D1187454

CRYSTALLIZATION OF POLYMERS

CRYSTALLIZATION OF POLYMERS

Leo Mandelkern

Professor of Chemistry
Florida State University

McGraw-Hill Book Company

New York   San Francisco   Toronto   London

Crystallization of Polymers

Library of Congress Catalog Card Number 63-21540

39865

to Berdie

For her infinite patience and understanding

PREFACE

We have been witnessing in recent years an unprecedentedly high degree of scientific activity. A natural consequence of the intensity of this endeavor is an ever-expanding scientific literature, much of which contains information of importance and interest to many diverse disciplines. However, it is a rare scientific investigator indeed who has either the time or the opportunity to digest and analyze critically the abundance we enjoy. Nowhere is this problem more acute than in the studies of the properties and behavior of macromolecular substances. Because of the somewhat belated recognition of its molecular character, this class of substances has been susceptive to quantitative investigations only for the past 30 years. During this period, however, there has developed a very rapidly increasing amount of activity and knowledge, in the realm of pure research as well as in industrial and practical applications. The problems presented have engaged the attention of individuals representing all the major scientific disciplines. In this situation it was inevitable that many subdivisions of polymer science have evolved. It appeared to the author that some of these areas could be subjected to a critical and, in some instances, a definitive analysis. Such endeavors also serve the purpose of acting as connecting links between the different specialities. At the same time they tend to underscore the more general and fundamental aspects of the scientific problems.

The present volume was suggested and stimulated by the aforementioned thoughts. We shall be concerned here with the phenomena and problems associated with the participation of macromolecules in phase transitions. The term crystallization arises from the fact that ordered structures are involved in at least one of the phases. The book is composed of three major portions which, however, are of unequal length. After a deliberately brief introduction into the nature of high polymers, the equilibrium aspects of the subject are treated from the point of view of thermodynamics and statistical mechanics, with recourse to a large amount of experimental observation. The second major topic discussed is the kinetics of crystallization. The treatment is intentionally very formal and allows for the deduction of the general mechanisms that are involved in the process. The equilibrium properties and the kinetic mechanisms must, in principle, govern the morphological characteristics of the crystalline state, which is the subject matter of the last chapter. The latter topic has been under intensive investigation in recent years. Many new concepts have been introduced which are still in a state of continuous revision. Consequently, a very detailed delineation of morphological structure has not been attempted. Instead, the discussion and interpretation have been restricted to the major features, which find their origin in the subject matter of the previous chapters.

Although many of the problems that fall within the scope of this work appear to be in a reasonable state of comprehension, there are some important ones that are not. It is hoped that these have become at least more clearly defined. Although no effort has been made to present a bibliographic compilation of the literature, care has been taken to avoid the neglect of significant work. Primary emphasis has been placed on principles, and this consideration has been the main guide in choosing the illustrative material. In this selection process a natural prejudice exists for material with which one is most familiar. This partiality, which appears to be an occupational hazard, has not been completely overcome in the present work. A great deal of what has been learned from studies of the simpler polymers can be applied to the properties and function of the more complex polymers of biological interest. Consequently, whenever possible, a unified approach has been taken which encompasses all types and classes of macromolecules, their diverse origin and function notwithstanding.

It was the author's pleasure and very distinct privilege to have the opportunity to be associated with Prof. P. J. Flory's laboratory some years ago. The author owes to him a debt, not only for the introduction to the subject at hand, but also for an understanding of the problems of science in general and polymer science in particular. As will be obvious to the reader, this book leans very heavily on his gifted and inspired teachings and research. However, the responsibility for the contents and the interpretations that are presented rests solely with the author.

The generous assistance of many friends and colleagues is gratefully acknowledged. Dr. N. Bekkedahl read and criticized a major portion of the manuscript and rendered invaluable aid to the author. Criticisms and suggestions on various chapters were received from Drs. T. G. Fox, W. Gratzer, G. Holzworth, H. Markowitz, and D. McIntyre. Dr. R. V. Rice and Mr. A. F. Diorio generously contributed electron micrographs and X-ray diffraction patterns for illustrative purposes.

The permission granted by *Annals of the New York Academy of Science; Chemical Reviews; Die Makromolekulare Chemie;* Faculty of Engineering, Kyushu University; John Wiley & Sons, Inc.; *Journal of the American Chemical Society; Journal of Applied Physics; Journal of Cellular and Comparative Physiology; Journal of Physical Chemistry; Journal of Polymer Science; Kolloid-Zeitschrift; Polymer; Proceedings of the National Academy (U.S.); Proceedings of the Royal Society; Review of Modern Physics; Rubber Chemistry and Technology; Science;* and *Transactions of the Faraday Society* to reproduce material originally appearing in their publications is gratefully acknowledged.

Leo Mandelkern

Tallahassee, Florida
May, 1963

CONTENTS

INTRODUCTION

Among the many scientific accomplishments of the past three decades has been the recognition that polymer molecules possess the unique structural feature of being composed of a very large number of chain units covalently linked together. This property is common to all macromolecules despite their diverse origin and widely differing chemical and stereochemical structure. It is therefore possible to study this class of substances from a unified point of view which encompasses the relatively simpler polymers that are prepared in the laboratory as well as the more complex ones of nature. The characteristic thermodynamic, hydrodynamic, physical, and mechanical properties possessed by high polymeric substances can be explained, in the main, by their covalent structure and the attendant large size of the individual molecules.

Although one is dealing with molecules that contain thousands of chain bonds, macromolecular systems still retain the ability to exist in different states. This property is common to all substances, high polymers included. Two of the states of matter observed for mono-

1

meric substances, the liquid and crystalline states, are also found in polymers. The liquid or amorphous state is characterized by some amount of free rotation about the single bonds connecting the chain atoms. Hence a single polymer molecule can assume a large number of spatial configurations.†

For a collection of such molecules in this state, the structural units of the different chains are arranged in a random, disoriented array and are essentially uncoordinated with one another. However, under appropriate conditions of temperature, pressure, stress, or solvent environment, a spontaneous ordering of portions of the chain molecules can take place. This ordering results from a strong preference for the chain bonds to assume a set of highly favored specific orientations or rotational states. Therefore, in contrast to the amorphous or liquid polymer, the individual molecules now exist in a state of configurational order. The individual ordered chains, or portions of them, can usually be organized into a regular three-dimensional array with the chain axes parallel to one another. The geometric structure of the individual molecules may be such that they are fully extended, or they may be held in a helical configuration, or they may fold back upon one another as circumstances dictate. The significant factor is that a state of three-dimensional order is developed which resembles very closely, in its major aspects, the crystalline state of monomeric substances. This very general kind of structural arrangement of the constituent molecules is termed the crystalline state of polymers.

It appears almost axiomatic that an individual polymer molecule that possesses a high degree of chemical and structural regularity among its chain elements should be capable of undergoing crystallization. Indeed, crystallization has been observed in a wide variety of such polymers. It is found, moreover, that a significant amount of known structural irregularity can be tolerated without impeding the crystallization process. However, even for a polymer possessing a regular structure, conditions must be found that are kinetically favorable for crystallization to occur in the time allotted for observation. For example, polyisobutylene, a polymer of apparently regular struc-

---

† In discussing the detailed three-dimensional structure of monomeric compounds, the term configuration is used to describe spatial arrangements of chemical bonds that cannot be altered unless the bonds are broken and then re-formed. The term conformation has been used to describe arrangements that arise from rotations about single bonds. For long chain molecules, we wish to describe the over-all structure of the molecule. Since this is primarily a statistical concept, neither of the above usages is adequate by itself. To avoid ambiguity in the present context, we reserve the word configuration to describe the over-all spatial structure of a macromolecule.

ture, can be easily crystallized by stretching. For a long time this polymer was not thought crystallizable without the application of an external stress. However, it has been demonstrated that crystallinity can be induced merely by cooling. However, many months must elapse, at the optimum temperature, before the development of the crystalline state can be definitely established. Kinetic factors therefore appear to be quite important in this case. It is thus not surprising that some polymers thought to have a regular structure have not as yet been crystallized. Some notable examples are polymers prepared from *m*-fluorostyrene, *p*-chlorostyrene, and 2-vinylnaphthalene, to cite but a few cases.[1]† Although evidence has been presented that these polymers have a regular stereostructure, suitable crystallization conditions have not as yet been found.

Many of the important properties of polymeric systems reside in the details of the configuration of the individual chains.[2,3] This is particularly true with regard to their crystallization behavior. Hence it is appropriate that, before embarking on a discussion of the major subject at hand, some attention be given to the general principles involved in determining the structural configuration of long chain molecules.

1-1   Structure of Disordered Chains

The spatial geometry of a long chain molecule depends on the bond distances between the chain atoms, the valence angles, and the possibilities or potentialities of internal rotation about single bonds of portions of the molecule with respect to one another. The configuration for a given chain backbone (fixed bond lengths and valence angles) is completely specified by the rotation angles about each of its single bonds. The large number of configurations available to a given molecule results from the permissible variations in the rotational angle among the skeletal bonds. These configurations differ from one another according to the value of the rotational angle for each individual bond.

As a convenient starting point in developing the statistical methods utilized to analyze chain configurations and for the purpose of calculating the dimensions of real molecules, a hypothetical chain model made up of completely freely rotating single bonds is assumed. The geometric properties of such a chain model can be exactly calculated as long as long-range intramolecular interactions involving pairs of

† Superior numbers in text refer to numbered list of references at the end of each chapter.

units remotely separated along the chain contour are neglected.[2] The geometry of the chain can be conveniently described either by the distance between the chain ends or by the distance of a chain element from the center of gravity of the molecule. Because of the large number of different configurations available to a molecule, a distribution of end-to-end distances is calculated. This distribution function is Gaussian, and the mean-square end-to-end distance is found to be $\langle r^2 \rangle_{of} = nl^2$. Here l is the length and n the number of links in the chain. The subscripts designate that we are dealing with an isolated, freely rotating chain. It has also been shown that, for such a chain, the root-mean-square distance of an element from the center of gravity and the root-mean-square end-to-end distance are related by $\langle S^2 \rangle_{of}^{1/2} = \langle r^2 \rangle_{of}^{1/2}/6$. For the chain model assumed, a linear dimension depends on the square root of the number of bonds and hence is many times smaller than the extended length of the macromolecule. The most frequent configurations expected, therefore, are those which are very highly coiled. Calculations of the dimension of freely rotating chains have also been made for cases where more than one kind of bond and valence angle are present.[2,4] Hence, it is possible for a comparison to be made between the actual dimensions of many real chains and their freely rotating counterpart.

In real chains the freedom of internal rotations is impeded by the hindrance potential associated with each bond. Although a quantitative assessment of all the factors contributing to this potential cannot be given, interactions between orbitals of valency electrons in adjoining bonds would be expected to confer an angular periodicity to this function.[5] The potential function can be significantly modified, however, by steric interferences and by interactions between neighboring substituents attached to the main chain atoms. The hindrance potential (for single bonds in polymer chains) is expected to resemble that deduced for similar bonds in monomeric organic molecules.[6] For example, a threefold symmetric potential is appropriate to describe the rotational states of ethane. However, the potential for the central bond of butane is modified from this. Although three minima still exist in the potential function for this bond, they are not all of equal energy. The lowest minimum is for the planar or trans configurations. The other two minima represent gauche forms, which are obtained from the trans by rotations of $\pm 120°$. The two gauche forms are of the same energy and exceed that for the trans form by about 500 to 800 cal/mole. It has been assumed that a similar potential function is applicable to the hindered rotation of bonds in the long chain polyethylene molecule. Hence, for this polymer the lowest energy form is the planar all-trans configuration which corresponds to the fully extended chain. Although the trans state is energetically favored, gauche states are allowed at favorable temperatures so that it is still possible to generate highly irregular configurations.

For macromolecules more complicated in structure than polyethylene, the simple potential function described above must be drastically modified. However, they are still characterized by minima representing the highly favored rotational states. The angular position of each bond may be considered to occur effectively in one of the available minima. Bond rotations are thus limited to angular values that lie within fairly narrow ranges and that can be regarded as discrete states.[7] Within this approximation, an elegant mathematical method is available that allows for a quantitative description of the chain configuration and accounts for the interdependence of rotational potentials on the states of neighboring bonds. The partition function of the chain can be calculated using the method of the one-dimensional Ising lattice which was developed for the treatment of ferromagnetism.[8, 9] From this calculation, the average dimensions of the single isolated real chain can be deduced. These quantities are found to be invariably greater than that calculated for free rotation.

Physical-chemical methods allow for the measurement of the actual mean-square end-to-end distance of a polymer chain.[†] A compilation of values for the actual dimension of a variety of real chains is given in Table 1-1, as the ratio of the root-mean-square end-to-end distance for the unperturbed chain to the same quantity calculated as if the chain were freely rotating.

The values observed for the linear dimensions are significantly greater in all cases than those calculated on the basis of free rotation. This is undoubtedly a reflection of the influence of hindered internal rotation on the over-all configuration of the molecule. The largest ratios are observed for cellulose derivatives. However, the change in the dimensions of this polymer with temperature indicates that the chain becomes more freely rotating as the temperature is increased. The dimensions obtained for polystyrene and polyacrylonitrile are relatively high and undoubtedly reflect the influence of the chain substituents. Natural rubber, polyisobutylene, polydimethylsiloxane, and polyethylene possess values of the pertinent ratio that tend to be lower than average. The limited data available for proteins and polypeptides in the disordered state do not indicate any unusual con-

---

[†] The methods and principles involved in these measurements are given in great detail elsewhere.[2]

figurational characteristics.   These macromolecules possess dimensions comparable to those of the simpler chain molecules.   Although, for all polymers that have been investigated, the chain dimensions exceeded those for free rotation, the size of a fully extended chain is not approached.   This occurs despite the strong preference for the individual bonds to assume discrete rotational states.   The experi-

TABLE 1-1
Typical dimensions of disordered polymer chains

Polymer	T†	$(\langle r^2 \rangle_o / \langle r^2 \rangle_{of})^{1/2}$	Ref.
Polyethylene	140	1.85	(4)
Polystyrene (atactic)	25	2.44	(2)
	70	2.35	
Polyisobutylene	24	1.93	(10)
	95	1.84	
Polymethylmethacrylate	30	2.2	(2)
Polyacrylic acid	30	1.96	(2)
Natural rubber			
(1,4-*cis*-polyisoprene)	0–60	1.70	(11)
Gutta-percha			
(1,4-*trans*-polyisoprene)	30	1.45	(11)
Polyacrylonitrile	30	2.6	(12)
Polydimethylsiloxane	20	1.6	(13)
Cellulose tributyrate	30	4.9	(14)
	90	2.1	(14)
	130	1.8	(14)
Cellulose trinitrate	30	4.5	(15)
Poly-γ-benzyl-L-glutamate	25	2.0	(4)‡
Collagen (disordered form)	25	1.15	(4)‡

† Unless otherwise indicated, the temperature is always given in degrees centigrade without any additional notation.

‡ $\langle r^2 \rangle_{of}$ is calculated assuming the transform for the peptide unit.

mental results indicate that, even though the permissible bond orientations are restricted, as long as some choice exists, a highly irregular, coiled-up configuration will be generated.

1-2   The Ordered Polymer Chain

Under suitable conditions the permissible rotational states can be restricted even further.   A given bond or sequence of bonds will now be limited to rotational angles that correspond to the lowest minima in the potential function describing the hindrance to rotation.   Consequently, a highly ordered chain structure is evolved with the concomitant loss of the configurational versatility that characterizes the disordered chain. For example, for polyethylene the trans position represents the orientation with the lowest energy. When successive bonds in the chain assume this orientation, a fully extended planar zigzag configuration results, as is illustrated in Fig. 1-1. An extended planar, or nearly planar, ordered configuration is characteristic of many polymers including polyamides, polyesters, cellulose derivatives, polydienes, and one of the chain forms of the polypeptides.

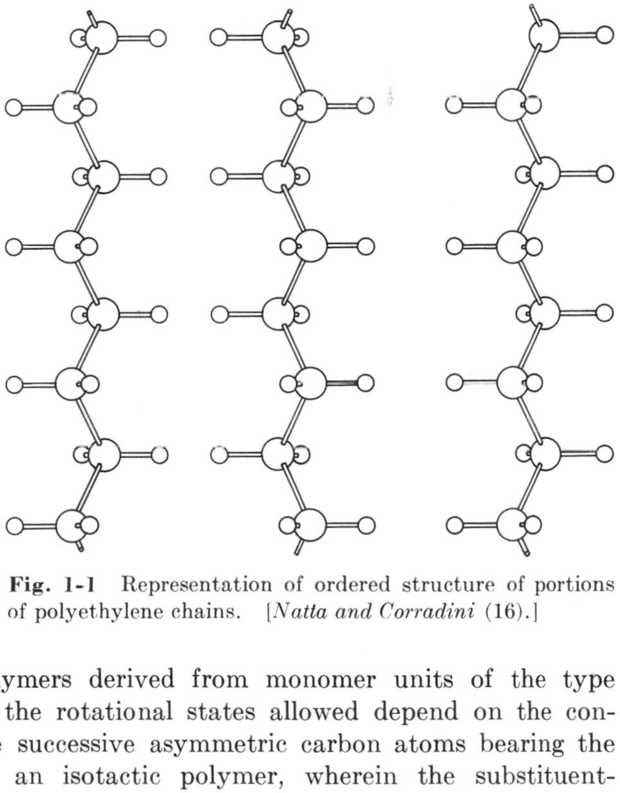

Fig. 1-1 Representation of ordered structure of portions of polyethylene chains. [*Natta and Corradini* (16).]

In vinyl polymers derived from monomer units of the type —CH_2—CH_2—R the rotational states allowed depend on the configurations of the successive asymmetric carbon atoms bearing the substituent. For an isotactic polymer, wherein the substituent-bearing carbon possesses the same tetrahedral configuration, the planar zigzag chain is excluded because of the steric interferences between the neighboring R groups. In the trans state successive substituent groups are within 2.5 to 2.6 A of each other. This distance is too small since it leads to gross overcrowding. The problem posed can be alleviated by having alternate bonds assume gauche positions. In this geometric pattern the substituent groups are adequately separated. If the required rotations are executed in a regular manner so that the bond orientation sequence trans-gauche is followed, then a helical chain structure is formed. Since there are two gauche positions, if the rotations are always executed in the same direction, either a right-handed or left-handed helix can be generated from the same molecule. If the substituent group is not too bulky, it is found that the helix contains three chemical repeating units for each geometrical repeating unit. A helix of this type is illustrated in Fig. 1-2a.[15,17] This helical form allows the substituent groups to be sufficiently far apart. The nearest distances between nonbonded carbon atoms now become 3.2 A in isotactic polypropylene and 3.3 A in isotactic polystyrene.

Polymers containing more bulky side groups require more space, so that much looser helices are formed. Some typical examples of the latter type are illustrated in Fig. 1-2b, c, and d. These structures give rise to larger repeating units. For example, poly-3-methyl-butene-1, in which the side group is $CH(CH_3)_2$, has a repeating unit that comprises four monomer units. This bulky side group leads to more acute overcrowding so that the angle of the gauche bond is changed from 120° to about 100° and instead of having the strict trans position at 0° it is modified to about −26°. For polymers in which the branching occurs at the second atom of the side chain, as in poly-4-methyl-hexene-1, the helix is comprised of seven monomer units in two geometric turns (Fig. 1-2b). Its structure is explained by the same type of bond rotations but with smaller deviations from that of pure trans and gauche positions being required. Polyvinyl naphthalene and poly-o-methylstyrene form fourfold helices (Fig. 1-2d) while the helix formed by poly-m-methylstyrene contains eleven monomer units in three turns. Isotactic polymethylmethacrylate forms a helix that contains five chemical units in two turns. Hence a diversity of helical structures, which depend on the nature of the substituent group, can be generated from isotactic polymers.

In syndiotactic polymers, the carbon atoms containing the substituent group possess an alternating D, L tetrahedral configuration. The steric problems between neighboring side groups is therefore not nearly as severe as for the isotactic structures. It is therefore possible to develop an ordered chain structure that is planar or nearly planar and fully extended. In these structures each bond is in the trans state. Planar zigzag extended structures are observed for polyvinyl chloride and poly-1,2-butadiene. The geometrical repeating unit encompasses two chemical repeating units and is approximately twice the comparable distance for the nonsubstituted polyethylene chain. The ordered structure for syndiotactic polymers is not required, however, to be

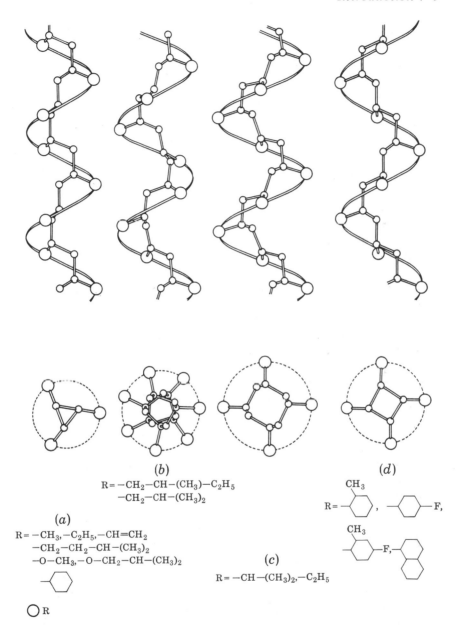

$$R = -CH_2-CH-(CH_3)-C_2H_5$$
$$-CH_2-CH-(CH_3)_2$$

(b)

(d)

(a)

$$R = -CH_3, -C_2H_5, -CH=CH_2$$
$$-CH_2-CH_2-CH-(CH_3)_2$$
$$-O-CH_3, -O-CH_2-CH-(CH_3)_2$$

(c)

$$R = -CH-(CH_3)_2, -C_2H_5$$

$R =$ (cyclohexyl with CH_3), (cyclohexyl with F), (cyclohexyl with CH_3 and F), (decalin with F),

○ R

Fig. 1-2 Representation of some typical ordered helical structures for isotactic polymers. [*Natta and Corradini* (16).]

planar.   Indications are that syndiotactic polypropylene possesses a helical structure.[1]

For polyisobutylene the pairs of methyl groups on the alternate chain carbon atoms give rise to a severe overcrowding between the side groups.   These steric difficulties cannot be alleviated by any combination of bond rotations which are restricted to the trans or gauche states.   The bonds in this molecule therefore possess a unique hindrance potential which bears no resemblance to the threefold potential used to describe the rotational states in polyethylene and other chain molecules containing a carbon-carbon skeleton.   A helical structure is generated in polyisobutylene by rotating each bond 82° from its trans state.   In this helix, eight chemical units correspond to five turns of the geometric repeating unit.[17,18]   A regularly ordered structure results when the direction or sign of the rotation is the same for each bond.   A statistically disordered structure evolves when the sign of the rotation is allowed to change at alternate bonds.

Polytetrafluoroethylene also forms an ordered structure.   The fully ordered configuration is a slowly twisting helix that comprises 13 CF_2 groups in a repeat.[19]   Each chain bond is rotated 20° from the precise trans position.   The reason for this distortion is that, if the structure were planar zigzag, the nonbonded fluorine atoms would be uncomfortably close to one another.   The rotation about each chain bond again relieves the overcrowding.

Helically ordered chain structures are not limited to molecules containing a carbon-carbon backbone structure.   They also manifest themselves in polypeptides, proteins, and nucleic acids.   A very important ordered structure for polypeptides is the alpha-helix deduced by Pauling, Corey, and Branson.[20]   In this structure (as contrasted with the extended ordered configuration of a polypeptide chain) the maximum number of hydrogen bonds between the carbonyl oxygen and amino nitrogen are formed intramolecularly.   The hydrogen bonding occurs between every third amino acid residue along the chain.   A nonintegral helix results which contains 3.6 residues per turn.   The peptide group is planar, in analogy to deductions from crystallographic studies of similarly constituted monomeric substances, and each CO and NH group forms a hydrogen bond.   A comparison of the structure of an alpha-helically ordered polypeptide chain with a 3.5 helix formed by an isotactic vinyl polymer is shown in Fig. 1-3. In the latter case, the structure is not stabilized by any intramolecular bonding.   Poly-L-proline is a polyimino acid and as such does not possess the capacity for the formation of intramolecular hydrogen bonds.   However, because of the influence of steric factors, an ordered chain configuration exists (poly-L-proline II) which is helical and has the imide grouping planar and in the trans state.[21]

The ordered structures of nucleic acids appear to involve more than one chain molecule. The structure of deoxyribonucleic acid (DNA), as deduced by Watson and Crick[22] and Wilkins,[23] involves two intertwined chains helically woven so as to resemble a twisted ladder. The rungs of the ladder, which are presumed to render the

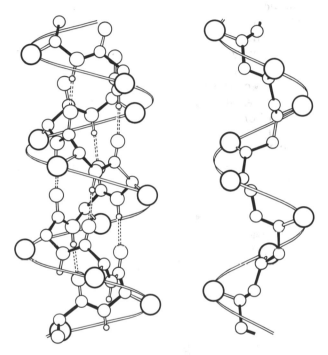

Fig. 1-3 Comparison of the alpha-helix formed by polypeptides (left) with a 3.5 helix generated by an isotactic polymer. [*Natta and Corradini* (16).]

structure stable, are formed through the hydrogen bonding of complementary purine and pyrimidine bases.

Although no effort has been made to discuss the intricate details of the problem, it is clear that a myriad of ordered structures can be developed in chain molecules. The structure found depends on the chemical nature of the molecule and results from the perpetuation of specific and definite bond orientations along the chain. This ordering process can also be aided and abetted by specific intramolecular interactions. Crystallization can then be schematically envisaged as the process of packing the individual ordered molecules into an organized three-dimensional array. Although the bond orientations represent the minimum energy for the chain as a whole, there should be a further decrease in free energy as the chain atoms and substituents from the different molecules are suitably juxtaposed relative to one another. The form of the individual molecules, as deduced from X-ray crystallography, is usually indicative of the bond configuration (or sequences of bond configuration) of minimum energy.[24] This can be tempered or modified somewhat by intermolecular forces which can cause a distortion in the structure of the individual molecules. The influence of chain packing is most important when a choice exists between configurations of nearly equal energy. This appears to be the case for rubber hydrochloride and certain of the polyesters and polyethers.[17]

The arrangements of the atoms in the crystalline regions of a polymer can be determined by the conventional methods of X-ray crystallography.[25] Although single crystals are usually not available to polymer crystallographers, many of the characteristics of the unit cell such as the crystal system, dimensions, and positions of the atoms have been deduced for a wide variety of polymers. Normal bond distances, angles, and other elements of structure appear to be the general rule. The role of the chemical repeating unit is analogous to the part played by molecules in crystals of low molecular weight organic compounds. A unit cell does not usually contain a complete molecule. It is not uncommon to find more than one chain traversing a unit cell; the unit cells are frequently composed of from one to eight chain units.

1-3 Morphological Features

When the structural features of crystalline polymers are examined, beyond a study of the geometry of the unit cell, it is necessary that the polycrystalline character be recognized. This situation becomes immediately apparent from X-ray diffraction studies. Several different categories of wide-angle X-ray patterns can be obtained from polymeric systems. When the polymer is noncrystalline, discrete Bragg reflections do not appear in the pattern. Only a diffuse halo is observed, as is illustrated in Fig. 1-4. This pattern is for noncrystalline natural rubber at 25°. A typical pattern obtained when a polymer is crystallized merely by cooling is given in Fig. 1-5 for a linear polyethylene specimen. Discrete Bragg reflections are now observed. These are in the form of a series of concentric circles. The photograph is very similar to that obtained from powder patterns of crystalline monomeric substances. This type of crystallization in

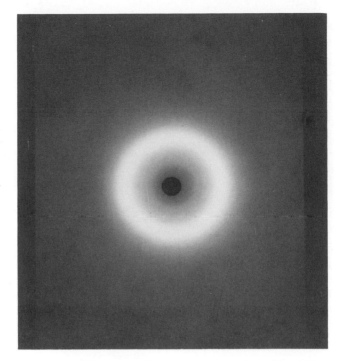

Fig. 1-4 Wide-angle X-ray patterns of noncrystalline natural rubber. (*Courtesy of A. F. Diorio.*)

polymers is termed random crystallization since from a macroscopic point of view there is, on an average, no preferred orientation of the crystallographic directions. On the other hand, different kinds of preferred orientation can also be developed and observed. The native state of many macromolecules of biological interest, such as the fibrous proteins, is characterized by a preferred crystalline orientation. Similar conditions can also be obtained in other polymers by mechanical methods. Examples of wide-angle X-ray diffraction patterns of three axially oriented crystalline polymers, natural rubber, linear polyethylene, and the naturally occurring fibrous protein collagen, are given in Fig. 1-6. The reflections have now become discrete spots as a result of the preferential orientation of different crystallographic planes. The natural rubber and polyethylene patterns are reminiscent of those obtained from a well-developed single crystal with rotational symmetry about an axis perpendicular to the incident X-ray beam. It should be noted that, despite this close similarity to the conventional single crystal pattern, the persistence of the diffuse halo can still be easily discerned. For the same crystallographic structure,

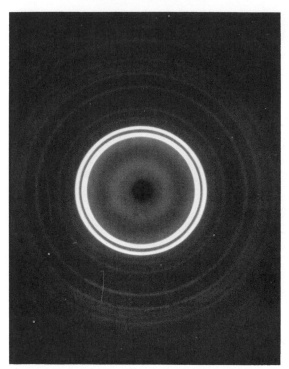

Fig. 1-5 Wide-angle X-ray diffraction patterns for linear polyethylene crystallized by cooling. (*Courtesy of A. F. Diorio.*)

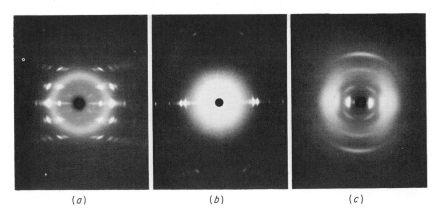

(*a*)   (*b*)   (*c*)

Fig. 1-6 Wide-angle X-ray diffraction patterns for axially oriented crystalline macromolecules.   (*a*) Natural rubber; (*b*) linear polyethylene; (*c*) native collagen fiber. (*Courtesy of A. F. Diorio.*)

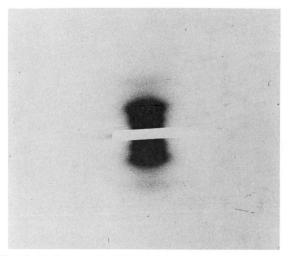

Fig. 1-7 Low-angle X-ray diffraction patterns of an axially oriented crystalline linear polyethylene specimen (26).

i.e., in the absence of polymorphism, recorded Bragg spacings are identical, whether the specimen is oriented or not. Other types of orientation are also possible and have been observed. Another example is biaxial orientation, wherein the polymer chains are all constrained to lie in a plane.

There is substantial evidence to indicate that, at all levels of morphology that are amenable to study, well-defined, though perhaps not too well-understood, organized structures exist. Low-angle X-ray studies indicate structures having linear dimensions that correspond to hundreds of angstroms.[26,27] A typical low-angle X-ray pattern from a highly axially oriented fiber of linear polyethylene is shown in Fig. 1-7. Several orders of diffraction, corresponding to a long period of 410 ± 20 A, are resolved in this specimen. In addition to the discrete maxima, diffuse scatter also occurs at the small angles. The light scattered by thin films of crystalline polymers can be interpreted in terms of structural entities whose size is in the range of several thousand angstroms.[28]

When viewed under the light microscope, thin films of crystalline homopolymers invariably display highly birefringent spherulitic structures. An example of this kind of crystalline body, grown in a thin polyethylene film, is illustrated in Fig. 1-8.[29] A more detailed discussion of these structures will be given subsequently. For present purposes it suffices to note that their presence is evidence of a further

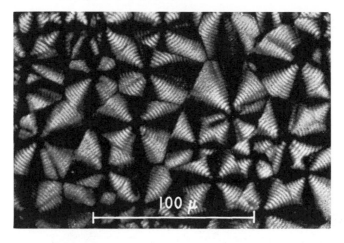

Fig. 1-8 Light micrograph of spherulitic structures grown in crystalline, linear polyethylene. [*Price* (29).]

structural organization of dimensions that encompasses several microns. Electron microscope studies of thin films, or of replicas of fracture surfaces, of crystalline polymers yield micrographs of the type illustrated in Fig. 1-9.[30] One observes structures by this technique which appear to be composed of very thin and twisted lamellae.

When homopolymers are crystallized from very dilute solutions, either lozenge-shaped platelets or crystals which possess a dendritic

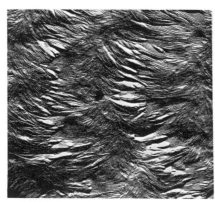

Fig. 1-9 Electron micrograph of melt crystallized linear polyethylene. [*Eppe, Fischer, and Stuart* (30).]

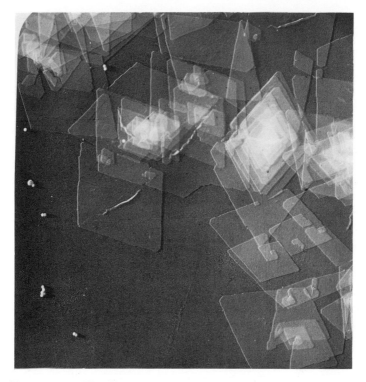

Fig. 1-10 Electron micrograph of linear polyethylene ($M_v = 50,000$) isothermally crystallized at 89° from a dilute tetralin solution. (*Courtesy of Dr. R. V. Rice.*)

habit are formed. Some typical electron micrographs of the crystals precipitated from dilute solution are shown in Figs. 1-10 and 1-11. The crystal habit that is observed depends on the molecular weight of the polymer and the crystallization conditions, such as the temperature and the nature of the solvent. A very striking feature is that the platelets are only about 100 to 200 A thick. In conjunction with selected-area electron diffraction studies, it can be concluded that a given chain must pass through these crystals many times. Hence, within the crystal, the polymer chain must assume some sort of folded configuration. A more detailed discussion of the folded chain configuration and the nature of the lamellar crystals is given in Chap. 9.

It has been recognized that there are many unique features and complications involved in delineating the detailed structure and configuration of a single isolated long chain molecule. The further organization of such molecules into a crystalline array poses further

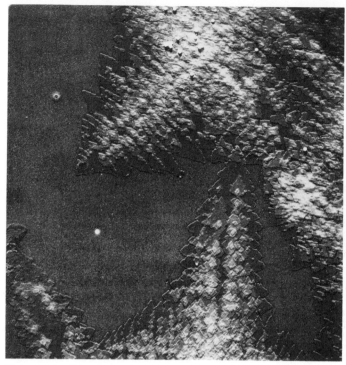

Fig. 1-11 Electron micrograph of linear polyethylene ($M_v =$ 50,000) isothermally crystallized at 60° from a dilute tetralin solution. (*Courtesy of Dr. R. V. Rice.*)

problems as must be apparent to even the most casual observer. In the subsequent chapters we endeavor to develop a systematic treatment and understanding of the nature of the crystalline state.

REFERENCES

1. Danusso, F.: *Polymer*, **3**: 423 (1962).
2. Flory, P. J.: "Principles of Polymer Chemistry," Cornell University Press, Ithaca, N.Y., 1953.
3. Flory, P. J.: "Lectures in Materials Science," p. 27, W. A. Benjamin, Inc., New York, 1963.
4. Flory, P. J.: Protein Structure and Function, *Brookhaven Symp. Biol.*, **13**: 89 (1960).
5. Wilson, E. B., Jr.: in "Advances in Chemical Physics," vol. II, Interscience Publishers, Inc., New York, 1959.
6. Mizushima, S.: "Structure of Molecules and Internal Rotation," Academic Press, Inc., New York, 1954.

7. Volkenstein, M. V.: *J. Polymer Sci.*, **29**: 441 (1958).
8. Kramers, H. A., and G. H. Wannier: *Phys. Rev.*, **60**: 252 (1941).
9. Newell, G. F., and E. W. Montroll: *Revs. Mod. Phys.*, **25**: 353 (1953).
10. Fox, T. G., Jr., and P. J. Flory: *J. Am. Chem. Soc.*, **73**: 1909 (1951).
11. Wagner, H. L., and P. J. Flory: *J. Am. Chem. Soc.*, **74**: 195 (1952).
12. Krigbaum, W. R.: *J. Polymer Sci.*, **28**: 213 (1958).
13. Flory, P. J., L. Mandelkern, J. Kinsinger, and W. B. Schultz: *J. Am. Chem. Soc.*, **74**: 3364 (1952).
14. Mandelkern, L., and P. J. Flory: *J. Am. Chem. Soc.*, **74**: 2517 (1952).
15. Hunt, M. L., S. Newman, H. A. Scheraga, and P. J. Flory: *J. Phys. Chem.*, **60**: 1278 (1959).
16. Natta, G., and P. Corradini: *Rubber Chem. Technol.*, **33**: 703 (1960).
17. Bunn, C. W., and D. R. Holmes: *Discussions Faraday Soc.*, **25**: 95 (1958).
18. Liquori, A. M.: *Acta Cryst.*, **8**: 345 (1955).
19. Bunn, C. W., and E. R. Howells: *Nature*, **174**: 549 (1954).
20. Pauling, L., R. B. Corey, and H. R. Branson: *Proc. Natl. Acad. Sci. U.S.*, **37**: 205 (1951).
21. Cowan, P. M., and S. McGavin: *Nature*, **176**: 501 (1955).
22. Watson, J. D., and F. H. C. Crick: *Nature*, **171**: 737, 964 (1953); *Proc. Roy. Soc. (London), Ser. A*, **223**: 80 (1954).
23. Wilkins, M. H. F., A. R. Stokes, and H. R. Wilson: *Nature*, **171**: 738 (1953).
24. Natta, G., P. Corradini, and P. Ganis: *J. Polymer Sci.*, **58**: 1191 (1962).
25. Bunn, C. W.: "Chemical Crystallography," Oxford University Press, London, 1946.
26. Mandelkern, L., C. R. Worthington, and A. S. Posner: *Science*, **127**: 1052 (1958).
27. Posner, A. S., L. Mandelkern, C. R. Worthington, and A. F. Diorio: *J. Appl. Phys.*, **31**: 536 (1960); **32**: 1509 (1961).
28. Stein, R. S.: in R. H. Doremus, B. W. Roberts, and D. Turnbull (eds.), p. 549, "Growth and Perfection of Crystals," John Wiley & Sons, Inc., New York, 1958.
29. Price, F. P.: *J. Polymer Sci.*, **37**: 71 (1959).
30. Eppe, R., E. W. Fischer, and H. A. Stuart: *J. Polymer Sci.*, **37**: 721 (1959).

FUSION OF
HOMOPOLYMERS

2-1 Introduction

During the transformation of a pure homopolymer from the crystalline or partially crystalline state to the liquid state, there are characteristic changes in physical and mechanical properties, in morphological and structural features, and in the extensive thermodynamic variables. For example, a crystalline homopolymer is typically a hard, rigid solid of high strength, whereas in the molten state a polymer may possess the properties of a liquid of low fluidity. However, if the molecular weight is sufficiently high, the liquid is instead endowed with the rubberlike characteristic of long-range elasticity. The influence of crystallinity on mechanical properties manifests itself by a change in the modulus of elasticity by a factor of about 10^3 to 10^5 upon melting; the mechanical strength of fibers can be attributed to the presence of oriented crystalline regions.

In well-developed crystalline specimens, wide-angle X-ray diffraction investigations yield reflections from a large number of crystalline planes, which are superimposed on diffuse scattering. After melting, these reflections disappear and only broad halos remain. Distinctive changes in the infrared spectra usually occur during the transformation. In addition, latent changes in the enthalpy and volume, which are commonly associated with a phase change, are observed.

The distinct differences in properties between the two states are very similar to those which occur during the melting of the crystals of a monomeric substance. The latter process is relatively well understood and can be formally described as a first-order phase transition. The laws of phase equilibria are applicable to this class of transformations. The completely general thermodynamic origin of these laws and their great potency in explaining diverse phenomena make it important to ascertain whether the observed similarities between the crystallization-melting process of monomeric and polymeric substances are merely coincidental or superficial or do, in fact, represent manifestations of the same fundamental process.

For a one-component system at constant pressure, a first-order phase transition is theoretically described by the fact that the transformation temperature is independent of the relative abundance of either of the phases being maintained in equilibrium. Melting is infinitely sharp; the characteristic temperature at which it occurs is defined as the melting temperature. This temperature is governed by the well-known relation

$$T_m = \frac{\Delta H}{\Delta S} \tag{2-1}$$

where ΔH and ΔS are, respectively, the enthalpy and entropy of fusion of the substance undergoing fusion. For the aforementioned conditions to be experimentally observed, an almost perfect internal arrangement of the crystalline phase is required. Moreover, large crystals are needed to minimize any excess contributions to the free energy caused by the surfaces or junctions between the two phases when compared with the free energy of fusion. Deviations from these idealized conditions must inevitably lead to a broadening of the melting range.

The criteria set forth above apply equally well to crystals of all substances. Long chain molecules packed in perfect array in crystallites of sufficiently large dimensions represent a state which is crystalline. The fact that the molecules may penetrate many unit cells is of no particular consequence. Accordingly, for this situation, as for any other crystalline substance, melting would be expected to be a first-order phase transition. If this condition is not fulfilled by experiment and detailed molecular theory, the foregoing premise will naturally have to be discarded.

From the viewpoint of molecular organization, it is evident that the crystalline state of polymers is quite complex. This is a consequence of its polycrystalline character and the fact that the crystallizing entities are not isolated elements of structure but are covalently linked together in molecules comprising many thousands of units. Experimental observations indicate that there is a wide range in the type of order that can be developed.[1,2,3] However, these observations do not necessarily imply that such a wide variety of states intermediate between the liquid and the perfect crystal is inherently characteristic of the crystalline state. If this situation represented the equilibrium state, it would be meaningless to consider a crystalline phase in polymers or attempt to investigate systematically its transformation to the liquid state. The observations could be the result of a compromise between the stringent requirements of equilibrium and the demands of a finite rate of crystallization. A spectrum of mesomorphic or metastable states would then be expected.

For the ordered regions in a crystalline polymer to be treated as a separate phase, the usual thermodynamic criteria must be satisfied. For a pure phase of one component, the chemical potential must be uniform throughout the phase and depend solely on the temperature and pressure. Obviously, for a poorly developed crystalline system, whether it is composed of polymer segments or of a monomeric substance, this condition will not be fulfilled. Under these circumstances, the chemical potential also depends on the degree of order and the crystallite size. The extent to which the idealized crystalline state can be approached must ultimately be judged, in terms of experiment, by the sharpness of the fusion process and the reproducibility of the melting temperature. It is to this question, of fundamental importance for the understanding of crystalline polymers, that we first direct our attention.

2-2   Nature of the Fusion Process

In experiments designed to study the fusion process and to determine the nature of the transformation, procedures must be adopted to ensure that conditions approaching equilibrium are attained. The most general considerations of the factors influencing the development of the crystalline phase from the molten state indicate that these requirements are best fulfilled when the transformation is carried out slowly at temperatures close to the melting temperature or by protracted annealing, at elevated temperatures, of the already formed crystalline phase. Experiments designed to yield results of thermodynamic significance must involve the measurement of thermodynamic quantities sensitive to small changes in the amount of crystallinity. In the case of polymers, many of the conventional methods are no longer adequate for determining the melting temperature.[4] In many

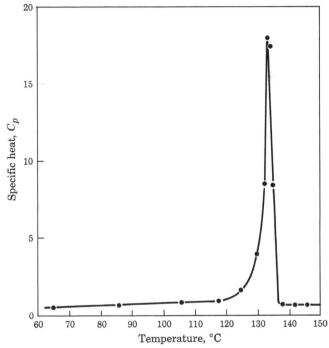

Fig. 2-1 Specific heat–temperature relations for linear polyethylene (Marlex-50). [*From Wunderlich and Dole* (5).]

instances, the measurement of changes in physical or mechanical properties is not sufficiently sensitive, so that melting temperatures determined by these methods bear only superficial resemblance to the desired quantities.

Specific heat measurements have been widely utilized in studying transformations of the type under discussion. In principle, this technique can yield valuable thermodynamic information. The data of Wunderlich and Dole[5] on a linear polyethylene specimen, which are illustrated in Fig. 2-1, are typical of the results obtained for an undiluted homopolymer. In this experiment, the polymer sample was allowed to cool slowly from the melt before the initiation of the measurements. The nature of the curve is reminiscent of a λ-type transition, which is characteristic of the order-disorder process of binary alloys. The specific heat rises sharply over a temperature range of 15 to 20°, reaches a finite maximum value, drops precipitously, and then levels off. For an ideal first-order phase transition of a one-component system, the specific heat should go to infinity at the transformation temperature. It is tempting to conclude from these observations that for polymeric systems transformations of the type under consideration cannot be classified as a first-order phase transition.

However, as Mayer and Streeter[6] have discussed in detail, there are certain inherent difficulties in classifying a transition solely according to the shape of its fusion curve. The question arises, for example, whether the transformation range would be appreciably sharpened by additional annealing or by adopting a slower heating schedule. The distinct possibility also exists that a still greater rise in the specific heat would be observed at the transformation temperature if the temperature interval of the experimental observations were decreased. Furthermore, the specific heat–temperature plot for a diffuse first-order transition is very similar to that of a λ-type order-disorder transition. Hence a description of the process and classification of the transition according to a cursory analysis of the fusion curve are both arbitrary and difficult. A more detailed investigation of the fusion, including the effects of the crystallization conditions and subsequent annealing processes on the transformation temperature, is clearly required.

The importance of the latter considerations is borne out by the pioneering study of Wood and Bekkedahl[7] on the crystallization and melting of natural rubber. They have shown that if, subsequent to crystallization, fusion is carried out utilizing rapid heating rates (on the order of 0.1° per min) the melting temperature observed is dependent on the crystallization condition. In particular, the melting temperature is a marked function of the crystallization temperature. The fusion curves that they obtained following isothermal crystallization at various temperatures are given in Fig. 2-2. The observed melting temperatures range from about 0 to 30°C and depend on the crystallization temperature, the melting temperature being higher for the higher crystallization temperatures. Qualitatively similar results have been obtained for a variety of other polymers when the fusion experiments were carried out in the manner described.[8–10] The fact that the crystallization temperature has such a decided influence on the melting temperature cannot be taken by itself as evidence of the lack of an equilibrium crystalline state and melting temperature in polymers. For it has been found that, if, subsequent to the crystallization of natural rubber[11] and of other polymers,[9-13] a slow heating schedule is adopted, a reproducible melting temperature independent of the previous thermal history of the sample is obtained. This melting temperature is independent of crystallization conditions, including the crystallization temperature, and is invariably significantly greater than that observed with fast heating rates. These results are explicable on the basis that at crystallization temperatures well below the

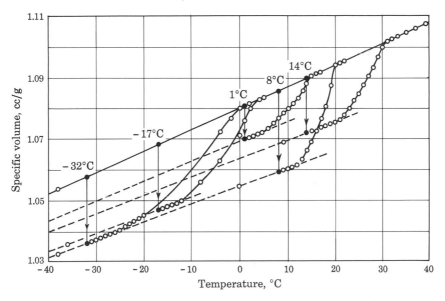

Fig. 2-2 Melting range of natural rubber as a function of the temperature of crystallization. [*From Wood and Bekkedahl (7a).*]

melting temperature morphological contributions or limitations on the perfection and size of the crystalline regions lower their thermodynamic stability. These effects, which find their origin in the kinetics and mechanisms of the crystallization process, cannot be alleviated when fast heating rates are employed. Hence, equilibrium considerations cannot be given to experimental observations carried out in this manner. However, when slow heating rates are employed after crystallization, annealing and recrystallization processes can exert their influence. The aforementioned observations indicate that equilibrium conditions are being approached.

For a majority of polymers, the measurement of the specific volume as a function of temperature offers a very simple and accurate method of studying the fusion process.   Moreover, and most important, it allows for rigorous control of the temperature and the convenient utilization of slow heating rates. Some typical results obtained for the fusion of homopolymers of different types by this technique are given in Fig. 2-3.   Slow heating rates were employed subsequent to essentially uncontrolled crystallization.   When sensitive methods of detection are used, it is found that below the melting

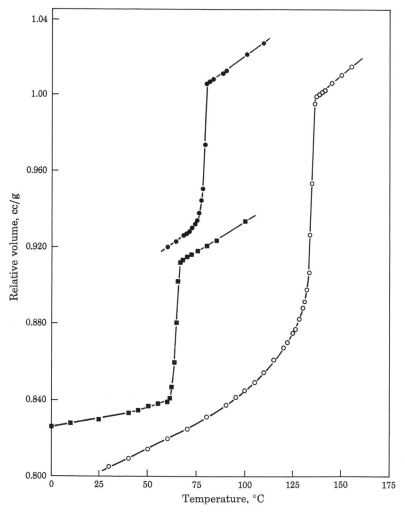

Fig. 2-3   Plot of relative volume against temperature: open circles, polymethylene; solid squares, polyethylene oxide; solid circles, polydecamethylene adipate (4).

temperature partial melting and recrystallization occur if the specimen is held at the temperature for a sufficient length of time. The points plotted in Fig. 2-3 represent the final specific volumes attained at a given temperature, usually after a period of 24 hr. When these procedures are adopted, the melting process is quite sharp, with a substantial portion of the melting occurring in an interval of 3 to 4°. The temperature at which the last traces of crystallinity disappear is well defined, and most significantly the abrupt termination of the fusion process is indicated. This temperature must therefore represent the disappearance of the most perfectly ordered regions that can be obtained under the limitation imposed by the crystallization conditions and the time invested in studying the fusion process. From these data, it could be expected that, if a similar heating schedule were followed in making specific heat measurements, the resemblance to the λ-type transition would disappear.

Another approach in the attempt to attain equilibrium conditions is to carry out the initial crystallization from the melt at a fixed temperature as close to the melting temperature as is practicable. This procedure must inevitably involve excessively long crystallization times for an adequate amount of crystallinity to be developed.[14] The results of such an experiment[15] are given in Fig. 2-4 for an unfractionated linear polyethylene (Marlex-50). The upper curve represents the data for a sample which, prior to the fusion studies, was crystallized from the melt in a manner similar to that utilized for the specific heat study of Fig. 2-1. The resulting specific volume of the specimen at 25° was 1.041. When heating rates of the order of 1° per day are used, the course of the fusion is marked by partial melting and recrystallization, as has been previously observed for other homopolymers. The melting is relatively sharp, and again the last traces of crystallinity disappear at a well-defined temperature, which for this specimen can be taken to be 137.5 $\pm$ 0.5. This temperature is several degrees higher than that determined by the specific heat method for the same polymer, a fact that can be attributed to the much slower heating rates utilized in the specific volume studies.

The lower curve in Fig. 2-4 represents the fusion for the same substance which, however, had initially been crystallized from the melt for 40 days at 130° (e.g., 7.5° below the melting temperature) and then slowly cooled to room temperature over a 24-hr period. This rather rigorous crystallization procedure yields a specimen with a specific volume of 1.018 at 25°, indicating a higher level of crystallinity and presumably the development of more nearly perfect crystallites. On subsequent heating, the partial melting–recrystallization process is now minimized.   However, a perceptible sharpening of the melting curve is observed, although the same melting temperature is obtained.

It can be demonstrated, therefore, that by appropriate experiment, involving either very slow crystallization or a very slow fusion process or a combination of both, there exists a well-defined temperature at which the last traces of crystallinity disappear.   This temperature is

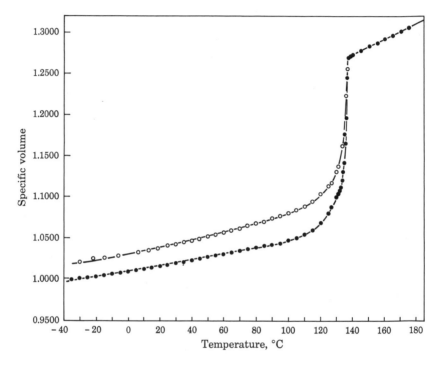

Fig. 2-4   Specific volume–temperature relations for unfractionated linear polyethylene (Marlex-50).   Open circles, specimen slowly cooled from melt to room temperature prior to fusion; solid circles, specimen crystallized at 130° for 40 days, then cooled to room temperature (15).

very reproducible and is independent of the crystallization conditions and previous thermal history of the sample.   The melting range for the unfractionated homopolymer illustrated is relatively narrow, being limited to a few degrees at most.   Although the melting of homopolymers is shown to be sharp and reproducible, the fusion process appears to violate one of the prime requirements of a first-order phase transition, namely, that at constant pressure the transformation temperature should be independent of the relative abundance of the two phases maintained in equilibrium.   There is no evidence or basis for belief that the ultimate in crystallization conditions and annealing procedures has as yet been applied. Any improvement in these factors must, of necessity, sharpen the melting range.

In the evolutionary process characterizing the study of the fusion of polymers, a major advance has been made by the use of sharp

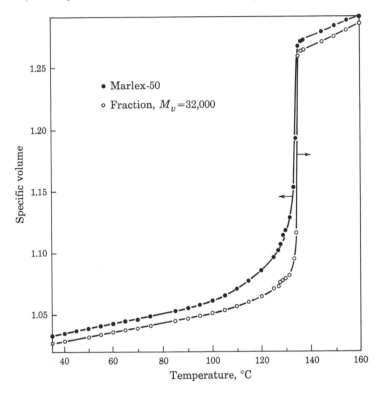

Fig. 2-5 Specific volume–temperature relations for linear polyethylene samples. Solid circles, unfractionated Marlex-50; open circles, fraction $M_v = 32,000$. Samples initially crystallized at 131.3° for 40 days. [*From Chiang and Flory* (16).]

molecular weight fractions.[16] In Fig. 2-5 a comparison is made of the fusion of unfractionated polyethylene (Marlex-50) and a fraction of molecular weight 32,000 obtained from the whole polymer. Prior to the initiation of fusion, the specimens were crystallized from the melt at 131.3°C for about 40 days, slowly cooled to 120°C over a period of 5 days, and finally cooled to room temperature over a 24-hr period. Slow heating rates were then employed. These procedures are very similar to those utilized in obtaining the lower curve of Fig. 2-4, with

almost identical results being obtained for the whole polymer in both
cases. However, as is clearly evident in Fig. 2-5, the melting of the
fraction is appreciably sharper, with over 80 per cent of the transformation occurring within a range of 2°. Over the same temperature
interval only 35 to 40 per cent of the melting process has taken place
for the unfractionated sample. The extremely broad molecular weight
distribution of the whole polymer[17] with its high content of low
molecular weight material is undoubtedly responsible for the observed
behavior. The results for a higher molecular weight fraction
(M = 490,000), crystallized under the same conditions, are also indicative of an extremely sharp melting process. The final traces of
crystallinity disappear at 138.7°C for this fraction, as compared with
137.5°C for the whole polymer.

The fusion curves typical of molecular weight fractions are comparable to those obtained for monomeric substances. Even for this
class of substances, the characteristic discontinuity of melting is
rendered more diffuse by rapid cooling of the melt to frozen states of
nonequilibrium and by the adventitious retention of impurities. The
differences between polymers and monomers is thus one of degree
rather than kind. More stringent measures are needed to approach
the equilibrium condition in the case of polymers.

The finite length of any real polymer chain introduces a certain
element of disorder into the system, namely, the chain ends. The
situation is analogous to that of an impure substance. If the chain
ends are not tolerated by the lattice, melting cannot be absolutely
sharp even under the most ideal conditions of crystallization and
annealing. Despite the expectation that the melting of a homopolymer must almost inevitably occur over a small but finite temperature range, the last vestiges of crystallinity should disappear at a
well-defined temperature. This deduction is amply confirmed by
careful experiment. According to the dictates of theory, this temperature is defined as the equilibrium melting temperature T_m of the
polymer. It represents the melting temperature of the hypothetical
macroscopic perfect crystal. In the theoretical limit of a homogeneous polymer of infinite molecular weight forming a perfectly
ordered crystalline phase, melting should occur sharply at a well-
defined temperature.† Theoretically, even a diffuse melting process
can be treated as a first-order phase transition.[18] It is perhaps noteworthy that for linear polyethylene this temperature is in close corre-

----

† In the sense used here, the perfect crystal is that with the lowest free energy.
Since a certain amount of lattice disorder can be tolerated at equilibrium, it does
not necessarily represent the structurally internally perfect ideal crystal.

spondence with the melting temperature extrapolated for a high molecular weight *n*-paraffin from an analysis of the thermodynamic data of low molecular weight homologs.[13,19,20,21]

For equilibrium to be maintained between two macroscopic phases of a one-component system at constant temperature, the pressure must be independent of the volume; i.e., the pressure does not depend on the relative abundance of either of the phases. A pressure-volume-temperature diagram for polyethylene is given in Fig. 2-6.[22] The

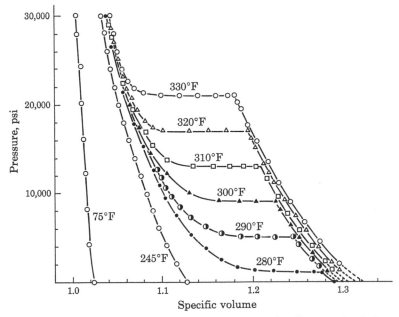

Fig. 2-6 Pressure-volume-temperature diagram for linear polyethylene (Marlex-50). [*From Matsuoka* (22).]

invariance of the pressure with the volume, characteristic of a first-order phase transition, is evident at the transformation temperature. The inexorable conclusion is reached, without recourse to the nature of the specimen being studied, that two phases must be in equilibrium. For the case in hand, these are obviously the crystalline and liquid phases of polyethylene.

The experimental results support the premise that the crystalline-liquid transformation in polymers possesses the characteristics of a first-order phase transition and therefore should be treated as such. This conclusion is reached from the formal analysis of experiment without the necessity of specifying the structural features of either of the phases.   The validity of this conclusion can be subjected to rather rigorous test as the concept of phase equilibria is extended to crystalline copolymers, multicomponent systems, and the effects of deformation on crystallization and melting.   The treatment of these apparently diverse subjects from this unified point of view is discussed in more detail in the following chapters.

The above deductions are contrary to that reached solely from morphological studies.[2,22]   As has been previously indicated, however, the matter is one requiring thermodynamic analyses.   At the melting temperature, therefore, equilibrium exists between the liquid and crystalline phases.   In principle, there are no reasons why equilibrium between the two phases cannot be developed and maintained at finite levels of crystallinity as well.   It is possible, therefore, to specify uniquely the properties of the crystalline phase as long as it is clearly recognized that the stipulations of equilibrium must be met.   For crystallization under conditions removed from equilibrium, this specification cannot be made.   The properties of the crystalline phase then depend on the mode by which the crystallinity was developed.   The development of higher levels of crystallinity, approaching equilibrium requirements, is not easily achieved and is governed by the nature of the crystallization mechanisms.   These problems are again common to the crystallization of polymers as well as monomeric substances.

The tortuous character of long chain molecules has intuitively led to the supposition that the crystalline state with the lowest free energy is one which contains a significant portion of amorphous regions.   The argument is based on the fact that the decrease in enthalpy incurred would be more than offset by the entropic gain attributable to the configurational freedom of the chain.   Hence, as the temperature is raised, chain segments would be progressively transferred to the amorphous regions.   Melting would then be a continuous process occurring over a broad temperature range.   Although this argument appears plausible in terms of the properties of a single chain, it is contrary to observations of the crystallization and melting of bulk polymers.

A molecular interpretation of this process involves the use of the methods of statistical mechanics.   This in turn requires the postulation of a molecular model for the system.   Two distinctly different models have been formulated and the necessary theoretical calculations performed.[24,25]   In one case, a given chain donates only one sequence to a crystallite.   In the other, the participation of a chain in a crystallite of fixed dimensions, appreciably less than the chain length, is unrestricted.   Common to both cases is the stipulation that crystallization is a three-dimensional process.   For both of these diverse models the conclusion is reached that the crystal-liquid transformation is a first-order phase transformation. Melting is predicted to occur sharply and discontinuously at a well-defined temperature. The anticipated entropic contribution of chain segments in random configuration at temperatures below T_m does not manifest itself. Close scrutiny of the calculations indicates this result is a consequence of the three-dimensional nature of the crystallite. The requirement that the termini of crystalline sequences (whether from many chains or from a single chain) must all lie in a plane normal to the chain axis is so stringent that if equilibrium prevails the concentration of chain units in the amorphous regions will be severely limited. The fraction of the material crystalline, $1 - \lambda$, will be very large and approach unity, while the equilibrium crystallite length will approach the extended length of the molecule.

These calculations explain in molecular terms why the fusion of high molecular weight polymers is a relatively sharp process that can be treated as a first-order phase transition. However, it can be expected that the large equilibrium length required below T_m would be difficult to attain experimentally. If the crystallite length ζ does not attain its equilibrium value, then the optimum stability of the system is reduced. Under these conditions,[24]

$$\frac{1}{T} - \frac{1}{T_m{}^\circ} = - \frac{R}{\Delta H_u} \frac{\ln D}{\zeta} \tag{2-2}$$

where $\ln D = 2\sigma_e / RT$. The excess free energy per mole of units at the crystallite ends is represented by σ_e. The depression of the melting temperature is smaller, the larger the values of ζ, since T is identified with the melting temperature of crystallites of length ζ. Equation (2-2) is identical to that obtained by considering the melting temperature of a crystallite restricted in the longitudinal direction to length ζ but unbounded in directions transverse to the chain direction. The depression of the melting point results from the contribution of the excess free energy at the crystallite ends to the total free energy of fusion. The formation and development of the crystalline phase are dependent on kinetic factors. Nonequilibrium melting temperatures that are observed, particularly on fast heating subsequent to crystallization, may very well reflect kinetic limitations on the size of ζ.

2-3 Effect of Molecular Weight

The influence of molecular weight on the equilibrium fusion process depends on the concentration of end groups and whether or not such units participate in the crystallization.   If chain ends are excluded from the crystallite for steric reasons, then, as has been previously indicated, they can be treated as a foreign ingredient that acts as a noncrystallizing component.   It is then possible to derive simple relationships between the melting temperature and the degree of polymerization.[24]   If the chain ends are present in the crystalline phase, a distinction must be made between the various possibilities that exist. For example, the end groups can be randomly distributed within the phase or they can be paired with one another.   The latter case is akin to that of the molecular crystals formed by the *n*-alkanes where the terminal units of the chains establish well-defined crystallographic planes.

For a system initially possessing a "most probable" molecular weight distribution defined by

$$w_x = x(1 - p)^2 p^{x-1} \qquad (2\text{-}3)$$

the end groups are distributed at random along the polymer chains. In this equation, w_x is the weight fraction of species composed of x units and p is a parameter representing the probability of the continuation of the chain from one unit to the next.   If these randomly distributed foreign units are excluded from the crystallites, then by straightforward thermodynamic arguments it is found that [24,26]

$$\frac{1}{T_m} - \frac{1}{T_m{}^\circ} = \frac{R}{\Delta H_u} \frac{2}{\bar{x}_n} \qquad (2\text{-}4)$$

T_m is the melting temperature of the specimen having a number-average degree of polymerization $\bar{x}_n$. $T_m{}^\circ$ is the melting temperature of the pure polymer of high molecular weight, and ΔH_u is the heat of fusion per chain repeating unit.   The quantity $2/\bar{x}_n$ represents the mole fraction of noncrystallizing units, and Eq. (2-4) results from the stipulation of the conditions for phase equilibrium.   According to this equation, as $\bar{x}_n$ is increased, the influence of molecular weight on T_m is expected to be severely diminished.   However, a careful study of the melting temperature of lower molecular weight polymers will allow for a critical assessment as to whether chain ends are excluded from the crystalline phase.

Evans, Mighton, and Flory[8] have studied the melting temperatures of samples of polydecamethylene adipate, prepared in such a manner as to possess the "most probable" molecular weight distribution.   Some typical results from this work are plotted in Fig. 2-7 according to Eq. (2-4). It is found that this equation is obeyed for values of $\bar{x}_n$ as low as several repeating units. Moreover, the value of ΔH_u obtained from the slope of the straight line of Fig. 2-7 is in good agreement with the value deduced by other methods. Although the melting temperature observed is the result of the disappearance of crystallites formed from the larger molecules, it depends on $\bar{x}_n$.

The data in Fig. 2-7 are for polyester chains terminated in the conventional manner with hydroxyl and carboxyl end groups. Low molecular weight decamethylene adipate polymers having very bulky end groups, such as benzoate, α-naphthoate, and cyclohexyl, were also prepared and their melting temperatures determined. Agreement

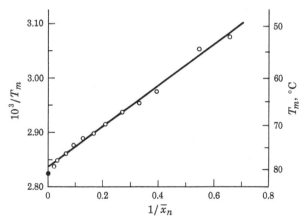

Fig. 2-7 $1/T_m$ against $1/\bar{x}_n$ for polydecamethylene adipates terminated with hydroxyl and carboxyl end groups. [*From Evans, Mighton, and Flory* (8).]

with Eq. (2-4) is again found. Within experimental error, the same value of ΔH_u is deduced for the above polymers as well as for the one terminated by hydroxyl and carboxyl groups. Since it is difficult to conceive that the bulky end groups could enter the crystallites, it can be concluded that, in general, terminal units will not occur within crystallites, irrespective of size. This conclusion is substantiated by the functional dependence of T_m on the number-average degree of polymerization.

For molecular weight fractions, where terminal units are no longer randomly distributed among the polymer chains, statistical mechanical methods are needed to deduce the relationship between melting temperature and molecular weight. For the model in which a chain contributes only one crystalline sequence to a crystallite, it is found that[24]

$$\frac{1}{T_m} - \frac{1}{T_m^\circ} = \frac{R}{\Delta H_u} \frac{1 + b}{x} \qquad (2\text{-}5)$$

where $b = [1 - (\zeta_e - 1)/x]^{-1}$ and ζ_e is the equilibrium crystallite length.

Except for the extremely low molecular weight species, T_m is essentially independent of chain length. For the values of ΔH_u usually observed, the limiting values of T_m should be reached for degrees of polymerization of several hundred at most. This has been verified for polyesters and polyamides[8] possessing the "most probable" molecular weight distribution as well as for fractions of polyethylene succinate[27] and of polyethylene.[28]

REFERENCES

1. Fuller, C. S., and W. O. Baker: *J. Chem. Educ.*, **20**: 3 (1943); W. C. Baker, C. S. Fuller, and N. R. Pape: *J. Am. Chem. Soc.*, **64**: 776 (1942).
2. Stuart, H. A.: *Ann. N.Y. Acad. Sci.*, **83**: 3 (1959).
3. Wycoff, H. W.: *J. Polymer Sci.*, **62**: 83 (1962).
4. Mandelkern, L.: *Chem. Rev.*, **56**: 903 (1956).
5. Wunderlich, B., and M. Dole: *J. Polymer Sci.*, **24**: 201 (1957).
6. Mayer, J. E., and S. F. Streeter: *J. Chem. Phys.*, **7**: 1019 (1939).
7a. Wood, L. A., and N. Bekkedahl: *J. Appl. Phys.*, **17**: 362 (1946).
7b. Wood, L. A., and N. Bekkedahl: *J. Res. Natl. Bur. Std.*, **36**: 489 (1946).
8. Evans, R. D., H. R. Mighton, and P. J. Flory: *J. Am. Chem. Soc.*, **72**: 2018 (1950).
9. Flory, P. J., L. Mandelkern, and H. K. Hall: *J. Am. Chem. Soc.*, **73**: 2532 (1951).
10. Mochel, W. E., and J. T. Maynard: *J. Polymer Sci.*, **13**: 235 (1954).
11. Roberts, D. E., and L. Mandelkern: *J. Am. Chem. Soc.*, **77**: 781 (1955).
12. Mandelkern, L., F. A. Quinn, Jr., and D. E. Roberts: *J. Am. Chem. Soc.*, **78**: 926 (1956).
13. Quinn, F. A., Jr., and L. Mandelkern: *J. Am. Chem. Soc.*, **80**: 3178 (1958).
14. Mandelkern, L.: in R. H. Doremus, B. W. Roberts, and D. Turnbull (eds.), "Growth and Perfection of Crystals," p. 499, John Wiley & Sons, Inc., New York, 1958.
15. Mandelkern, L.: *Rubber Chem. Technol.*, **32**: 1392 (1949).
16. Chiang, R., and P. J. Flory: *J. Am. Chem. Soc.*, **83**: 2857 (1961).
17. Tung, L.: *J. Polymer Sci.*, **24**: 333 (1957).
18. Rutgers, A. J., and S. A. Wouthuysen: *Physica,* **4**: 515 (1937).
19. Garner, W. E., K. van Bibber, and A. M. King: *J. Chem. Soc.*, 1533 (1931).
20. Meyer, K. H., and A. J. van der Wyk: *Helv. Chim. Acta*, **20**: 83 (1937).
21. Broadhurst, M.: *J. Chem. Phys.*, **36**: 2578 (1962).

22. Matsuoka, S.: *J. Polymer Sci.*, **42**: 511 (1960).
23. Kargin, V. A., and G. L. Slonimskii: *Usp. Khim.*, **24**: 785 (1955); V. A. Kargin: *J. Polymer Sci.*, **30**: 247 (1958).
24. Flory, P. J.: *J. Chem. Phys.*, **17**: 223 (1949).
25. Flory, P. J.: *J. Am. Chem. Soc.*, **84**: 2857 (1962).
26. Flory, P. J.: "Principles of Polymer Chemistry," p. 568, Cornell University Press, Ithaca, N.Y., 1953.
27. Ueberreiter, K., G. Kanig, and A. S. Brenner: *J. Polymer Sci.*, **16**: 53 (1955).
28. Tung, L. H., and S. Buckser: *J. Phys. Chem.*, **62**: 1530 (1958).

POLYMER-DILUENT SYSTEMS

chapter
3

3-1   Introduction

The authenticity of the conclusion that melting in polymeric systems is a first-order phase transition can be subjected to a rigorous test by studying the effect of an added monomeric second component on the transformation.   The appropriate relations that govern the fusion can be formally developed in a rigorous manner utilizing classical methods. We shall discuss this problem in some detail since exacting conditions can be imposed on the system and quantitative predictions made.   It is convenient to treat separately the more concentrated polymer-diluent mixtures as compared with dilute solutions.   In the latter category a distinction will also be made between the more flexible chain molecules and those which assume highly asymmetric configurations.

3-2   Concentrated Solutions

The composition range considered in this category is characterized by the random distribution of polymer segments throughout the mixture.

The Flory-Huggins equation has been shown to give an adequate representation for the free energy of mixing of polymer and diluent in the amorphous state.[1,2] From this expression, the chemical potential μ_1 of the diluent in the mixture relative to that of the pure component μ_1° can then be written as

$$\mu_1 - \mu_1^\circ = RT\left[\ln\,(1 - v_2) + \left(1 - \frac{1}{x}\right)v_2 + \chi_1 v_2^2\right] \quad (3\text{-}1)$$

while the chemical potential of the polymer molecule relative to the pure liquid polymer as a reference state can be expressed as[3]

$$\mu_2 - \mu_2^\circ = RT[\ln\,(1 - v_2) - (x - 1)(1 - v_2) + \chi_1 x(1 - v_2)^2] \quad (3\text{-}2)$$

In Eqs. (3-1) and (3-2), μ_2 is the volume fraction of polymer present in the mixture, x is the number of repeating units per molecule, and χ_1 represents the polymer-diluent interaction free energy.[3] The chemical potential per mole of polymer units in this formulation is obtained by dividing Eq. (3-2) by xV_1/V_u, the number of units per molecule. Thus[3]

$$\mu_u - \mu_u^\circ = RT\frac{V_u}{V_1}\left[\frac{\ln v_2}{x} + \left(1 - \frac{1}{x}\right)(1 - v_2) + \chi_1(1 - v_2)^2\right] \quad (3\text{-}3)$$

where V_u and V_1 are the molar volumes of the repeating unit and diluent, respectively. For polymers of high molecular weight, Eq. (3-3) reduces to

$$\mu_u - \mu_u^\circ = RT\frac{V_u}{V_1}[(1 - v_2) - \chi_1(1 - v_2)^2] \quad (3\text{-}4)$$

These expressions describe the thermodynamic properties of a two-component polymer melt.

The chemical potentials of the components in the crystalline phase that form from the mixture cannot be derived with such generality. They depend on restrictive conditions concerned with the number of components present and the nature of the mixing law governing the phase. These restrictions cannot be formulated in terms of general properties of polymer chains but depend on the chemical and crystal structure involved. A distinction can be made, however, between the cases where the diluent is either present or absent in the crystalline phase. When present, the role of the diluent must be enunciated in order to specify the chemical potential of both components.

For a large number of polymer-diluent mixtures the problem is greatly simplified since the diluent is prevented from entering the crystal lattice for steric reasons. This corresponds to a binary liquid mixture only one of whose components crystallizes over the complete composition range.   In this instance, the stipulation that equilibrium exist between the two phases requires that, in addition to the equality of temperature and pressure, the chemical potential of the crystallizing component in the two phases be identical.   At the melting point of a polymer-diluent mixture, which adheres to the above conditions, it is required that[4]

$$\mu_u^c - \mu_u^\circ = \mu_u^l - \mu_u^\circ \tag{3-5}$$

where the superscripts refer to the crystalline and liquid phases, respectively, and the pure molten polymer is taken as the reference state.   The difference in the chemical potential between a crystalline polymer unit and one in the pure liquid state can be written as

$$\mu_u^c - \mu_u^\circ = -\Delta F_u = -(\Delta H_u - T \Delta S_u) \tag{3-6}$$

By defining the ratio $\Delta H_u/\Delta S_u$ as T_m°, Eq. (3-6) can be written as

$$\mu_u^c - \mu_u^\circ = \Delta H_u \left(1 - \frac{T}{T_m^\circ} \right) \tag{3-7}$$

The tacit assumption has now been made that ΔH_u and ΔS_u do not vary with temperature.   By utilizing Eq. (3-4) for $\mu_u^l - \mu_u^\circ$, there is obtained

$$\frac{1}{T_m} - \frac{1}{T_m^\circ} = \frac{R V_u}{\Delta H_u V_1} [(1 - v_2) - \chi_1(1 - v_2)^2] \tag{3-8}$$

as the basic equation for the depression of the melting temperature with added diluent.

   Equation (3-8) bears close similarity to the usual expression for the melting temperature of a binary monomeric mixture, only one of whose components crystallizes.   The only difference for polymeric systems results from the new expression required to express the activity of the crystallizing component in the molten phase.   According to Eq. (3-8), the depression of the melting temperature depends on the volume fraction of diluent in the mixture and on its thermodynamic interaction with the polymer.   Other quantities being equal, a larger depression of the melting temperature should be observed with a good solvent (smaller values of χ_1) than with a poor one.   The size of the diluent molecule also affects the melting temperature, the depression being predicted to be greater for diluents of smaller molar volume. The larger the value of ΔH_u, the smaller is the expected melting point depression. ΔH_u, which represents the heat of fusion per mole of repeating unit, is an inherent and characteristic property of the chain repeating unit of a crystalline polymer. It should not be confused with the heat of fusion or latent enthalpy change ΔH_u^* obtained from calorimetric measurements. The latter quantity must, of necessity, depend on the amount of crystallinity initially present in the system. ΔH_u^* is less than ΔH_u except for the hypothetical completely crystalline polymer where the two quantities would be identical.

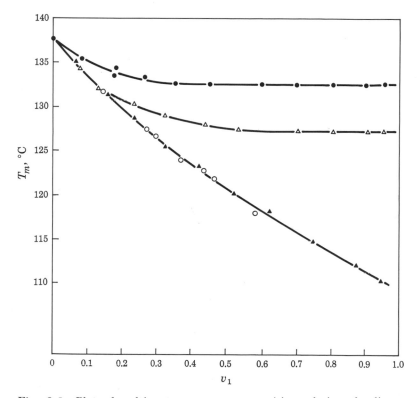

Fig. 3-1 Plot of melting temperature–composition relations for linear polyethylene for different diluents. Solid circles, *n*-butyl phthalate; open triangles, *o*-nitrotoluene; solid triangles, α-chloronaphthalene; open circles, tetralin. v_1 is volume fraction of the diluent present in the mixture (5).

For those systems in which diluent is excluded from the crystalline phase, a quantitative basis for the further assessment of the principles developed concerning the fusion process is given by Eq. (3-8). As has been indicated, different types of diluents are expected to affect the melting temperature of a given polymer in diverse ways, even at the same concentration. In Fig. 3-1 the melting temperature–composition relations of a linear polyethylene with different diluents are illus-

trated.[5,6] The two lower curves represent the results for tetralin and
α-chloronaphthalene as diluents. A continuous decrease of the melting temperature is observed as increasing amounts of diluent are
added. Such behavior is expected for these relatively good solvents.
The upper curves, which represent n-butyl phthalate and o-nitro-
toluene as diluents, are quite different. With the initial addition of
diluent, a small depression of the melting point is observed. However,
when a critical diluent concentration is reached, the melting temperature remains invariant with further dilution.

Similar effects have been observed with polychlorotrifluoroethylene,[7] poly(N,N'-sebacoyl piperazine),[8] and branched polyethylene[9]
when mixed with appropriate diluents. The observed invariance of
the melting temperature in these diluent mixtures can be given a
simple explanation when it is realized that when this phenomenon is
observed the molten state always consists of two immiscible liquid
phases. This is in contrast to the more commonly observed two-
component single liquid phase that is obtained on melting. Hence,
for the special cases cited, three phases must coexist in equilibrium at
the melting temperature. As a consequence of the phase rule, since
the pressure is maintained constant, the melting temperature must
remain invariant with composition. At the melting temperature,
therefore, crystalline macromolecular systems satisfy this requirement
of the phase rule. This is to be expected if the fundamental thesis of
the existence of a distinct macroscopic crystalline phase is accepted.

For those systems that show a continuous depression of the melting temperature with decreasing polymer concentration, a more direct
comparison with Eq. (3-8) can be made. According to this equation,
the initial slope of a plot of $1/T_m$ against the diluent concentration
$(1 - v_2)$ should be inversely proportional to ΔH_u. Any deviations
from linearity in a plot of this type are a reflection of the magnitude
of χ_1. Since χ_1 also depends on temperature, in order to utilize Eq.
(3-8) most conveniently, the assumption is made that $\chi_1 = BV_1/RT$,
where B represents the interaction energy density characteristic of the
solvent-solute pair.[10] Equation (3-8) can therefore be written as

$$\frac{1/T_m - 1/T_m^{\circ}}{v_1} = \frac{R}{\Delta H_u} \frac{V_u}{V_1} \left(1 - \frac{BV_1}{R} \frac{v_1}{T_m}\right) \qquad (3-9)$$

In making the assumption that χ_1 is inversely proportional to the
absolute temperature, any entropy contribution to the thermodynamic
interaction parameter has been neglected. More properly, χ_1 should
be equated to $BV_1/RT + (\frac{1}{2} - \psi_1)$, where ψ_1 is an entropy parameter.[10] When multiplied by v_1^2, the first term represents the Van Laar

heat of dilution; the second represents an additional contribution to the entropy of dilution beyond that calculated from the simple lattice theory. The neglect of the latter term can be justified by the small temperature range usually encompassed by experiment. Although the value of ΔH_u deduced from experiment should scarcely be affected by the approximation introduced, the value of B obtained may very well exceed the true Van Laar heat of mixing parameter.

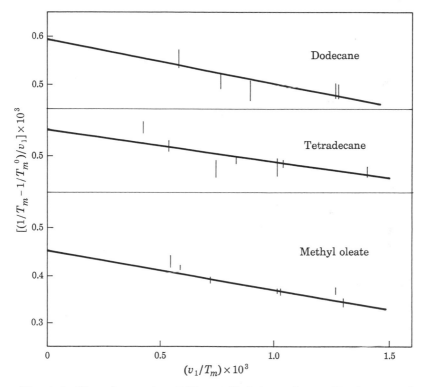

Fig. 3-2 Plot of quantity $(1/T_m - 1/T_m°)/v_1$ against v_1/T_m for natural rubber mixed with the indicated diluents (11).

Melting points of polymer-diluent mixtures crystallized and treated under conditions approaching equilibrium should therefore adhere to this equation. A plot of the quantity $(1/T_m - 1/T_m°)/v_1$ against v_1/T_m should yield a straight line; from the intercept of this straight line, ΔH_u for a given polymer can be deduced if the ratio V_u/V_1 is known.

Representative plots of experimental data treated in accordance with Eq. (3-9) are given in Figs. 3-2 and 3-3 for two distinctly different polymer types, natural rubber[11] and polydecamethylene terephthalate.[12]   Each of the polymers was mixed with varying amounts of different diluents.   In each case the data are well represented by a straight line.   The negative slopes in Fig. 3-2 are indicative of positive values of the quantity B for the interaction of each of the three diluents with natural rubber.   On the other hand, the slightly positive slope observed for the polydecamethylene terephthalate–benzophenone system denotes a negative value for this quantity.   Linear relations of the type illustrated have been observed for such a large number of

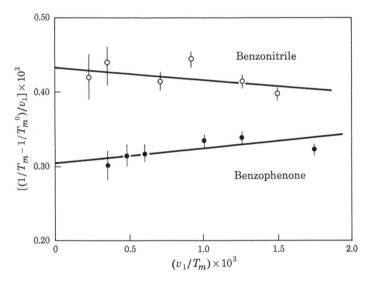

Fig. 3-3   Plot of quantity $(1/T_m - 1/T_m°)/v_1$ against v_1/T_m for polydecamethylene terephthalate with the indicated diluents. *From Flory, Bedon, and Keefer (12).*]

diverse polymer-diluent systems[5] that the functional relation of Eq. (3-9) has been clearly established.   Moreover, when cognizance is taken of the molar volume of the added component, the value of ΔH_u deduced for a given polymer is independent of the nature of the diluent used.   Some representative examples of the values obtained for ΔH_u from experiments of this kind are given in Table 3-1.   The agreement for a given polymer is excellent.   Hence, experiment strongly confirms the thesis that the quantity ΔH_u is a property of the crystallizing chain repeating unit and is independent of the nature of the diluent used. Since the necessary requirements are fulfilled, it can be concluded from a simple analysis that, at the melting temperature, equilibrium between the pure crystalline polymeric phase and the two-component liquid phase is established.

Studies of the depression of the melting point by diluent have been successfully employed by Flory and Garrett[13b] in investigating the thermodynamics of the crystal-liquid transformation of the fibrous protein collagen. By means of sensitive dilatometric techniques, the melting temperature of collagen (from rat-tail tendon and beef Achilles tendon)–anhydrous ethylene glycol mixtures was determined

TABLE 3-1
Typical results for ΔH_u as determined from Eq. (3-9)

Polymer	Diluent	ΔH_u, cal/mole of repeating unit
Polyethylene[6]	Ethyl benzoate	930
	o-Nitrotoluene	935
	Tetralin	990
	α-Chloronaphthalene	970
Natural rubber[11]	Tetradecane	1,040
	Methyl oleate	980
	Dodecane	1,100
Polydecamethylene terephthalate[12]	Benzonitrile	11,600
	Benzophenone	10,400
Polychlorotrifluoroethylene[7]	Toluene	1,220
	Mesitylene	1,100
	o-Chlorobenzotrifluoride	1,260
	Cyclohexane†	1,330

† Since the data for T_m scatter, the value obtained for ΔH_u is only approximate.

over a wide composition range. As illustrated in Fig. 3-4, the melting temperature–concentration relations are in accord with Eq. (3-9) except for the extremely dilute range. From the straight line of this figure a value for ΔH_u of 24 cal/g or 2250 cal/mole of peptide units is deduced when $T_m°$ is taken as 418°K. These results demonstrate that the melting process for the more complex crystalline macro-molecular systems such as the fibrous proteins can also be treated as a general problem in phase equilibrium. Consequently they can be studied and analyzed by the methods utilized for the simpler type of polymer systems.

There are complications, however, in analyzing the phase diagram for such systems. It is difficult to obtain the melting point of the pure undiluted polymer. The distinct possibility also exists that the diluent may enter the crystal lattice and actually become part of the crystallographic structure.   For example, for collagen and the nucleic acids the absorption of water is accompanied by an increase in the equatorial X-ray spacings,[14,15] indicative of the diluent entering the ordered phase.   Under these circumstances, the conditions for equilibrium stipulated by Eq. (3-5) are no longer sufficient, and an additional requirement must be fulfilled.   Specifically, it is now required that

$$\mu_1{}^l = \mu_1{}^c \qquad\qquad (3\text{-}10)$$

Moreover, Eq. (3-6) for the expression $\mu_u{}^c - \mu_u{}^\circ$ may no longer be

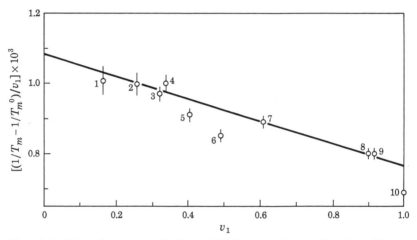

Fig. 3-4 Plot of quantity $(1/T_m - 1/T_m{}^\circ)/v_1$ against v_1 for the collagen–ethylene glycol system.   [*From Flory and Garrett* (13b).]

satisfactory if there are any interactions or mixing of polymer units and diluent molecules in the crystalline phase.   The simplest example of this type would be the formation of a solid solution in the ordered state.   Hence, when dealing with the two-phase equilibrium of a two-component system, both components being present in each phase, the activity as a function of the composition of each component in each of the phases must be specified in order to arrive at the melting temperature–composition relation.   For these situations, analysis of the experimental observations is more complex than is indicated by Eq. (3-9) and cannot be easily generalized.

Certain simplifying assumptions have been made in analyzing the results for collagen.[13]   It is assumed that a fixed amount of diluent (independent of total composition) is firmly bound to the protein while the remainder is loosely held, so that at the melting temperature the latter can be relegated to the amorphous regions. Under these conditions, Eq. (3-5) will again stipulate the requirements for equilibrium, the chemical potential of the polymer unit in the crystalline phase will be a constant independent of total composition, and Eq. (3-9) should be fulfilled. However, in this instance T_m° does not represent the melting point of the pure undiluted polymer but that of the polymer-diluent complex and hence is not independent of the nature of the added second component. Utilization of this approximate procedure must necessarily lead to a greater uncertainty in the deduced value of ΔH_u than is usually expected when the aforementioned complications do not exist.

Heretofore attention has been focused principally on the lowering of the melting temperature of a pure homopolymer by added diluent. The equilibrium requirements can also be examined at finite levels of crystallinity at temperatures below T_m where λ is less than unity. If the diluent is uniformly distributed throughout the amorphous phase, the polymer composition in this phase v_2' varies with the degree of crystallinity $(1 - \lambda)$ according to the relation

$$v_2' = \frac{v_2\lambda}{1 - v_2 + v_2\lambda} \tag{3-11}$$

At phase equilibrium the chemical potential of the polymer unit in the pure crystalline phase must be equal to that in the liquid phase at the composition given by Eq. (3-11). Consequently it is found that

$$\frac{1}{T_\lambda} - \frac{1}{T_m^\circ} = \frac{R}{\Delta H_u} \frac{V_u}{V_1} (v_1' - \chi_1 v_1'^2) \tag{3-12}$$

where T_λ represents the temperature of equilibrium for a degree of crystallinity $1 - \lambda$ corresponding to a volume fraction of diluent v_1'. In effect, therefore, Eq. (3-12) specifies the equilibrium degree of crystallinity that exists at temperature T_λ for a total or nominal composition v_2. When $\lambda = 1$, $v_2' = v_2$ and Eq. (3-8) is regained.

As in the case of a homopolymer, Eq. (3-12) again leads to the expectation that the last traces of crystallinity will disappear at a well-defined temperature. However, for the polymer-diluent mixtures the melting range should be broadened, the breadth of the melting process depending on the amount and type of diluent added, becoming more expanded as the concentration of diluent is increased. This expectation is confirmed by studies on a wide variety of polymer-diluent systems.[5,6]

Experimental studies by Chiang and Flory[16] of the specific volume–temperature relations of polyethylene–α-chloronaphthalene mixtures through the melting range are particularly suited to test the thesis that phase equilibrium can be maintained at finite levels of crystallinity.   These experiments were conducted under carefully controlled crystallization conditions, and the specific volumes can be easily converted to the degree of crystallinity.   The results of these experiments are given in Fig. 3-5.   The solid lines represent the experi-

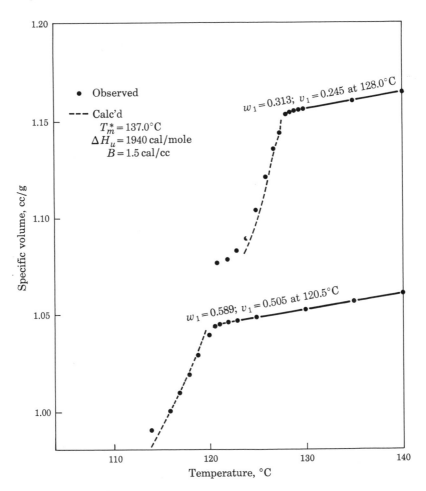

Fig. 3-5   Relationship of specific volume to temperature for mixtures of polyethylene ($M = 50,000$) with α-chloronaphthalene of the indicated weight (w_1) and volume (v_1) fractions.   Dashed lines represent calculations according to Eq. (3-12), assuming equilibrium between the crystalline and liquid phases.   [*From Chiang and Flory* (16).]

mental observations, while the dashed lines are calculated from Eq. (3-12) using values for ΔH_u and χ_1 previously determined from studies of the melting temperature–composition relations for this polymer. The agreement between the theoretical expectation and experimental observations is excellent in this composition range for levels of crystallinity ranging up to about 50 per cent. For systems containing lesser amounts of diluent, small deviations between theory and experiment are observed; they can be attributed to the enhanced difficulties of establishing equilibrium. These observations conclusively demonstrate that equilibrium between two distinct phases exists even when appreciable levels of crystallinity are developed. One of these phases has the properties of the liquid mixture while the other has that of the pure crystalline polymer. The concept that a partially crystalline polymer, when crystallized from the bulk or concentrated solution, is composed of crystalline and amorphous regions is further strengthened. The proposals[17–19] that such systems are merely imperfect or distorted crystals and devoid of amorphous content find no substantiation in terms of a thermodynamic analysis of experiment. The morphological basis for these suggestions must therefore be reexamined.

3-3 Dilute Solutions

The melting or dissolution of a crystalline polymer at high dilution is widely observed, as is the inverse process of a polymer crystallizing out of a dilute solution. The dissolution process results in the separation of the constituent molecules and is usually accompanied by a simultaneous change in molecular configuration. However, it is also possible at high dilution for the individual polymer molecules to maintain the configuration typical of the crystalline state. This is particularly true if steric requirements favor the perpetuation of a preferred bond orientation or if the crystalline structure is maintained by intramolecular bonding. For the latter case further alterations in the thermodynamic environment can result in a structural transformation involving the individual molecules, each molecule being converted to a configuration typical of the amorphous state. This intramolecular transformation has been popularly termed the helix-coil transition because of the two different chain configurations that are usually involved. Postponing a discussion of the latter phenomenon, we consider first the crystallization behavior of the simpler-type macromolecules where an ordered configuration is not maintained in dilute solutions.

A homogeneous dilute solution is characterized by a nonuniform polymer segment distribution throughout the medium, in contrast to the situation prevailing in more concentrated systems.[10] The individual molecules are isolated from one another; hence there are regions in space that are devoid of polymer. This distinguishing feature of mixtures dilute in polymeric species is very important in considering the crystal-liquid transformation in this composition range. The lattice treatment of polymer solutions previously utilized is now in error and requires revision for the present situation. Only when the solvent is sufficiently poor, so that the molecules freely interpenetrate one another, is the effect of this circumstance neutralized.

The chemical potential of the solvent species in dilute solution is expressed in virial form in modern theory.[10] By use of the Gibbs-Duhem equation, the chemical potential of the polymer unit in the molten phase can be calculated. When the indicated calculation is performed, however, it is found that the corrections are much too small to have any appreciable effect on the melting temperature. Hence, for present purposes the chemical potential of the polymer unit as given by Eq. (3-3) can be utilized. If the chemical potential of a unit in the crystalline phase is again expressed by Eq. (3-6), then, at the melting temperature,

$$\frac{1}{T_m} - \frac{1}{T_m{}^\circ} = \frac{R}{\Delta H_u} \frac{V_u}{V_1} \left[\left(1 - \frac{1}{x} \right) v_1 - \chi_1 v_1{}^2 - \frac{\ln v_2}{x} \right] \qquad (3\text{-}13)$$

which is very similar to Eq. (3-8) obtained for more concentrated systems. Deviations from the latter form when $x \to \infty$ would be expected only at extremely high dilutions; other deviations which might occur for very small values of x would be difficult to detect experimentally. Therefore, the melting point–composition relations or solubility relations are expressible as a continuous function that encompasses the complete composition range.

The temperature-concentration relations for the dissolution in tetralin of finely divided samples of polyethylene, originally crystallized in the bulk at high temperatures, are given in Fig. 3-6.[20] These observations are indicated by the solid circles in the plot and fall on the same smooth curve as the melting temperatures obtained dilatometrically at the higher polymer concentrations. The latter points are indicated by the open circles. Thus, in accordance with theory, the melting temperature–composition relations from pure polymer to very dilute solutions can be represented by a continuous function given by Eq. (3-8).

However, when the crystallization is initially conducted from a solution of given composition and the melting temperature (or solubility point) subsequently determined, differences exist in the temperatures determined by the two methods. Material crystallized from solution invariably displays a lower melting temperature. Melting temperatures determined by the latter method for polyethylene-tetralin mixtures are given by the open squares of Fig. 3-6. These differences initially manifest themselves at about 50 per cent polymer

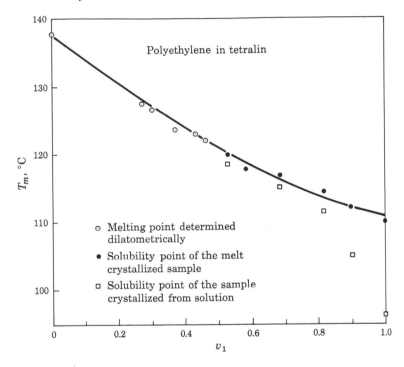

Fig. 3-6 A plot of the solubility temperature against volume fraction diluent v_1 for polyethylene in tetralin. Open circles, melting points determined dilatometrically; solid circles, solubility point of melt crystallized samples; open squares, solubility point of solution crystallized sample. [*From Jackson, Flory, and Chiang* (20).]

composition and become progressively more pronounced with further dilution. For the very dilute solutions about a 12° difference in the melting temperatures is observed. Since the liquid state is the same for the two cases, irrespective of the mode of crystallization, the disparity in the melting temperatures must reside in differences in the nature of the crystalline phases. The lower melting temperatures observed after crystallization from solution indicate that a metastable crystalline form is obtained under these conditions. This metastability could arise for a variety of reasons. In this connection it is significant that platelike crystals of folded chains are the usual morphological form observed after crystallization from dilute solution.

For present purposes it suffices to take cognizance of these observations so that caution is exercised in analyzing the experimentally observed melting temperature–composition relations. The melting temperature of the most stable species is required at all concentrations, so that for purposes of determining ΔH_u the dilute range should be avoided unless bulk crystallized polymer is utilized.

When the complete composition range from pure polymer to very dilute solution is encompassed, utilizing a good solvent as the added second component, the range of melting temperatures can be quite large. The tacit assumption that ΔS_u and ΔH_u are independent of temperature can be seriously questioned, and the entropy contribution to χ_1 must be taken into account. Although Eq. (3-8) still describes the equilibria, the appropriate thermodynamic quantities may no longer remain constant.

The melting point–composition relation (3-8) is, in effect, an expression of the temperature limit of the solubility of a crystalline polymer in the given solvent. At a given concentration the solubility temperature is not very sensitive to molecular weight except for the very low molecular weight species. Therefore the crystallization of a polymer from a dilute solution cannot provide a very effective method of molecular weight fractionation even if equilibrium solubility conditions are achieved. It is more likely, however, that as the liquid phase is cooled, the crystallization of the polymer will be governed primarily by rate factors. Thus further difficulties in efficiently separating the molecular weight species can be envisaged. In order to separate effectively a heterogeneous crystalline polymer into its constituent molecular weight components by precipitation from dilute solution, it is necessary that crystallization be avoided and the polymer separate out as a liquid phase. This can be established by appropriate phase-diagram studies.

3-4 Helix-Coil Transition

Although dispersed polymer chains usually adopt the random coil configuration in very dilute solutions, important exceptions are observed. These occur principally among macromolecules of biological interest. Physical-chemical measurements have established[21–23] that many of the simpler synthetic polypeptides are capable of existing as independent alpha-helices at high dilution in appropriate solvent

media. Similarly the ordered structure of the synthetic polynucleotides, among which are compound helices comprised of two or three
interwoven polymer chains, can also be maintained in dilute solution.[24-27] The solubilization of the naturally occurring nucleic acids,
as well as many of the fibrous proteins, with the preservation of the
molecular organization has been demonstrated. For example, the
dissolution of the fibrous protein collagen can be accomplished, with
the characteristic ordered structure of the collagen protofibril being
preserved.[28,29] In the instances cited, the preservation and stability
of the ordered structure can be attributed to the action of specific
secondary bonding. For the alpha-helical structures intramolecular
hydrogen bonds between peptide groups along the main chain are
involved. For the compound helical structures interchain hydrogen
bonding is involved.

Specific types of intramolecular bonding are not, however, necessary for ordered structures to persist in dilute solution. For example,
poly-L-proline can exist in solution in either of two forms, one of which
has been established to be helical.[30] Since this polymer is a polyimino
acid, intramolecular hydrogen bonds are not possible. The helical
form is undoubtedly perpetuated in this case by steric hindrances
imposed by the bulky pyrrolidine ring. Other chains in which the
steric hindrance is very severe could possibly also exist, even when
dispersed in dilute solution. Polar forces between neighboring substituents could also cause the perpetuation of a given bond orientation
without the imposition of hydrogen bonds.

When individual isolated molecules exist in helical form, environmental changes, particularly in the temperature or in the solvent composition, can cause a disruption of the ordered structure, with the
chain configuration becoming that of a random coil. This reversible
intramolecular transformation has been termed the helix-coil transition and represents an elementary manifestation of polymer melting
and crystallization. Many examples of transformations of this type
are available from the experimental studies of Doty and his collaborators.[24-26] For example, the simple polypeptide poly-L-glutamic
acid exists as a randomly coiled molecule in dilute neutral or alkaline
solution. However, when the pH is lowered below about 5.0, the
alpha-helical form is stabilized. The transformation from the coil
$\rightleftarrows$ helix manifests itself in changes in various physical-chemical properties, as illustrated in Fig. 3-7. Thus, as the charge on the molecule is
decreased, as indicated by the decreased state of ionization, a large
increase is observed in the optical rotation $[\alpha]$. Concomitantly the
intrinsic viscosity $[\eta]$ also increases. The small pH range over which

these changes occur is indicative of the cooperative nature of the transformation and displays strong similarity to melting processes.

A similar type of transition can also be demonstrated for the synthetic polynucleotides. As an example, when mixed in dilute solution,
polyadenylic acid and polyuridylic acid form an ordered two-stranded
helical structure. When this system is heated, an intramolecular
transition is induced in the vicinity of 50°C, as illustrated in Fig. 3-8.
Among the properties affected during this configurational charge are
the absorbance (at about 250 mμ) and the optical rotation. These
alterations in properties occur over a narrow temperature interval

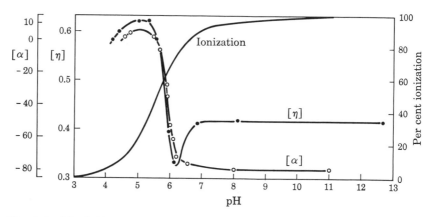

Fig. 3-7   The helix-coil transition in poly-L-glutamic acid as it is affected by the
variation of pH. [*From Doty* (23).]

characteristic of melting. The collapse of the ordered structure of
multichain molecules in dilute solution results concomitantly in the
separation of the individual chains, each in randomly coiled form.
Under careful conditions of experiment, regeneration of the native
ordered structure can be accomplished even for such complex systems
as collagen[31] and deoxyribonucleic acid.[32]

Extensive theoretical attention has been given to intramolecular
transitions. We shall discuss in detail the theory for the transformation of those polypeptide chains which exist in either the alpha-helical
or random coil form in dilute solution. The existence of the ordered
structure in helical form is attributable to the stability given to the
molecule by the intramolecular hydrogen bonds between neighboring
units. Specifically, according to Pauling and Corey,[33] the hydrogen
atom of each main chain amide group forms a hydrogen bond with the
oxygen atom of the third preceding group. Hence the bond orientation of successive units is dependent upon one another and there is a

tendency for this configuration to be sustained along the chain. Schellman[34] has pointed out that the stereochemistry of an alpha-helix requires that three successive hydrogen bonds, involving three peptide units, be severed in order that one repeating unit of the ordered struc-

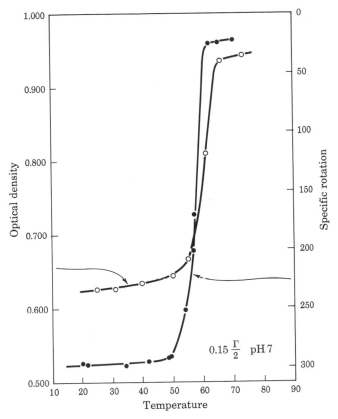

Fig. 3-8 The helix-coil transition in synthetic polynucleotides. The variation in specific rotation and optical density with temperature of a dilute solution of the complex formed by polyadenylic and polyuridylic acid. [*From Doty, Boedtker, Fresco, Hall, and Haselkorn* (27).]

ture be disrupted. The necessary fulfillment of this condition in order for a repeating unit to gain the configurational freedom of the random coil state is the basis for the cooperative nature of the transformation. Once the enthalpy has been expended for the realization of the greater entropy of the random coil state, the latter configuration is favored. The transformation from the helix to the random coil should thus be relatively abrupt, with changes in such independent variables as temperature, pressure, or composition.

The simplest, but very illuminating, quantitative formulation of this problem is due to Schellman.[34]   It is assumed that the individual molecules existed completely in either the helical (H) or the coil (C) form.   For the equilibrium process

$$H \rightleftarrows C \tag{3-14}$$

$$\frac{(C)}{(H)} = K = \exp \frac{-\Delta F_t}{RT} \tag{3-15}$$

where ΔF_t is the difference in free energy per molecule between the ordered and random forms.   For a sufficiently high molecular weight so that the influence of the terminal residues can be neglected, $\Delta F_t = x \, \Delta F_u$. ΔF_u is the change in free energy per repeating unit, there being x repeating units per molecule.   When ΔF_u is zero, the concentration of molecules in each of the forms is identical.   Since the number of units per molecule x is assumed to be large, a small change in ΔF_u, in the vicinity of $\Delta F_u = 0$, can cause the ratio of $(C)/(H)$ to change drastically.   The development of one configuration at the expense of the other, with the alteration of an independent variable, such as the temperature or composition, of the surrounding medium, could be sufficiently sharp as to resemble a phase transition.   Since x is large, the enthalpy change for the molecule as a whole will be large. Consequently the equilibrium constant K must change very rapidly with temperature.   As a measure of the breadth of the transition, the rate of change with temperature of the fraction of the molecules in randomly coiled form is examined.   At the transition temperature, $T = T_t$ when $\Delta F_t = 0$, this rate of change can be expressed as[34]

$$\left(\frac{d\{(C)/[(C) + (H)]\}}{dT} \right)_{T=T_t} = \frac{x \, \Delta H_u}{4RT_t^2} \tag{3-16}$$

Since ΔH_u is estimated to be of the order of several kilocalories per mole, the transition is relatively sharp and appears to possess the characteristics of a first-order phase transition.   However, only in the limit of pure polypeptide chains of infinite molecular weight is the transition infinitely sharp.   If the molecular weight is not large, the range of the transition is considerably broadened.

The formulation of the problem presented above is based on the assumption that the individual molecules exist completely in either one or the other of the two possible configurations.   For molecules of high molecular weight this is not a completely satisfactory hypothesis. Although the helical form clearly represents the state of lowest enthalpy, whereas the random coil represents the one with the greatest configurational entropy, intermediate chain configurations comprised of alternating random coil and helical regions could represent the thermodynamically most stable configurational state, the one of minimum free energy.†

The more elaborate methods of statistical mechanics are now needed to investigate this possibility. A variety of theoretical treatments of this problem has been presented.[35—43] A strong similarity exists among the different theories. A one-dimensional ordered array of amino acid residues is taken as the model. The number of ways in which formed or unformed hydrogen bonds can be distributed along the chain, chain ends being treated as special cases, are enumerated. This enumeration is restricted by the stereochemical requirements of an alpha-helix, with appropriate statistical weights being assigned to the different arrangements. In its more general aspects the problem resembles the one-dimensional Ising lattice used as a model for the theory of ferromagnetism. The various theories differ in the detailed manner in which the partition function for the isolated chain is generated. However, the same general conclusion is reached, namely, that a fairly sharp transition is still possible even though helical and random coil sequences actually coexist within the same molecule.

A more quantitative basis for this conclusion is seen by examining the theory developed by Zimm and Bragg.[35] For a simple polypeptide chain of uniform structure, the transformation depends on two parameters. One of these, designated as s, can be identified with $K^{1/x}$ of Eq. (3-15), while the other, σ, enters into the partition function for each ordered sequence which follows a succession of randomly coiled units. Thus $-RT \ln \sigma$ can be treated as a measure of the free energy change for three amide residues being transposed from the random state to initiate a helical portion of the chain, as compared with the change that occurs when one segment is added to a section of pre-existing helix. Therefore σ, which is a quantity much less than unity, can be looked upon as an inverse measure of the cooperative interactions favoring continuation of the ordered structure.

The matrix method is utilized to evaluate the partition function of the chain. For long chains the fraction of residues in helical form is

† The problem posed here differs fundamentally from that discussed in the previous chapter. In the present case a one-dimensional system is being treated. Formerly, the problem involved a three-dimensional crystallite which required all crystalline sequences to terminate in the same plane.

given by[35]

$$\theta = \frac{d \ln \chi}{d \ln s} \tag{3-17}$$

where χ is the largest root of the equation

$$\chi = \tfrac{1}{2}\{1 + s \pm [(1 - s)^2 + 4\sigma s]^{1/2}\} \tag{3-18}$$

According to the theory, s assumes a critical value at unity. It is in the neighborhood of this critical value that the transition from random to helical configuration occurs. The sharpness of the transition depends on the value of σ and on the chain length. For low molecular weights a more complicated expression is derived for θ, and the chains either are randomly coiled or contain only one unbroken helical section. When the chain length exceeds the order of several hundred amide residues, the transition becomes essentially independent of molecular weight and is quite sharp. When σ equals unity, there is no interaction between the states of the successive units so that the fraction of hydrogen-bonded units shows only a gradual rise with s. However, when σ approaches zero, indicative of very intense cooperative interaction, there is an extremely sharp transition at $s = 1$.

It can be shown[44] that for long molecules the breadth of the transition can be characterized by the range in which s changes between limits set by

$$-\sigma^{1/2} < \frac{1 - s}{s} < \sigma^{1/2} \tag{3-19}$$

Over this range the helix content should diminish from about three-fourths to one-fourth. Since $-RT \ln s$ is equal to ΔF_u, in the vicinity of T_t where $s \cong 1$,

$$\frac{ds}{dT} = \frac{\Delta H_u}{RT^2} \tag{3-20}$$

Hence the temperature interval of the transition is given to good approximation by

$$\Delta T = \frac{2RT^2\sigma^{1/2}}{\Delta H_u} \tag{3-21}$$

The transition becomes sharper as ΔH_u is increased or σ decreased.

A quantitative comparison between the statistical mechanical theory outlined and experimental observation has been made for different molecular weight samples of poly-γ-benzyl glutamate in

dilute solutions of dichloroacetic acid–ethylene dichloride mixtures.[45]
The results of this comparison are given in Fig. 3-9.   The solid curves
represent the best fit between experiment and theory for the three
samples of differing degrees of polymerization.   Good agreement is
obtained, and the increased sharpness of the transition with increasing
molecular weight is apparent.   The best fit is obtained if σ is assigned
the value 2×10^{-4} and ΔH_u is 900 cal/mole.   According to Eq. (3-21),
these parameters indicate that the breadth of the transition should be

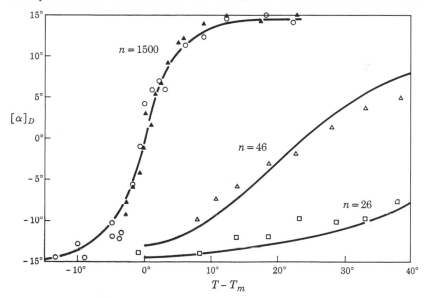

Fig. 3-9   Theoretical and experimental comparison of the helix-coil transition
of poly-γ-benzyl-L-glutamate in dilute solution of an ethylene dichloride–
dichloroacetic acid mixture.   The experimental points are the optical rotation
$[\alpha]_D$ plotted as a function of the temperature T minus the transition temperature
T_m.   The solid curves represent the best fit of theory for samples of various
degrees of polymerization n.   [*From Zimm, Doty, and Iso* (**45**).]

about 5° for very high molecular weight samples.   The above analysis
is, of course, predicated on the assumption that the equilibrium distribution between the helical and random coil sequences is actually
attained along the chain.   The thermodynamic parameters deduced
are of significance only if these conditions are, in fact, met.

   For the more complex compound helices, the initiation of a
random coil region within the ordered structure requires the disruption
of a larger number of peptide or nucleotide units.   Hence the parameter corresponding to σ should be much smaller for such systems.

Therefore, if the other quantities involved were of the same order of magnitude, the breadth of the transition for a multichain structure should be smaller than for one containing only a single chain.

The analogy between the helix-coil transition and a transition restricted to a one-dimensional lattice is clear.   Landau and Lifshitz[46] have shown generally that thermodynamic equilibrium is not possible between two arbitrarily long homogeneous phases in contact at a point.   The two phases must mix with one another to some extent. The statistical mechanical calculation of the helix-coil transition is consistent with this conclusion.   This characteristic of one-dimensional systems causes the transition to be diffuse and allows for coexistence of the two phases over a finite temperature range.   Therefore, in strict interpretation, transitions of the helix-coil type cannot qualify as being true phase transitions.   However, despite the diffuseness of the transition, the dependence of the transition temperature on the independent variables of the system follows the dictates of phase equilibria theory.

This type of transition is unique in the sense that the coordinated action of many molecules is not required.   It is restricted to the very dilute portion of the complete phase diagram.   As the concentration of molecules which have adopted the helical configuration is increased, intermolecular interactions begin to assert themselves.   The cooperative character of the transition is further enhanced.   The dimensional order of interdependence increases from 1 in the case of a dilute solution to 3 for the concentrated system.   The melting transition is then formally identical to that of the dense crystalline phase previously discussed.

The globular proteins are believed to be composed of short helical regions interspersed between less-ordered regions.   Detailed X-ray diffraction studies confirm this hypothesis for hemoglobin and myoglobin.[47,48]   This type of organization of chain elements results in an over-all molecular structure of relatively low asymmetry.   Despite this, however, relatively sharp structural transitions are observed. The transformation range is much narrower than would be expected solely from the restricted length of the helical regions.   It has been pointed out that interactions between side chains of neighboring units within an individual helix would enhance the sharpness of the transition.[49]   More important perhaps is the possibility that the transformations of the individual helices within the molecule do not occur independently.   If the helices lie in close proximity to one another, the system is effectively a concentrated one and the cooperative character of the transition is further increased.

3-5 Transformations Not Involving Molecular Configurational Changes

When a polymer molecule possesses an ordered structure, it is necessarily restricted to a unique configuration. A highly asymmetric, rodlike molecule results, characterized by a length many times greater than its breadth. Such a collection of molecules, wherein the individual species are uncorrelated and randomly arranged relative to one another, can exist as independent entities in a sufficiently dilute solution. However, rodlike molecules of high axial ratio cannot be arranged at random at high density because of space requirements; i.e., as the density of polymer is increased, sufficient volume is no longer available to allow for the maintenance of a disordered array. This qualitative concept leads to the conclusion that at high concentration a completely disordered or isotropic solution of asymmetrically shaped macromolecules is not possible. Hence either a change in molecular configuration must occur or a more ordered arrangement must develop as the polymer concentration is increased.

A quantitative treatment of this phenomenon has been given by Flory.[50] In the theoretical development a lattice technique is utilized to enumerate the number of configurations available to n_2 rigid, rodlike polymer molecules with an asymmetry x (the ratio of molecular length to its breadth) and partial orientation about an axis and to n_1 monomeric solvent molecules. When the usual Van Laar heat of mixing term is employed, the free energy of mixing can be expressed as

$$\frac{\Delta F_M}{kT} = n_1 \ln v_1 + n_2 \ln v_2 - (n_1 + yn_2) \ln \left[1 - v_2 \left(1 - \frac{y}{x} \right) \right]$$
$$- n_2[\ln (xy^2) - y + 1] + \chi_1 x n_2 v_1 \quad (3\text{-}22)$$

where v_1 and v_2 are the respective volume fractions and y is a parameter which is a measure, or index, of the disorientation of the molecules. This parameter can vary from unity, characteristic of a perfectly ordered array, to x typifying a state of complete disorder. When $y = 1$, Eq. (3-22) reduces to the free energy of mixing for a regular solution and when $y = x$ it yields a result essentially identical to that for the mixing of rigid polymer chains.[51] Thus for a fixed molecular asymmetry x, Eq. (3 22) is an expression for the free energy of mixing as a function of the composition and the disorientation index y.

When the composition and molecular asymmetry are kept constant, Eq. (3-22) goes through a minimum and then a maximum as the disorientation parameter y is increased. Since there are no external restraints on the disorientation index, y assumes the value that minimizes ΔF_m. By appropriate differentiation it is found that for a given v_2 and x the value of y which fulfills this condition is the smaller of the two solutions of the equation

$$v_2 = \frac{x}{x - y}\left[1 - \exp\left(-\frac{2}{y}\right)\right] \tag{3-23}$$

If v_2^* is the minimum concentration which allows for a solution of this equation, a necessary condition for the existence of an isotropic phase (a state of complete molecular disorder) is $v_2 < v_2^*$. It can be shown that

$$v_2^* = \frac{8}{x}\left(1 - \frac{2}{x}\right) \tag{3-24}$$

represents the maximum concentration allowable for the stable existence of an isotropic phase or the minimum concentration required for stable anisotropy (a state of partial equilibrium order of the molecules). Thus the maximum concentration at which the molecules can exist in random arrangement relative to one another is inversely related to the axis ratio for large x. This conclusion depends only on the asymmetry of the molecules and is reached without invoking the action of any intermolecular forces. In the absence of diluent ($v_2 = 1$), it is calculated that a length-diameter ratio of about $2e$ would be sufficient to cause spontaneous ordering of the phase.

From the free energy function given by Eq. (3-23), together with the equilibrium stipulation of Eq. (3-22), the chemical potentials of each of the components in the two phases, the isotropic phase with $y = x$ and the phase where the molecules are in a state of equilibrium disorder (not completely disordered), can be derived. The conditions for equilibrium between the two phases at constant temperature and pressure can then be established by equating the chemical potentials of each of the components in each phase. We treat first the case of athermal mixing, where χ_1 is equal to zero, so that there is no net interaction between the molecules. The variation of the chemical potentials of each of the components is such that separation into two phases, one isotropic and one ordered, must occur at relatively high dilution.[50] For $x = 100$ the composition of the two phases in equilibrium is $v_2 = 0.0806$ for the dilute phase and $v_2' = 0.1248$ for the slightly more concentrated phase. The more dilute phase is isotropic, the orientation of the particles being uncorrelated with those of their neighbors. The more concentrated phase is highly anisotropic, particles in a given region being fairly well aligned relative to a common axis. This can be termed a "tactoidal" phase. Phase separation occurs in this instance solely as a consequence of particle asymmetry, unassisted and unabetted by any intermolecular interactions. As the molecular asymmetry is increased, the polymer concentrations of both phases diminish; however, the concentration of the ordered phase is never much greater than that of its isotropic conjugate. The polymer concentration ratio of the two phases appears to approach a limit of 1.56 as x increases.

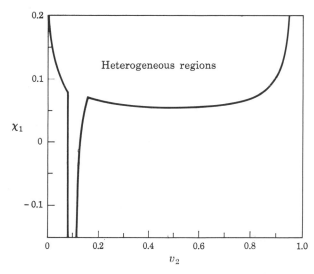

Fig. 3-10 Theoretical calculation of phase equilibria in solutions of rodlike particles. Composition of phases, v_2, in equilibrium for $x = 100$, and values of the interaction parameter χ_1 plotted on the ordinate. The curve for isotropic solutions is on the left and that for ordered phases on the right. The heterogeneous regions lie between the two curves. [*From Flory* (50).]

As χ_1 becomes slightly positive, the theoretical possibility develops, within a limited range of values of this parameter, for the coexistence of the two anisotropic phases. Thus two heterogeneous regions can exist, one representing the equilibrium between two conjugate relatively concentrated anisotropic phases and the other between the dilute isotropic and anisotropic phases just discussed. For $x = 100$ the two heterogeneous regions merge at $\chi_1 = 0.070$. For values of χ_1 equal to or exceeding 0.07, equilibrium exists only between a dilute isotropic phase and a concentrated anisotropic phase. The complete diagram depicting the phases that can coexist in such a system is given in Fig. 3-10 for the illustrative case of $x = 100$. The configuration of the polymer molecules remains unaltered in the different phases. In this diagram it is seen that a relatively small increase in χ_1 can cause a drastic increase in the polymer concentration of the anisotropic phase, from $v_2 \cong 0.15$ to $v_2 > 0.9$. Hence a comparatively small positive interaction energy causes the concentration of the anisotropic phase to approach that of a pure polymer, while the polymer concentration in the isotropic phase remains quite small. The magnitude of the interaction parameter required for phase separation is relatively small. It is much less than the value of 0.5 necessary to bring about liquid-liquid phase separation of randomly coiled polymers of infinite molecular weight. The basis for this difference is the greater configurational entropy possessed by the randomly coiled molecules in dilute solution. The entropy due to mixing of rigid, rodlike molecules at equilibrium disorder is much less and approaches that of the ideal mixing law. Consequently lower interaction energies suffice to cause the instability of the isotropic phase.

Specific interactions between chain substituents, beyond those incorporated in the Van Laar mixing term, produce a further ordering of the concentrated or precipitated phase. For asymmetric particles of uniform structure, only a small further sacrifice in entropy suffices for the formation of an ordered array of crystalline regularity. Despite the inexactitudes inherent in a lattice model, the theory outlined offers a basis for the understanding of the spontaneous formation of fibrillar structures from dilute solutions of macromolecules. The latter process is involved in the macroscopic formation of the fibrous proteins and in many of the macromolecular systems involved in cell processes. The value of the parameter χ_1 can be varied by suitable change of solvent composition or by alterations of the temperature. Depending on the relative contributions of enthalpy and entropy to this parameter, it either increases or decreases with an increase in temperature.

Examples of the type of transformation described exist primarily among polymers of biological interest. Robinson, Ward, and Beevers[50] observed that dilute solutions of poly-γ-benzyl-L-glutamate in various organic solvents, wherein the alpha-helical form is maintained, spontaneously separate into a dilute birefringent phase at a concentration that depends on the degree of polymerization. In the alpha-helix the axial ratio must increase with increasing molecular weight. Since the dilute tactoidal phase is observed in a variety of solvents, a lack of sensitivity to specific solvent interaction is indicated, in accordance with the theoretical prediction. The high asymmetry of the particles is the major factor in causing the phase separation.

A specific example of the phase separation observed for this

polymer in dioxane is given in Fig. 3-11.[44]   The polymer concentrations in the two phases coexisting in equilibrium are plotted as a function of the axial ratio or degree of polymerization and are represented
by the solid lines.   The birefringent phase is only slightly more concentrated than the dilute isotropic phase.   The dashed lines represent
the composition of the two phases as calculated from theory.   The
ratio of the observed concentration of the two phases is in good accord

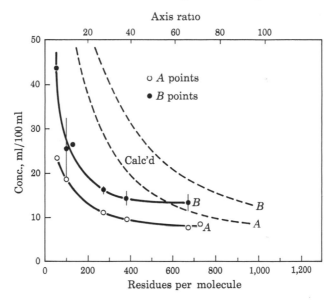

Fig. 3-11   Composition of coexisting isotropic (open circles)
and birefringent tactoidal (solid circles) phases of poly-γ-
benzyl-L-glutamate in dioxane at ordinary temperature plotted against the average degree of polymerization on the
lower abscissa.   The upper abscissa scale represents the
axial ratio calculated from the structure of the alpha-helix.
Dashed curves are calculated from the theory of phase equilibria in solutions of rodlike particles.   [*From Flory* (44).]

with theory.   The dependence of the composition of each of the two
phases on the axial ratio, however, shows a considerable departure from
theoretical expectation, particularly at the lower values.   Hermans[53]
has shown that, for the same polymer, the maximum volume fraction
v_2^* at which solutions are homogeneously isotropic follows the dictates
of Eq. (3-24).   Despite the quantitative shortcomings, it can be concluded that the formation of the dilute birefringent phase is a consequence of the particle asymmetry and develops for the reasons outlined
above.

According to theory, if a slightly positive interaction parameter is operative, the anisotropic phase will become highly concentrated in polymer. Phase separation will occur at a critical value of this parameter, with the transition occurring without any change in molecular configuration. Although quantitative verification of this expectation has not as yet been demonstrated, several observations are amenable to interpretation from this point of view. For example, poly-L-proline can exist in dilute aqueous solution in a highly asymmetric helical form with the chain units, assuming a trans configuration relative to the imide bond.[30] If the temperature is raised, a highly concentrated polymer phase will precipitate. It can be shown that no change in the configuration of the individual molecules occurs during this separation. On cooling, the dilute isotropic solution is formed once again.[54] This transition between the two phases can receive qualitative explanation in terms of the aforementioned principles if it is assumed that χ_1 increases with increasing temperature. This condition is not uncommon in polar systems.

The solubilized collagen molecule, or tropocollagen, is a highly asymmetric molecule about 3,000 A long and 15 A in breadth, according to light scattering measurements.[29] When the temperature or solvent composition of dilute solutions of these molecules is varied, different states of aggregates or fibrils are developed, depending on the environmental conditions.[55] Included in the fibrillar forms that can be regenerated is the native structure. These processes again represent examples of a transformation occurring without any change in molecular configuration. The organized state that develops depends on specific interactions between the molecules which are governed or regulated by the nature of the solvent. The theory outlined can serve as a basis for further quantitative study of these observations which can be taken as models for the naturally occurring processes of fibril formation.

The different phase equilibria and transformations in polymer-diluent mixtures that have been discussed can be epitomized by the schematic diagram of Fig. 3-12. Process 1 represents the usual melting or crystallization of polymers with a configurational change occurring during the transformation. A diluent may or may not be present in the amorphous state, III, while state I represents the pure crystalline phase. Transformations in this category were discussed in Secs. 3-2 and 3-3. The formation of an isotropic dilute solution, II, wherein the molecules maintain the configuration characteristic of state I, is designated as process 2. This can be thought of as a dissolution process, but in distinction to process 1 molecular configuration is maintained. The inverse process represents the formation of a pure ordered phase from a dilute solution of anisotropic molecules. The "helix-coil" transformation is then represented by process 3. The dilute tactoidal phase I′ is formed from the dilute isotropic phase by process 2′ by a slight increase in the polymer concentration. This schematic diagram points out certain similarities between the various processes and the importance of considering the complete composition

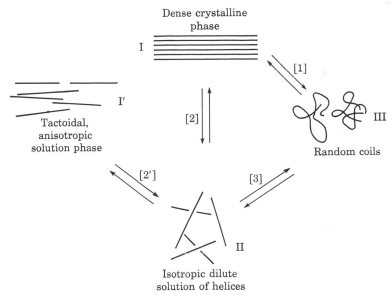

Fig. 3-12 Schematic representation of transitions and phase equilibria involving polymer chains in ordered configurations. [*From Flory* (44).]

range to describe the behavior adequately. For example, the helix-coil transition is seen as a manifestation of process 1 in dilute solution. The continuity between the helix-coil transition and regular melting has been established for collagen. For certain polymer systems a point in the phase diagram may exist at low polymer concentrations where three phases representing the pure ordered phase, the randomly coiled state, and the state of the individual asymmetric molecules coexist. This bears an analogy to the triple point for the coexistence of solid, liquid, and vapor of monomeric substances.

3-6 Melting Induced by Chemical Reactions

Melting and crystallization are governed not only by the independent variables such as temperature, pressure, and composition but also by appropriate chemical reactions.   All that is required in order to shift the equilibrium is an alteration of the chemical potential of the polymer unit in either or both of the phases.   This can be accomplished, for example, by reaction between reagents in the surrounding medium and functional groups along the polymer chain.   One of the phases will then develop at the expense of the other.   Chemical reactions are not limited to dilute solutions of isolated macromolecules but can take place over the complete composition range.   Thus, in analyzing the problem, the polymer composition must be carefully specified.

A diversity of reactions can be considered in this general classification.   For example, one type could involve complexing between a reactant in the surrounding medium and a specific substituent group along the polymer chain.   It is possible that the steric requirements of the complex formed would be such that it could exist only in the amorphous state.   In this state the necessary accommodations could be made by adjustments in the chain configuration.   Therefore, an increase in the extent of complexing would shift the crystal-liquid equilibrium to favor melting.   However, if the reactant entered the crystalline phase, a new compound would be formed possessing its own characteristic melting temperature.   Another possibility is that only some of the chain units would be structurally altered.   In this instance, a homopolymer would be converted to a copolymer.   The characteristics of the crystallization of this class of polymers would then be developed.

For crystallizable polyelectrolytes, electrostatic effects would be expected to affect the equilibrium between the two states.   It seems unlikely, for example, that a charged substituent and its associated counterion could be accommodated in the usual crystal lattice. Experiment indicates that melting can indeed be induced in such polymers by changes in the ionic nature of the surrounding medium. The dilute solution helix-coil transition of poly-L-glutamic acid[23] and poly-L-lysine[23] is affected by alterations of the pH of the medium. Poly-L-lysine has an amino group in the side chain of the repeating unit which is positively charged at pH values below about 9.5 and is neutral above about pH 10.5.   It is observed that the helical form is stable only in the uncharged state so that, as the pH is lowered, transformation to the random coil state occurs isothermally.   Similarly, for poly-L-glutamic acid the helical form is stable below pH 5 where the carboxyl side groups are largely un-ionized.   Transformation to the random coil form occurs as the pH is raised.   The stability of the ordered structure of other polyelectrolytes is similarly affected.   The melting temperature of DNA from calf thymus is lowered from 86° to

about 25° by a reduction in the ionic strength or pH.[56]   In the absence
of an added electrolyte, T_m falls below room temperature.   Similar
behavior has also been noted in the synthetic polyribonucleotides.
We can conclude, therefore, that the accommodation of a charged
substituent in the ordered state is thermodynamically less favored
than in the amorphous state.   A shift in the equilibrium between the
two states can thus be accomplished by control of the pH of the
medium.

It has also been suggested by Scheraga[57] that, besides purely
electrostatic effects, changes in pH can alter the nature of side chain
hydrogen bonding in polypeptides and proteins.   The disruption of
such hydrogen bonds, when they are an integral part of the crystal
structure, would promote melting.   Chemical reactions that cause the
formation or severance of intermolecular cross-links must also affect
the stability of ordered structures.   The role of cross-links will be discussed in detail subsequently (see Chap. 6).   For polypeptides and
proteins this is of importance in view of the relative chemical ease with
which intermolecular disulfide bonds can be controlled.   Other types
of chemical reactions which could affect the crystal-liquid transition
can be envisaged.   It is not the intent to consider here all the diverse
possibilities.

The quantitative formulation of the coupling of the crystal-liquid
transformation with a chemical reaction involves specifying the phases
in which the reaction occurs and the modifications induced in the
chemical potential of the repeating unit.   The reaction can be treated
by the usual methods of chemical equilibrium, the results of which are
then imposed on the conditions for phase equilibrium.   The many
possibilities that exist must be individually treated according to this
procedure.   For illustrative purposes we give attention to a simple
type of complexing reaction restricted solely to the amorphous
phase.[34,58]

Consider a polymer molecule P containing n substituents each
capable of complexing in the amorphous phase with reactant C according to the scheme

$$P + rC \rightleftharpoons P \cdot C_r \qquad (3\text{-}25)$$

where the total concentration of polymer species P and $P \cdot C_r$ remains
unchanged.   The equilibrium constant for the reaction can be written
as

$$K_r = \frac{n!}{(n-r)!\,r!} K^r \qquad (3\text{-}26)$$

where K is the equilibrium constant for the individual complexing reaction.   Each site of reaction is assumed to be independent of any other.   The combinatorial factors represent the number of ways in which the reactant can be distributed among the n possible substituents.   The extent of the reaction r can be expressed as

$$r = \frac{na_c K}{1 + a_c K} \tag{3-27}$$

where a_c is the activity of species C.   The free energy change due to the reaction is

$$\Delta F_{\text{react}} = -nRT \ln (1 + Ka_c) \tag{3-28}$$

The change in chemical potential per repeating unit is

$$\mu_u^* - \mu_u = -N_A RT \ln (1 + Ka_c) \tag{3-29}$$

where μ_u^* represents the chemical potential of the complexed unit and N_A is the mole fraction of chain units bearing the reactive substituent. If more than one reactive site per chain unit exists, the appropriate numerical factor must be appended to Eq. (3-29).   By applying the usual conditions for phase equilibria, the melting point equation becomes[58]

$$\frac{1}{T_m} - \frac{1}{T_m^\circ} = \frac{R}{\Delta H_u} \frac{V_u}{V_1} (v_1 - \chi_1 v_1^2) + \frac{RN_A}{\Delta H_u} \ln (1 + Ka_c) \tag{3-30}$$

For experiments carried out at fixed polymer concentration, usually in dilute solutions, the last term on the right in Eq. (3-30) represents the depression of the melting temperature, at the given composition, due to the chemical reaction.   If the factor Ka_c is small, then[37]

$$T_m(v_2) - T_{m,r}(v_2) \cong \frac{RT_m^2(v_2)N_A Ka_c}{\Delta H_u} \tag{3-31}$$

$T_m(v_2)$ represents the melting temperature of the unreactive mixture at the composition v_2 and $T_{m,r}(v_2)$ is that after complexing.   Structural transformations in dilute solutions of globular proteins which are induced by the action of urea have been found to obey Eq. (3-31).[59,60] For this reactant both the carbonyl oxygen and the amino hydrogen of the peptide group are assumed to be involved so that the right-hand side of Eq. (3-31) must be increased by a factor of 2.

More generally, and particularly for open systems, the more complete Eq. (3-30) must be employed.   The sensitivity of the melting temperature to the chemical reaction is embodied in the last term of the equation.   For example, if there is a very strong affinity for complexing, i.e., if K is large, only a small change in the activity (or concentration) of the reactant will suffice to cause a marked shift in the equilibrium. Melting or crystallization can therefore be carried out by isothermal processes. Conversely, if K is small, a large value of the activity may be required to lower the melting temperature. However, in the vicinity of the melting point small changes in a_c will still drastically alter the concentration of the various species.

The foregoing is intended to exemplify a specific type of chemical process which has as a consequence the shifting of the melting temperature. All processes that affect the chemical potential of the polymer unit must affect the nature of this equilibrium. Further discussion of the influence of chemical reactions on melting will be included in the treatment of contractile processes and the mechanochemistry of fibrous macromolecules.

REFERENCES

1. Huggins, M. L.: *J. Phys. Chem.*, **46:** 151 (1942); *Ann. N.Y. Acad. Sci.*, **41:** 1 (1942); *J. Am. Chem. Soc.*, **64:** 1712 (1942).
2. Flory, P. J.: *J. Chem. Phys.*, **10:** 51 (1942).
3. Flory, P. J.: "Principles of Polymer Chemistry," p. 513, Cornell University Press, Ithaca, N.Y., 1953.
4. Flory, P. J., R. R. Garrett, S. Newman, and L. Mandelkern: *J. Polymer Sci.*, **12:** 97 (1954); Ref. 3, pp. 568ff.
5. Mandelkern, L.: *Rubber Chem. Technol.*, **32:** 1392 (1959).
6. Quinn, F. A., Jr., and L. Mandelkern: *J. Am. Chem. Soc.*, **80:** 3178 (1958); **81:** 6533 (1959).
7. Bueche, A. M.: *J. Am. Chem. Soc.*, **74:** 65 (1952).
8. Flory, P. J., L. Mandelkern, and H. K. Hall: *J. Am. Chem. Soc.*, **73:** 2532 (1951).
9. Richards, R. B.: *Trans. Faraday Soc.*, **42:** 10 (1946).
10. Flory, P. J., and W. R. Krigbaum: *Ann. Rev. Phys. Chem.*, **2:** 383 (1951); also Ref. 3, pp. 508ff.
11. Roberts, D. E., and L. Mandelkern: *J. Am. Chem. Soc.*, **77:** 781 (1955).
12. Flory, P. J., H. D. Bedon, and E. H. Keefer: *J. Polymer Sci.*, **28:** 151 (1958).
13a. Garrett, R. R., and P. J. Flory: *Nature*, **177:** 176 (1956).
13b. Flory, P. J., and R. R. Garrett: *J. Am. Chem. Soc.*, **80:** 4836 (1958).
14. Zaides, A. L.: *Kolloidn. Zh.*, **16:** 265 (1954).
15. Feughelman, M., R. Langridge, W. E. Seeds, A. R. Stokes, H. R. Wilson, C. W. Hopper, M. H. F. Wilkins, R. K. Barclay, and L. D. Hamilton: *Nature*, **175:** 834 (1955).
16. Chiang, R., and P. J. Flory: *J. Am. Chem. Soc.*, **83:** 2857 (1961).
17. Kargin, V. A., and G. L. Slonimskii: *Usp. Khim.*, **24:** 785 (1955); V. A. Kargin: *J. Polymer Sci.*, **30:** 247 (1958).

18. Stuart, H. A.: *Ann. N.Y. Acad. Sci.*, **83**: 3 (1959).
19. Geil, P.: *J. Polymer Sci.*, **47**: 65 (1960).
20. Jackson, J. B., P. J. Flory, and R. Chiang: *Trans. Faraday Soc.*, **59**: 1906 (1963).
21. Doty, P., A. M. Holtzer, J. H. Bradbury, and E. R. Blout: *J. Am. Chem. Soc.*, **76**: 4493 (1954); P. Doty, J. H. Bradbury, and A. M. Holtzer: *J. Am. Chem. Soc.*, **78**: 947 (1956); J. T. Yang and P. Doty: *J. Am. Chem. Soc.*, **78**: 498 (1956); **79**: 761 (1957).
22. Doty, P., K. Iamhori, and E. Klemperer: *Proc. Natl. Acad. Sci. U.S.*, **44**: 474 (1958); P. Doty, A. Wada, J. T. Yang, and E. R. Blout: *J. Polymer Sci.*, **23**: 851 (1957).
23. Doty, P.: *Revs. Mod. Phys.*, **31**: 107 (1959).
24. Warner, R. C.: *J. Biol. Chem.*, **229**: 711 (1957).
25. Rich, A., and D. R. Davies: *J. Am. Chem. Soc.*, **78**: 3548 (1956); G. Felsenfeld and A. Rich: *Biochim. Biophys. Acta*, **26**: 457 (1957); A. Rich: *Nature*, **181**: 521 (1958); A. Rich: *Biochim. Biophys. Acta*, **29**: 502 (1958).
26. Fresco, J. R., and P. Doty: *J. Am. Chem. Soc.*, **79**: 3928 (1957).
27. Doty, P., H. Boedtker, J. R. Fresco, B. D. Hall, and R. Haselkorn: *Ann. N.Y. Acad. Sci.*, **81**: 693 (1959).
28. Cohen, C.: *Nature*, **175**: 129 (1955); *J. Biophys. Biochem. Cytol.*, **1**: 203 (1955).
29. Boedtker, H., and P. Doty: *J. Am. Chem. Soc.*, **77**: 248 (1955); **78**: 4267 (1956).
30. Harrington, W. F., and M. Sela: *Biochem. Biophys. Acta*, **27**: 24 (1958).
31. Rice, R. V.: *Proc. Natl. Acad. Sci. U.S.*, **46**: 1186 (1960).
32. Marmur, J., and D. Lane: *Proc. Natl. Acad. Sci. U.S.*, **46**: 453 (1960); P. Doty, J. Marmur, J. Eigner, and C. Schildkraut: *Proc. Natl. Acad. Sci. U.S.*, **46**: 461 (1960).
33. Pauling, L., R. B. Corey, and H. R. Bransom: *Proc. Natl. Acad. Sci. U.S.*, **37**: 205 (1951).
34. Schellman, J. H.: *Compt. Rend. Trav. Lab. Carlsberg, Ser. Chim.*, **29**: 230 (1955).
35. Zimm, B. H., and J. K. Bragg: *J. Chem. Phys.*, **28**: 1246 (1958); **31**: 526 (1959).
36. Gibbs, J. H., and E. A. DiMarzio: *J. Chem. Phys.*, **28**: 1247 (1958); **30**: 271 (1959).
37. Peller, L.: *J. Phys. Chem.*, **63**: 1194, 1199 (1959).
38. Rice, S. A., and A. Wada: *J. Chem. Phys.*, **29**: 233 (1958).
39. Hill, T. L.: *J. Chem. Phys.*, **30**: 383 (1959).
40. Schellman, J. H.: *J. Phys. Chem.*, **62**: 1485 (1958).
41. Zimm, B. H.: *J. Chem. Phys.*, **33**: 1349 (1960).
42. Nagai, K.: *J. Phys. Soc. Japan*, **15**: 407 (1960); *J. Chem. Phys.*, **34**: 887 (1961).
43. Lifson, S., and A. Roig: *J. Chem. Phys.*, **34**: 1963 (1961).
44. Flory, P. J.: *J. Polymer Sci.*, **49**: 105 (1961).

45. Zimm, B. H., P. Doty, and K. Iso: *Proc. Natl. Acad. Sci. U.S.*, **45**: 1601 (1959).
46. Landau, L. D., and E. M. Lifshitz: "Statistical Physics," p. 482, Pergamon Press, Ltd., London, 1958.
47. Kendrew, J. C., R. E. Dickerson, B. E. Strandberg, R. G. Hart, D. R. Davies, D. C. Phillips, and V. C. Shore: *Nature*, **185**: 422 (1960).
48. Perutz, M. F., M. G. Rossmann, A. F. Cullis, H. Muinhead, G. Will, and A. C. T. North: *Nature*, **185**: 416 (1960).
49. Scheraga, H. A.: *J. Phys. Chem.*, **65**: 699 (1961).
50. Flory, P. J.: *Proc. Royal Soc. (London)*, *Ser. A*, **234**: 73 (1956).
51. Flory, P. J.: *Proc. Royal Soc. (London)*, *Ser. A*, **243**: 60 (1956).
52. Robinson, C.: *Trans. Faraday Soc.*, **52**: 571 (1956); *Discussions Faraday Soc.*, **25**: 29 (1958).
53. Hermans, J., Jr.: *J. Colloid Sci.*, **17**: 638 (1962).
54. Gornick, F., and L. Mandelkern: Unpublished results.
55. Highberger, J. H., J. Gross, and F. O. Schmitt: *J. Am. Chem. Soc.*, **72**: 3321 (1950); *Proc. Natl. Acad. Sci. U.S.*, **37**: 286 (1951).
56. Doty, P., J. Marmur, and N. Sueoka: *Brookhaven Symp. Biol.*, **12**: 1 (1959).
57. Scheraga, H. A.: *J. Phys. Chem.*, **64**: 1917 (1960).
58. Flory, P. J.: *J. Cellular Comp. Physiol.*, **49**: (Suppl. 1) 175 (1957).
59. Foss, J. G., and J. A. Schellman: *J. Phys. Chem.*, **63**: 2007 (1959).
60. Nakajima, A., and H. A. Scheraga: *J. Am. Chem. Soc.*, **83**: 1575 (1961).

FUSION OF COPOLYMERS

4-1 Introduction

The introduction into a polymer of units that differ chemically, stereo-chemically, or structurally from the predominant chain repeating elements imposes restrictions on the crystallization and fusion processes. The distinct possibility exists that in such macromolecules not all the chain elements can participate in the crystallization. For purposes of classification and logical treatment of their crystallization behavior, polymer chains that possess nonidentical units are termed copolymers. In this category are true chemical copolymers, wherein chemically differing groups are incorporated into the chain, as well as chains containing isomeric units. Polymers possessing other types of chain irregularities, as, for example, branch points, are also conveniently placed in this grouping. However, for reasons to be discussed subsequently, systems possessing intermolecular cross-links require special treatment.

The problems involved in the crystallization and melting of copolymers cannot be uniquely formulated. This arises from the fact that, when a copolymer crystallizes, participation in the transformation by all the differing chain elements is not an a priori requirement. A wide variety of possibilities exist. These depend on the crystallization conditions, the concentration of the different chain units present, their sequence distribution, and the stereochemical relations that exist among the various units. Thus, from a theoretical point of view, model systems are treated, and careful distinctions must be made when examining real systems. A common situation encountered with synthetic polymers and simpler type of chain molecules is that in which only the units that occur in major proportion crystallize. Specific cases exist, however, where the other chain units present enter into the same crystal lattice.

For protein molecules, where the constituent polypeptide chains are composed of many different amino acid residues arranged in specified sequence distribution, similar problems are presented. When stereochemical identity exists among the units, it can be assumed that they can all enter into the same lattice. However, in the absence of this identity, this assumption is not warranted. Besides influencing the melting behavior of this important class of macromolecules, the deduction of the detailed crystal structure of these systems from X-ray diffraction studies depends on the knowledge of which specific units are involved in the crystallization. The tacit assumption that all units are involved could lead to serious misinterpretation of the chain microstructure.

In studying the general problem of the fusion of copolymers, not only must consideration be given to the effect of compositional and structural changes on the melting temperature but a careful distinction must be made among the various possible modes of crystallization.

4-2   Theory

The theory of the equilibrium crystallization of copolymers is due to Flory.[1] Following his development, we shall discuss a model copolymer which contains only one type of crystallizable unit, designated as A units. In the initially molten state, these units occur in a specified distribution of sequence lengths as a consequence of the copolymer constitution. The noncrystallizable comonomeric units will be designated as B units. Thus the crystalline state is comprised of crystallites of varying length. The length of a crystalline sequence is conveniently expressed by ζ, the number of A units of a given chain that traverses the crystallite from one end to the other. The longitudinal development of the crystallites is restricted by the occurrence of the

noncrystallizing B elements along the polymer chain.   The lateral
development is governed by the availability or concentration of
sequences of suitable length in the residual melt and by the decrease in
free energy that occurs when a sequence of ζ A units is transferred
from the amorphous to the crystalline phase.

A quantitative formulation is developed by relating to the melt
composition the probability P_ζ that a given A unit in the amorphous
polymer is located within a sequence of at least ζ such units.   Let w_j
represent the probability that a unit chosen at random from the
amorphous regions of the copolymer is an A unit and also is a member
of a sequence of j A units terminated at either end by B units.   Further, let $P_{\zeta,j}$ be the probability that the specific A unit selected is
followed in a given direction by at least $\zeta - 1$ additional units of this
kind.   Then[1]

$$P_{\zeta,j} = \frac{(j - \zeta + 1)w_j}{j} \qquad j \geq \zeta$$

$$P_{\zeta,j} = 0 \qquad j < \zeta \tag{4-1}$$

and
$$P_\zeta = \sum_{j=\zeta}^{\infty} P_{\zeta,j} = \sum_{j=\zeta}^{\infty} \frac{(j - \zeta + 1)w_j}{j}$$

Solving for successive values of ζ yields the difference equation

$$w_\zeta = \zeta(P_\zeta - 2P_{\zeta+1} + P_{\zeta+2}) \tag{4-2}$$

Equations (4-1) and (4-2) are quite general and do not depend on the
presence or absence of crystallites.   The quantities P_ζ and w_ζ can be
related to the constitution of both the initially molten polymer and to
the partially crystalline one.   The conditions for equilibrium between
the two phases can then be established.

In the completely molten copolymer, prior to the development of
any crystallinity,

$$w_\zeta{}^\circ = \frac{X_A \zeta \nu_\zeta{}^\circ}{N_A} \tag{4-3}$$

where N_A is the total number of A units in the copolymer, X_A the corresponding mole fraction, and $\nu_\zeta{}^\circ$ the number of sequences of ζ A units
initially present in the melt.   We assume that the probability of an A
group being succeeded by another A group is independent of the
number of preceding A groups in the sequence.   This probability is
designated as p, and Eq. (4-3) can be written as

$$w_\zeta{}^\circ = \frac{\zeta X_A(1 - p)^2 p^\zeta}{p} \tag{4-4}$$

By combination with Eq. (4-1), there is obtained

$$P_\zeta{}^\circ = X_A p^{\zeta-1} \qquad (4\text{-}5)$$

for the initially molten copolymer.

When crystallization occurs and thermodynamic equilibrium is maintained, the probability $P_\zeta{}^e$ that in the noncrystalline regions a given A unit is located in a sequence of at least ζ such units is given by

$$P_\zeta{}^e = \exp\left(-\frac{\Delta F_\zeta}{RT}\right) \qquad (4\text{-}6)$$

where ΔF_ζ is the standard free energy of fusion of a sequence of ζ A units from a crystallite ζ units long. ΔF_ζ can be expressed as

$$\Delta F_\zeta = \zeta \,\Delta F_u - 2\sigma_e \qquad (4\text{-}7)$$

where ΔF_u is the free energy of fusion per mole of units and σ_e is the surface free energy per repeating unit at the crystallite ends. Crystallites are considered to be sufficiently large in directions transverse to the chain axis so that the contribution of the excess lateral surface free energy to ΔF_ζ can be neglected. Equation (4-6) can then be expressed as

$$P_\zeta{}^e = \frac{1}{D} \exp\left(-\zeta\theta\right) \qquad (4\text{-}8)$$

where

$$\theta = \frac{\Delta H_u}{R}\left(\frac{1}{T} - \frac{1}{T_m{}^\circ}\right) \qquad (4\text{-}9)$$

and

$$D = \exp\left(-\frac{2\sigma_e}{RT}\right) \qquad (4\text{-}10)$$

If crystallites of lengths ζ, $\zeta + 1$, and $\zeta + 2$ are present and are in equilibrium with the melt, then Eqs. (4-8) and (4-2) can be combined to give

$$w_\zeta{}^e = \zeta D^{-1}[1 - \exp(-\theta)]^2 \exp(-\zeta\theta) \qquad (4\text{-}11)$$

as the expression for the residual concentration in the melt of sequences of A units which are ζ units long.

From the above, the necessary and sufficient condition for crystallization can be stated as

$$P_\zeta{}^\circ > P_\zeta{}^e \qquad (4\text{-}12)$$

for one or more values of ζ. Similarly, the condition $w_\zeta{}^\circ > w_\zeta{}^e$ for one or more ζ is a necessary but not sufficient condition for crystallization. Equations (4-4) and (4-11), which describe the initial and equilibrium distributions of sequences in the melt, are both functions of the sequence length ζ. There is therefore a critical value, $\zeta = \zeta_{cr}$, at which the two distribution functions are equal. This is expressed analytically as

$$\zeta_{cr} = \frac{-\{\ln (DX_A/p) + 2 \ln [(1 - p)/(1 - e^{-\theta})]\}}{\theta + \ln p} \qquad (4\text{-}13)$$

For values of $\zeta < \zeta_{cr}$, w_ζ^e is greater than w_ζ° while for $\zeta > \zeta_{cr}$ the converse is true. Thus ζ_{cr} represents the limiting size above which crystallites can exist at equilibrium; crystallites below this size cannot be maintained in equilibrium.

Utilizing Eqs. (4-5) and (4-8), the inequality of Eq. (4-12) can be expressed as

$$\frac{X_A}{p} p^\zeta > \frac{1}{D} e^{-\theta\zeta} \qquad (4\text{-}14)$$

Except for copolymers exhibiting a high tendency for alternation, $1/D$ is greater than X_A/p. Thus the inequality (4-14) becomes

$$\theta > - \ln p \qquad (4\text{-}15)$$

or, alternatively,

$$\frac{1}{T} - \frac{1}{T_m^\circ} > - \frac{R}{\Delta H_u} \ln p \qquad (4\text{-}16)$$

A limiting temperature must therefore exist above which the inequality (4-16) cannot be fulfilled. At temperatures higher than this, crystallization cannot occur. This limiting temperature is clearly the equilibrium melting temperature of the copolymer, T_m. Hence

$$\frac{1}{T_m} - \frac{1}{T_m^\circ} = - \frac{R}{\Delta H_u} \ln p \qquad (4\text{-}17)$$

It is therefore expected that, for a copolymer in which only one type of unit is capable of crystallizing, the melting point depression will depend on the heat of fusion per mole of crystallizing unit and on the sequence propagation probability p but not otherwise directly on the composition. The parameter D, related to the end surface free energy, does not explicitly appear in the expression for the melting point depression. Equation (4-17) is derived on the basis of total equilibrium prevailing throughout the system. This implies that the longitudinal growth of the crystallites is impaired only by the occurrence of noncrystallizable units along the chain and that lateral development is restricted solely by the thermodynamic conditions specified. If equilibrium does not prevail, the above are not applicable, and appropriate cognizance must be taken of the departures from equilibrium in analyzing experimental data.

When the aforementioned conditions are satisfied, the dependence of the melting temperature on the concentration of crystallizable units resides in the relationship between the sequence propagation probability p and the over-all composition. For a random-type copolymer, p can be identified with X_A, and Eq. (4-17) becomes

$$\frac{1}{T_m} - \frac{1}{T_m{}^\circ} = -\frac{R}{\Delta H_u} \ln X_A \qquad (4\text{-}18)$$

For an ordered or block-type copolymer, characterized by the crystallizable units occurring in very long sequences, p greatly exceeds X_A. The depression of the melting temperature is not as great as for random copolymers. For alternating types of copolymers, p is less than X_A, and a much greater depression of the melting temperature is observed.† On the basis of Eq. (4-18), relatively large depressions of the melting temperature can easily be expected for random-type copolymers. For example, for a random copolymer of the hydrocarbon type to which values of $\Delta H_u = 1000$ cal/mole and $T_m{}^\circ = 400°\text{K}$ are assigned, a depression of the melting point of $61°$ is calculated when $X_A = 0.8$. When $X_A = 0.6$, a depression of $115°$ should theoretically be observed.

The theory also allows for an estimate of the fraction of the A units that are crystalline at temperatures less than T_m. This estimate is obtained by totaling all the sequences of A units involved in crystallites. This procedure leads to a slight overestimation of the degree of crystallinity, since sequences greater than ζ units in length may be participating in crystallites only ζ units long. If $w_\zeta{}^c$ is the concentration of sequences of ζ units involved in a crystallite, then

$$w_\zeta{}^c = w_\zeta{}^\circ - w_\zeta{}^e \qquad (4\text{-}19)$$

and w_c, the fraction of A units in the crystalline state, is given by

$$w_c = \sum_{\zeta=\zeta_{cr}}^{\infty} w^c = \sum_{\zeta=\zeta_{cr}}^{\infty} (w_\zeta{}^\circ - w_\zeta{}^e) \qquad (4\text{-}20)$$

By utilizing Eqs. (4-4) and (4-11) for $w_\zeta{}^\circ$ and $w_\zeta{}^e$, respectively, there is obtained

$$w_c = \frac{X_A}{p}(1-p)^2 p^{\zeta_{cr}}\{p(1-p)^{-2} - e^{-\theta}(1-e^{-\theta})^{-2}$$
$$+ \zeta_{cr}[(1-p)^{-1} - (1-e^{-\theta})^{-1}]\} \qquad (4\text{-}21)$$

with ζ_{cr} being given by Eq. (4-13).

† When the alternation tendency in the copolymer is very great, it is possible for the quantity X_A/p to exceed $1/D$. The inequality (4-15) is therefore no longer fulfilled, and Eq. (4-16) is not applicable. The requirements of inequality (4-14) can still be observed for very small values of ζ. For this special situation crystallinity develops by the preferential formation of crystallites of shorter length.

Theoretical curves depicting the variation in the degree of crystallinity with temperature can be constructed from Eq. (4-21) by the assignment of appropriate parameters.   Representative plots are given in Fig. 4-1 for random copolymers containing the indicated concentrations of crystallizable units.   Parameters utilized in the calculations

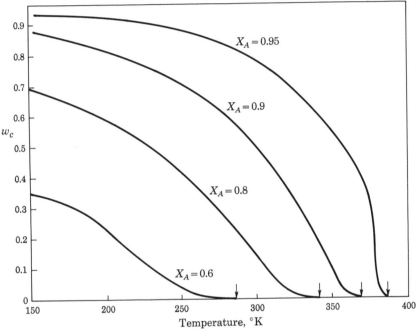

Fig. 4-1   Theoretical plot according to Eq. (4-21) of the fraction of crystalline A units, w_c, as a function of temperature for random-type copolymers of different compositions.   Short vertical arrows indicate melting temperature T_m of copolymer.   For case illustrated, $T_m{}^\circ = 400°$K, $\Delta H_u = 10^3$ cal/mole, and $\ln D = -1$.

are $T_m{}^\circ = 400°$K, $\Delta H_u = 10^3$ cal/mole, and $\ln D = -1$.   The theoretical curves in this figure contrast quite markedly with those expected and observed for pure homopolymers.

At comparable temperatures the level of crystallinity is severely reduced as the concentration of noncrystallizing units is increased.   A significant feature of these plots is the diffuseness of the fusion curves. Crystallinity disappears over a very wide temperature range, the breadth of the melting range increasing with the increased concentration of the noncrystallizable units.   Thus, even for a polymer that contains only 5 mole per cent of B units the final 50 per cent of the crystallinity will disappear over a 25° interval.   The introduction of even small amounts of chain irregularities therefore significantly alters the fusion curve.

Another salient feature of the curves is the persistence of very small but finite amounts of crystallinity over an appreciable temperature interval before its complete disappearance. The breadth of this interval markedly increases with an increase in concentration of non-crystallizable units. For the 60 per cent copolymer, it encompasses about 30°. Although the total amount of crystallinity that persists in this manner is very small, it is nevertheless significant. The disappearance of these small amounts, in fact, determines the equilibrium melting temperature.

The unique features of the fusion of copolymers outlined above are primarily consequences of the broad distribution of sequence lengths in a random copolymer, with its concomitant effect on the longitudinal crystallite sizes that can be developed. At a given temperature, only those sequences whose length exceeds ζ_{cr} can participate in the crystallization process, ζ_{cr} being a function of the temperature. As the temperature is varied, both the composition and sequence distribution of the amorphous phase change. These factors in turn govern the fraction of A units that can participate in the crystallization. Thus the diffuse melting curves have a natural explanation. The shapes of the melting curves depend on the value of the parameter D but are not very sensitive to it. As the melting temperature is approached, ζ_{cr} assumes very large values, while the concentration of sequences that exceed this length becomes quite small. This accounts for the expectancy, illustrated in Fig. 4-1, of the persistence of small amounts of crystallinity at temperatures just below T_m.

Because of their diffuseness, the fusion curves of Fig. 4-1 do not appear to be typical of a first-order phase transition. However, melting curves of this type are natural consequences of the constitution of random copolymers. Furthermore, at T_m, w_c and all its derivatives vanish, so that a true discontinuity exists and T_m can be theoretically identified with the equilibrium melting temperature of the copolymer. This temperature is a true thermodynamic melting temperature and represents the temperature at which crystallites composed of very long sequences of A units disappear. It is this temperature that must be utilized in Eq. (4-18). Below this temperature a finite amount of crystallinity will exist, while above this temperature crystallinity must vanish. The fact that this temperature is theoretically required is quite important since it can be anticipated that the determination of the disappearance of small amounts of crystallinity will be a difficult experimental problem.

It has been widely observed that the melting of copolymers is a diffuse process, with crystallinity disappearing over a broad temperature range.   In addition, it is known that it is more difficult to develop high levels of crystallinity in a copolymer than in homopolymers. The major conclusions of the theoretical development are, in fact, substantiated by experiment.   Since chain irregularities can be introduced into a polymer without change in the chemical nature of the chain repeating unit, diffuse melting has not always been recognized as the consequence of the copolymeric character of such systems.   It is therefore quite easy to conclude erroneously that diffuse melting is also a characteristic of the fusion of homopolymers.   On the other hand, theory clearly demonstrates that the detailed analysis of the fusion process under conditions approaching equilibrium offers a very sensitive method of detecting the presence of chain irregularities in a crystallizable polymer.

4-3   General Experimental Results

The fusion process that is actually observed for some typical copolymers can now be examined in terms of the theoretical development. As a typical set of examples, we shall examine the melting behavior of a series of copolymers containing a preponderance of methylene

$-CH_2-$ units, with small proportions of counits of the type $-\overset{\overset{\textstyle R}{|}}{C}H-$ being incorporated into the chain.[2]   Copolymers with $R = n\text{-}C_3H_7$ or CH_3 or C_2H_5 have been studied.   The polymers were prepared by the copolymerization of mixtures of diazomethane and the corresponding higher diazoalkanes.   Special measures were adopted to assure the random distribution of counits in the chain.   Crystallization was allowed to occur while the temperature of the initially molten copolymer was reduced gradually by small increments in the vicinity of the melting temperature over a period of many days.   This procedure provides the optimum opportunity for an approach to equilibrium. Specimens well suited for study and comparison with theory are thus provided.

In Fig. 4-2 specific volume–temperature plots are given for a series of such copolymers.   Slow heating rates were utilized subsequent to the crystallization, the temperature being raised 1° per day in the interval $T_m - 15$ to T_m.   The copolymer composition indicated for each curve is presented as the ratio of $CHR/100CH_2$.   Typically sigmoidal melting curves are observed, as is expected for copolymers.

The transformation occurs over a wide temperature interval, with the melting range becoming broader as the concentration of noncrystallizable units is increased. Small amounts of crystallinity persist at temperatures just below T_m, in accordance with the theoretical conclusions. The merging with the liquidus appears to be a gradual and asymptotic process.

Careful examination of the data in the vicinity of the melting temperature gives no evidence of a discontinuity. This is consistent

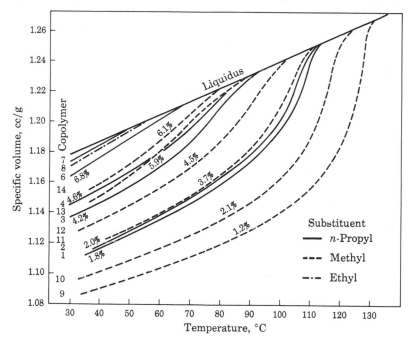

Fig. 4-2 Melting curves for polymethylene copolymers containing the indicated substituents as coingredients. Composition of copolymers is indicated as per cent of coingredient present. [*From Richardson, Flory, and Jackson (2).*]

with theory which, although predicting a discontinuity, assigns to it a magnitude beyond the reach of experimental observation. The theoretically desired T_m refers to this experimentally inaccessible discontinuity. To determine an experimental T_m, the supercooled liquidus is established. The temperature at which measurable departure from the liquidus vanishes is taken to be the experimental T_m. At best, melting points determined in this manner can be compared with the theoretical relations.

In Fig. 4-3 the dashed line represents the melting temperature–

composition relation calculated according to Eq. (4-18), taking ΔH_u = 970 cal/mole CH_2 and T_m° = 411.7°K.[2] The experimental points fall considerably below the calculated curve. Differential thermal analyses studies of methyl and ethyl branched polymethylenes yield essentially the same results.[3] The observation of melting temperatures less than those theoretically predicted is widespread among

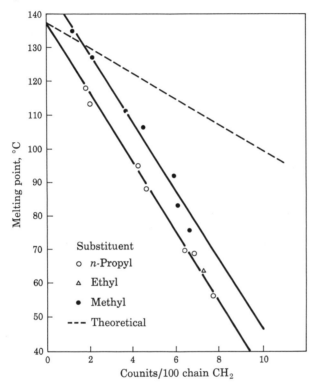

Fig. 4-3 The melting temperature of the polymethylene copolymers as a function of the composition. The theoretical curve is calculated from Eq. (4-18). [*From Richardson, Flory, and Jackson* (2).]

copolymers.[4] These results can be explained in part by the difference in the melting temperature that can be experimentally observed and that required by theory. Theoretically, at temperatures just below the true melting point, the degree of crystallinity falls to a level too low to be detected by the usual experimental means.

It is noted that the melting temperatures for the ethyl and n-propyl copolymers fall on the same line. However, the copolymers containing methyl side groups are consistently higher. The fact that the points for the methyl series do not extrapolate to $T_m°$ in the limit of vanishing counit concentration indicates that very small quantities of this counit have little effect on T_m. This suggests the formation of a solid solution, i.e., a crystalline phase that accommodates the

$$\begin{matrix} & CH_3 \\ & | \\ -C&H- \end{matrix}$$ unit at equilibrium. On the other hand, the steady decrease

in T_m observed in the ethyl and n-propyl series indicates the separation of a pure crystalline phase.

These conclusions appear to be in contradiction with deductions from X-ray diffraction studies on similar systems.[5,6] In these studies an increase in the dimensions of the a axis of the unit cell of polyethylene is observed when methyl, ethyl, n-propyl, and n-butyl substituents are introduced. However, the X-ray diffraction measurements were carried out at temperatures far removed from T_m. At these temperatures, it would be possible for crystallites containing the counits to be stable while at higher temperatures they would not. Another factor of importance is the decrease in crystallite size with an increasing proportion of counits. Reduction in crystallite size introduces a serious error in the determination of the true X-ray diffraction spacing. Hence the discrepancy between the phase diagram and X-ray diffraction studies may be more apparent than real.

The degree of crystallinity can be calculated from the specific volume data and is plotted in Fig. 4-4 for the n-propyl and ethyl copolymers. The dotted lines in Fig. 4-4 are calculated according to Eqs. (4-13) and (4-21), using a single set of values for the parameters $T_m°$, ΔH_u, and ln D for all the copolymers. The parameter p is identified with the mole fraction of CH_2 units in each copolymer. Since $T_m°$ and ΔH_u are determined independently, there is only one arbitrary parameter, ln D, available to fit the entire set of curves. When this parameter was used, the best fit between theory and experiment was accomplished in the temperature range where the degree of crystallinity undergoes the most rapid changes. The observed degrees of crystallinity for a given copolymer depart from the theoretical curve at both low and high degrees of crystallinity. The problems at the low levels of crystallinity have been discussed and can be attributed to limitations on the sensitivity of observation and to the kinetic difficulty of gathering together those rarely occurring long sequences that are required for formation of stable crystallites at high temperatures. The deviations that occur at higher levels of crystallinity can be attributed to the restrictions imposed by the crystalline regions previously generated at higher temperatures during the cooling cycle. The interconnections resulting from prior crystallization greatly impeded the subsequent crystallization of the remaining crystallizable sequences.

In order to achieve the best fit, a value of -11.5 is assigned to the quantity ln D. This corresponds to a surprisingly large interfacial free energy σ_e of 170 ergs/cm² or 4600 cal/mole of chains emerging from

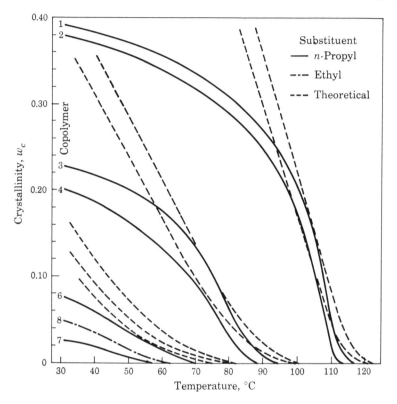

Fig. 4-4 The degree of crystallinity (calculated from the specific volume data) as a function of temperature for the copolymers with n-propyl and ethyl substituents. The theoretical curves are calculated from Eqs. (4-13) and (4-21). [*From Richardson, Flory, and Jackson* (2).]

the (001) surface. This quantity is much larger than the corresponding value usually assigned to nonpolymeric crystals. However, a direct comparison should not be made. For crystals formed from long chain molecules there are included contributions to the free energy associated with the dissipation of crystalline order throughout the depth of the interfacial layer. This large value for the interfacial free energy for the (001) crystal boundary becomes quite important in discussing crystal nucleation in polymeric systems.

Despite the lack of complete agreement between theory and experiment, much of which can be attributed to experimental shortcomings and inaccessibility, the data in Figs. 4-2 and 4-4 display all the major characteristics of the calculated theoretical fusion curves. Hence they can generally be expected to be typical of the fusion of random-type copolymers, irrespective of the nature of the noncrystallizing chain units that are introduced.

4-4 Copolyesters and Copolyamides

Copolymers formed by the methods of condensation polymerization usually can be characterized by a sequence propagation probability parameter p that is independent of copolymer composition and extent of conversion. Moreover, in such systems the quantity p can be equated to the mole fraction of crystallizable units which is easily susceptible to analytical determination. The fusion of copolyesters and copolyamides takes place over a broad temperature range, and the melting curves are again sigmoidal in character.[7,8] As a consequence, the melting temperature is usually a poorly defined experimental quantity.

The melting temperature–composition relations for some representative copolyesters and copolyamides are illustrated in Fig. 4-5. Copolymers of this type, whose units crystallize independently of one another, display certain characteristic features. The melting temperatures depend only on composition and are independent of the chemical nature of the coingredient that is introduced, as is illustrated for the copolymers of polyethylene terephthalate and those of polyhexamethylene adipamide. This observation is consistent with wide-angle X-ray observations, which indicate that only one of the units participates in the crystallization. This is in accordance with the random distribution of sequences in the copolymer. As the concentration of the added ingredient is sufficiently increased, it can itself undergo crystallization at the expense of the other component. The melting point–composition relations for this component follow an independent curve, so that a eutectic-type minimum results at the intersection of the two curves. This is typical behavior of random copolymers when studied over the complete composition range.

For experiments conducted under conditions such that the requirements of theory are adhered to, the melting temperature–composition relations of each branch of the curves of Fig. 4-5 should be described by Eq. (4-18). Consequently the relation between $1/T_m$ and $- \ln X_A$

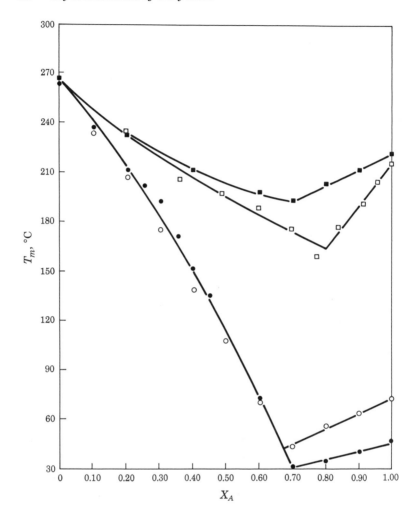

Fig. 4-5 Melting temperature–composition relations for various copolyesters and copolyamides. Solid circles, polyethylene terephthalate/
adipate; open circles, polyethylene terephthalate/sebacate; solid squares,
polyhexamethylene adipamide/sebacamide; open squares, polyhexamethylene adipamide/caproamide. [*From Edgar and Ellery* (9), *Sonnerskog* (10),
and Izard (11).]

for some typically selected copolyesters and copolyamides is plotted
in Fig. 4-6. For each of the examples, which cover a wide range in
copolymer composition, the melting point data are well represented by
a straight line, in accordance with theory. In each instance the
straight line extrapolates to the melting point of the pure homo-

polymer. Similar results are obtained for other copolyesters and copolyamides.

The slope of the straight lines obtained in this type of plot is related to the value of ΔH_u. As an example, from the melting temperature–composition data for copolyesters of decamethylene adipate–decamethylene isophthalate a value of ΔH_u of 3800 cal/mole of repeating units is obtained. This value is appreciably lower than the

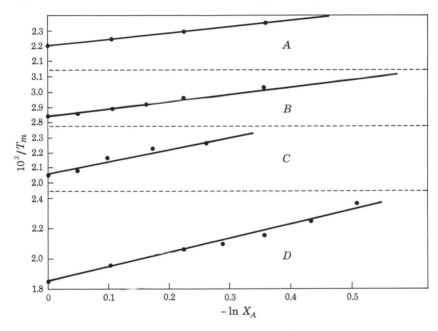

Fig. 4-6 Plot of $1/T_m$ against $-\ln X_A$ for copolyamides and copolyesters. *A*, *N,N'*-sebacoyl piperazine/isophthaloyl piperazine copolymer (4); *B*, decamethylene adipate/decamethylene isophthalate copolymer [*from Evans, Mighton, and Flory* (8)]; *C*, caproamide–hexamethylene adipamide copolymer [*from Sonnerskog* (10)]; *D*, ethylene terephthalate–ethylene adipate copolymers [*from Edgar and Ellery* (9).]

10,200 cal/mole of repeating units determined for the same polymer by an analysis of the melting point depression of various monomeric diluents. Thus, although the melting points of this random copolymer depend on composition in the manner predicted, the value of ΔH_u that is deduced is significantly lower than that determined by another method. This appears to be a general conclusion based on the results for several different systems, as is indicated by the data in Table 4-1. In this table results are given for systems where ΔH_u has been determined by both the diluent and copolymer methods. The values of ΔH_u determined from an analysis of copolymer melting are always lower by varying amounts than the values obtained by the diluent method. There is an apparent discrepancy which resides in either the experimental methods or the subsequent analysis.

This problem is similar to the systematic observation of melting points lower than predicted which has been previously discussed in connection with the melting of polymethylene copolymers. Fundamentally this is a consequence of the paucity of crystallites composed of long sequences of A units even if complete equilibrium were established. For this idealized situation a fictitious melting temperature

TABLE 4-1
Comparsion of the copolymer and diluent methods in determining ΔH_u

Polymer	ΔH_u, cal/g	
	Copolymer method	Diluent method
Poly (decamethylene adipate)	13.4 (Ref. 8)	36 (Ref. 12)
Poly (decamethylene sebacate)	13.8 (Ref. 8)	36 (Ref. 8)
Poly (N-N'-sebacoyl piperazine)	19.8 (Ref. 7)	24.5 (Ref. 7)
Poly (decamethylene sebacamide)	23 (Ref. 8)	24.5 (Ref. 13)

would be observed because of the limited sensitivity of experimental methods. According to theory, the difference between the temperature recorded at a small but finite amount of crystallinity and the true melting temperature increases as the concentration of A units is decreased. The functional relation between the copolymer composition and the experimentally observed melting temperature can, in fact, be approximated by an equation of the same form as Eq. (4-18). The melting temperature observed when a small but finite amount of crystallinity persists can be calculated from Eq. (4-21). The results of such a computation are plotted in Fig. 4-7, with the same parameters used as in the construction of the curves of Fig. 4-1. Random-type copolymers containing up to 40 per cent noncrystallizable units were treated in this calculation. The different curves in Fig. 4-7 represent the melting point–composition relations for various levels of sensitivity. The lower curve is for the ideal situation where the disappearance of the long crystalline sequences can be detected. The remaining curves represent cases where, although melting is thought to be complete, 1, 2, and 5 per cent, respectively, of the fraction of A units are still crystalline. Within the experimental error of recording temperature,

straight lines are obtained for all cases, indicating a pseudo adherence
to Eq. (4-18).   The straight lines calculated have progressively
increasing slopes.   Thus if Eq. (4-18) is applied to such data, the
value of ΔH_u deduced will be invariably lower than the true value.
For example, for the hypothetical polymer considered, ΔH_u is equal to
1000 cal/mole, whereas if the experimental technique were such that

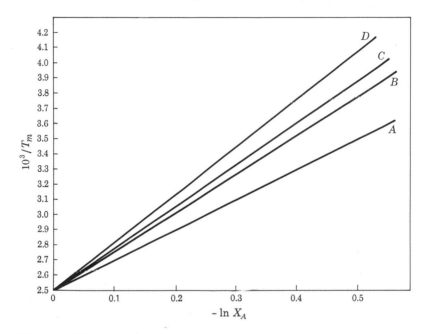

Fig. 4-7   Plot of calculated values of $1/T_m$ against $-\ln X_A$ for random-type
copolymers, assuming various levels of sensitivity. A, complete disappearance of crystallinity; B, C, and D, 1, 2, and 5 per cent crystallinity persist,
respectively.   Calculated from Eq. (4-21) using $T_m{}^\circ = 400°K$, $\Delta H_u = 10^3$
cal/mole, $\ln D = -1$.

the disappearance of the last 1 per cent crystallinity were not detected,
a value of 780 cal/mole would be deduced.   The value of ΔH_u obtained
by the copolymer method is thus very dependent on the sensitivity of
the method used to detect the disappearance of crystallinity.   The
situation described above represents the difficulties encountered in
interpreting   the   melting   temperature–composition   relations   of
random copolymers.   Although apparent adherence to Eq. (4-18)
is observed, the value of ΔH_u deduced will be in error.   The diluent
method is therefore deemed more reliable in determining the value
of ΔH_u.

4-5   Geometric Isomerism

Chain units that are identical chemically but are isomeric to one another can impart to a polymer molecule a copolymeric character as far as its crystallization behavior is concerned.   For example, polymers prepared from the 1,3 dienes are subject to chain irregularities.   For polybutadiene the following three types of chain structure can exist:

$$
\left(
\begin{array}{c}
\underset{|}{\overset{H_2}{C}} \qquad \underset{|}{\overset{H}{C}} \\
\diagup \quad \diagdown \quad \diagup \quad \diagdown \diagup \\
C \qquad\qquad C \\
| \qquad\qquad | \\
H \qquad\qquad H_2
\end{array}
\right) \qquad \text{1,4 trans}
$$

$$
\left(
\begin{array}{c}
\underset{|}{\overset{H_2}{C}} \qquad \underset{|}{\overset{H_2}{C}} \\
\diagup \quad \diagdown \qquad \diagup \quad \diagdown \\
C=C \\
| \quad | \\
H \quad H
\end{array}
\right) \qquad \text{1,4 cis}
$$

$$
\left(
\begin{array}{c}
H \\
| \\
CH_2-C \\
| \\
CH \\
\| \\
CH_2
\end{array}
\right) \qquad \text{1,2 vinyl}
$$

Thus polyisoprene, polychloroprene, polybutadiene, and other polymers of this class contain units that can exist in the trans 1,4 or cis 1,4 configuration as well as containing pendant vinyl groups that can be in the D or L configuration.   The diene polymers that occur naturally, hevea rubber and gutta-percha, contain an overwhelming concentration of groups either in the cis or trans configuration.   These polymers crystallize readily, and their melting is typical of that of homopolymers. However, the chain composition or microstructure of the synthetically prepared diene polymers depends on the methods and mechanism of polymerization.   This in turn governs their crystallization behavior. Marked deviation from that of homopolymers can be expected and is in fact observed.

Polychloroprene[14] and polybutadiene[15] prepared by free radical emulsion methods contain varying proportions of the different units, the composition of the copolymer being controlled by the polymerization temperature.[14,16,17,18] A quantitative analysis of the polymer microstructure is obtained by means of infrared absorption spectroscopy. In the composition range in which the crystallization behavior

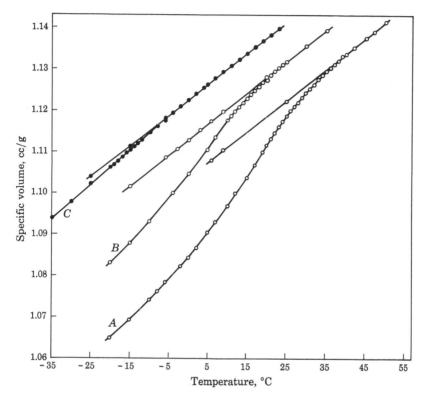

Fig. 4-8 Plot of specific volume against temperature for polybutadienes of varying concentration of crystallizing trans 1,4 units. For curve A, $X_A = 0.81$; for curve B, $X_A = 0.73$; for curve C, $X_A = 0.64$. Curves B and C are arbitrarily displaced along the ordinate (15).

has been studied in detail, only the trans 1,4 units are capable of crystallizing. Under appropriate conditions, crystallization occurs in such a polymer when as little as 55 to 60 per cent of the crystallizable units is present.[15]

In Fig. 4-8 specific volume–temperature plots, as determined from dilatometric studies utilizing slow heating rates subsequent to the development of crystallinity, are given for three different polybutadienes whose concentration of crystallizing units ranges from $X_A = 0.64$ to $X_A = 0.81$. Typical sigmoidal melting curves consistent with the copolymeric character of the molecule are obtained. The transformation occurs over a wide temperature interval, with the melting range becoming broader as the concentration of noncrystallizable units is increased. The final portion of the melting curve encompasses a larger temperature interval as the concentration of crystallizing units is decreased.

In the examples illustrated, recourse was again taken to establish the supercooled liquidus as an aid in the determination of T_m. The melting temperatures for these polymers depend on composition in the manner described by Eq. (4-18), but for the reasons previously discussed the validity of the deduced value of ΔH_u remains in doubt.

Diene-type polymers can also be prepared by the methods of anionic polymerization[19,20,24] with *cis*-1,4 and *trans*-1,4 polyisoprene and polybutadiene as well as 1,2-polybutadiene being reported. By these methods of synthesis, a wide range in the concentration of the various chain units can be achieved. Thus polybutadienes can be prepared that contain an adequate concentration of cis 1,4 units so that the crystallization of these species can be accomplished. The melting behavior of these polymers is again similar to that of the emulsion-polymerized polybutadienes where the trans 1,4 units crystallize.[19] Although the melting points differ, the general behavior is typically copolymeric. By these methods of polymerization, polymers of isoprene can be prepared that are sufficiently regular in structure that they possess properties very similar to those of their naturally occurring counterparts. However, a small but significant concentration of chain irregularities exists, which alters the ease of crystallization when compared with the homopolymer. This can be attributed to the depression of the melting temperature by the small concentration of noncrystallizable units.[4]

For a diene polymer containing units that are originally either all in the trans or all in the cis configuration it is possible to effect an isomerism of a portion of the units by chemical methods without severing any chain bonds. Reaction of this type can be carried out by use of thiol acids,[25] sulfur dioxide,[26] and the utilization of high-energy radiation with appropriate sensitizer.[27] Isomerization is expected on the basis of similar experiments carried out with monomeric olefins. The isomerization occurs via a free radical mechanism, with a double bond temporarily converted to a single bond of the transitory adduct. Subsequent regeneration of the double bond occurs; whether the same or a new configuration evolves depends on the concentration of the reactants and the equilibrium requirements of the experimental conditions. Configurational changes of the chain units can thus be brought about in much larger proportion than is reflected in the concentration of additives introduced into the system.

Spectroscopic analysis confirms the fact that cis-trans isomerization can be accomplished by these procedures in diene polymers.[28] Cuneen, Higgins, and Watson[28] have shown that the infrared absorption spectra of natural rubber and gutta-percha treated with sulfur dioxide revealed structural changes that increased with the time of reaction until equilibrium was achieved. For example, after treatment with sulfur dioxide for 24 hr at 140°C both the initially all-1,4-*cis*-polyisoprene and the initially all-1,4-*trans*-polymer displayed identical infrared spectra. For each of the polymers, therefore, an equilibrium mixture of chain units in the cis and trans configuration occurs. It is found that there are 57 per cent trans double bonds and 43 per cent cis double bonds at equilibrium. This ratio of cis to trans corresponds to the equilibrium composition, at the same temperature, of a mixture of cis and trans isomers of 3-methylpent-2-ene.

From the point of view of the crystallization behavior of polymers, by these methods one converts a homopolymer into a copolymer. If the reaction proceeds at random, a random type of copolymer should develop; it would contain a much greater concentration of structural irregularities than would be apparent from the concentration of reactant. It would then be expected that significant alterations should occur in the melting temperature, the fusion process, the crystallization kinetics, and in other properties of the polymer that are related to crystallization. These expectations are, in fact, borne out. For example, the melting temperature of gutta-percha can be significantly lowered so that it is an amorphous substance at room temperature and possesses the elastic properties associated with a noncrystalline polymer above its glass temperature. Similarly, significant depressions of the melting temperature have been achieved in 1,4-*cis*-polybutadiene, by isomerizing a portion of the cis configurations to trans.[27] As will be discussed in Chap. 8, the copolymeric nature of these polymers must inevitably lead to a large retardation in the rate of crystallization. This is in accord with experimental observations.[27] The underlying principles governing the crystallization and melting behavior of random copolymers do not depend on the nature of the chain irregularities or the methods by which they are introduced into the molecule.

The chemical formula for a portion of a polypeptide chain can be

written as

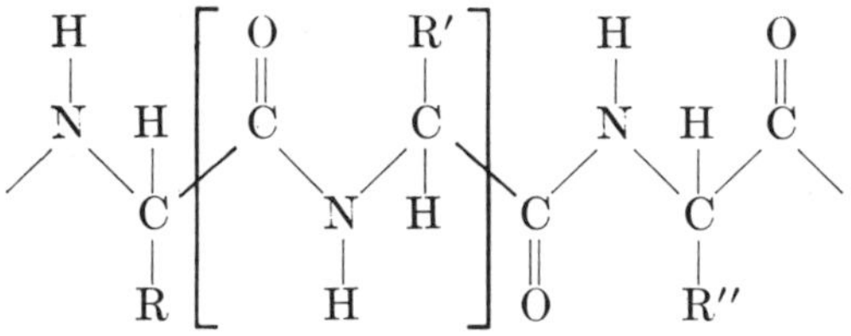

with the repeating unit indicated by the chain elements contained within the bracket. A polypeptide containing identical R groups is a homopolymer, and the crystallization behavior depends solely on the nature of the amino acid residue of which it is comprised. On the other hand, if several different R groups are present, the copolymeric character of the molecule becomes evident.

In addition to chemical differences among the chain repeating units, a certain type of geometric isomerism can also exist for chemically identical repeating units. According to Pauling and Corey,[29] the bond between the carbon atom containing the carbonyl oxygen and the nitrogen atom has about 40 per cent double bond character because of resonance between the structures:

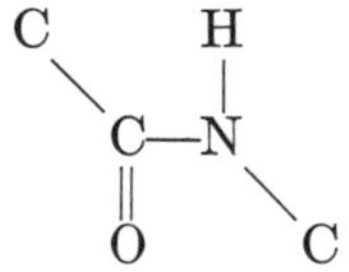

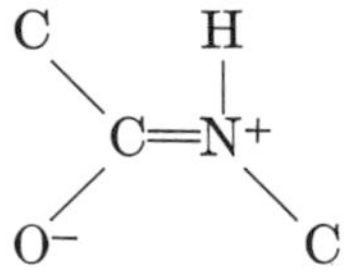

As a result of the double bond character of this linkage, the amide group must be nearly coplanar. Hence, as is indicated below, a choice of either a cis or trans configuration exists. According to Pauling and

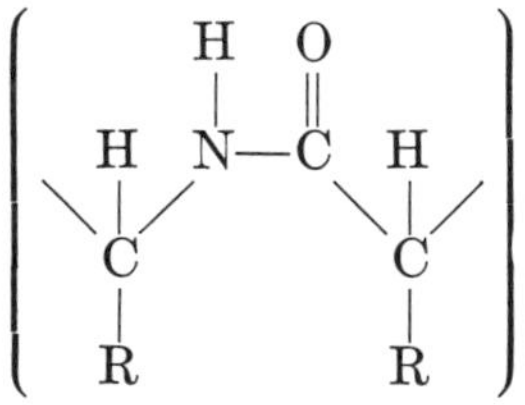

Cis configuration of amide group in polypeptide structures

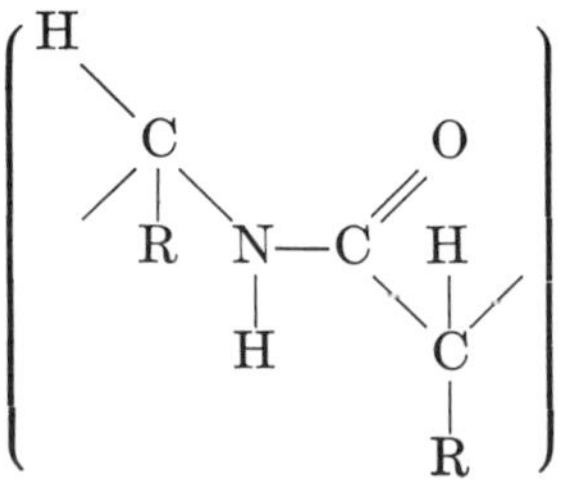

Trans configuration of amide group in polypeptide structure

Corey[29] and Mizushima,[30] the trans configuration of the amide group in polypeptide chains is, in general, the more stable one. If all units in a molecule assume the same configuration, homopolymer-type behavior is expected. If, on the other hand, the two different configurations, even of identical chemical repeating units, occur in the same chain, then crystallization behavior typical of a copolymer would be expected (except for the unlikely situation in which units in either configuration can enter the same crystal lattice).

By analogy with the results for the diene polymers, therefore, the transformation of a homopolypeptide to a copolymer can, in principle, be accomplished by the conversion of units from one configuration to another. This conversion must involve rotation about the carbonyl carbon–nitrogen bond and could be induced by appropriate chemical reactions. If the reaction involves a transitory structure, where the double bond character of the peptide linkage is only temporarily lost, conversion from one configuration to another could be accomplished. The situation could also exist where certain reactions, such as the binding of specific ions, favor one of the resonance structures. The particular peptide bonds involved could completely lose their double bond character by this process. In this case the regeneration of the double bond character would require the reversion of the chemical reaction. In either case, whether geometrical isomerism develops or the peptide bond becomes more characteristically single bonded, the thermodynamic stability of the crystalline state, relative to the liquid state, is severely reduced.

Various mechanisms for the melting of polypeptide homopolymers can be envisaged. The melting of the homopolymer can occur by processes wherein the cis or trans configuration is maintained in the melt similar to the melting of the all-*cis* or all-*trans*-polyisoprene. It is also possible for a cis-trans isomerism to be induced, again in analogy to the polyisoprenes. This would lower the stability of the system and result in melting. A more freely rotating chain structure could also be developed, if all or even a portion of the peptide linkages lost their double bond character. Melting would result from this process also. The structure of the chains in the liquid state would differ from one another for these various cases. Statistically, however, they can still be represented as random coils. Careful distinction between the different melting processes and the nature of the molten state that results must obviously be made. However, the ease by which the crystal-to-liquid transformation can be induced by a wide variety of chemical reagents in polypeptide-containing macromolecular systems is not surprising.

4-6   Stereoisomerism

In certain classes of polymers it is possible for stereoisomerism to exist among chemically identical chain repeating units.   The concentration and sequence distribution of the stereoisomers along the chain have an important bearing on the crystallizability and melting of such polymers.   An important class of polymers possessing asymmetric or pseudo-asymmetric carbon atoms are those which adhere to the general formula

$$\left(\begin{matrix} H & X \\ | & | \\ -C-C- \\ | & | \\ H & Y \end{matrix}\right)_n$$

where X and Y represent two different substituents attached to alternate carbon atoms.   Polymers of this class can be prepared from the α-olefins and appropriately substituted vinyl monomers.   A more complex type of stereoisomer is formed when each of the carbon atoms contains different substituents, as in the case of a polymer prepared from a 1,2-substituted ethylenic monomer.   For the simpler case illustrated, if one arbitrarily represents the chain in an extended planar zigzag form, the X or Y substituent can be located on the same or opposite side of the plane of the zigzag with respect to the same substituents of adjacent monomer units.   When the pseudo-asymmetric carbon atoms each assume identical configurations or when the configurations alternate or vary in a definite and prescribed manner throughout the molecule, homopolymer-type crystallization is expected.   However, a wide variety of arrangements of the chain units in a nonregularly repeating configuration is obviously also possible.   It is not surprising, therefore, that for a long time polymers of this type could not be crystallized because of the lack of sufficient stereoregularity among the chain elements.

In a notable synthetic accomplishment, Natta and coworkers[31] have demonstrated that crystallizable vinyl polymers from monomers bearing different substituents and also crystallizable polymers from the α-olefins can be prepared by methods of anionic polymerization. The method by which stereocontrol is achieved in this type of polymerization has not been fully clarified.   It appears to result in part from the directing influence of the initiating complex.   Subsequently, following an earlier suggestion by Huggins,[32] stereoregular polymers from vinyl monomers have been prepared by free-radical polymerization methods.[33-36]   In this case stereocontrol is presumed to result from the directing influence of the free end of the propagating species. Variation in stereoregularity is achieved by varying the polymerization temperature, advantage being taken of the small difference in activation energy for the addition of units in the two different possible configurations.[33,37]

Two extreme conditions of chain microstructure can be envisaged. In one case the successive units in the chain possess identical configurations, and the resulting polymer is termed isotactic. In the other case successive alternation of the two possible configurations occurs; such a polymer is termed syndiotactic.[31] A polymer molecule need not be completely isotactic nor completely syndiotactic. There is possible a variety of intermediate situations that can range from random sequence distributions of the two types of structure, with only one type participating in the crystallization, to that of an ordered copolymer where both the syndiotactic and isotactic structures can independently crystallize in the same molecule. Units that are isotactic relative to one another can be converted to the syndiotactic configuration only by the severance and reformation of the connecting covalent bond. The recognition of the copolymeric character of stereoirregular polymers allows for a systematic analysis and investigation of their properties.

The necessary apparatus with which to treat the crystallization and fusion of such polymers is already embodied in Flory's[1] theory of the crystallization of copolymers. It remains only to consider the relation between the general theory and the stereoirregular-type copolymer. Coleman[38] has treated this problem by assuming that the generation of stereosequences is determined by random processes. The fundamental problem is to develop relations between the sequence probability parameter p and the probability of generating either an isotactic or a syndiotactic sequence in the growing chain.

As an example, let us take the following schematic representation of the polymerization of a head-to-tail vinyl polymer where chain propagation occurs by a free radical mechanism:[38]

$$-\left[\begin{matrix} H & X \\ | & | \\ C-C \\ | & | \\ H & Y \end{matrix}\right]_4-\left[\begin{matrix} H & Y \\ | & | \\ C-C \\ | & | \\ H & X \end{matrix}\right]_3-\left[\begin{matrix} H & Y \\ | & | \\ C-C \\ | & | \\ H & X \end{matrix}\right]_2-\left[\begin{matrix} H & X \\ | & | \\ C-C \\ | & | \\ H & Y \end{matrix}\right]_1 \cdot$$

Here units 3 and 2 are said to be in isotactic placement with one another whereas units 4 and 3 are in syndiotactic placement. The propagation-rate constants for either isotactic or syndiotactic placements are designated as k_α and k_β, respectively. As a first approximation in treating the problem, it is assumed that k_α and k_β are independent of the existing placements in the chain, including the last placement. With this basic assumption, the probability α that the next unit added to the growing chain will be in isotactic placement with unit 1 can be written as

$$\alpha = \frac{k_\alpha}{k_\alpha + k_\beta} \qquad (4\text{-}22)$$

while the probability that the unit will be in syndiotactic placement can be expressed as

$$\beta = \frac{k_\beta}{k_\alpha + k_\beta} \qquad (4\text{-}23)$$

The probability of the occurrence of a given type of placement is therefore constant. However, the two probabilities are unequal except for the special case where $k_\alpha = k_\beta$ from which it follows that $\alpha = \beta = 0.5$. Polymers whose microstructure is so defined are termed atactic. It is not required that $k_\alpha = k_\beta$. A difference in the free energy of activation for the respective propagation steps leads to differences in the values of k_α and k_β. In particular, even for small differences in the enthalpy of activation, one type of propagation is favored over the other as the temperature is lowered.[33,37] In this instance, the concentration of crystallizable units and their sequence distribution are governed by the relative rates of propagation.

Under conditions where only isotactic sequences can participate in the crystallization, p and X_A of Eqs. (4-17) and (4-21) are equal and can be identified with α, the fraction of repeating units that are in isotactic placement with their nearest neighbors in a given direction. Similar results hold when crystallization of only syndiotactic units is possible. $T_m{}^\circ$ can be identified with the equilibrium melting temperature of either the completely isotactic or syndiotactic polymer. Consequently the crystallization and melting of stereoirregular polymers that are formed in accordance with the aforementioned assumption should be identical to that of other random-type copolymers previously described. The problem resolves itself into the quantitative determination of the concentration of units in each type of placement.

Other mechanisms of chain propagation, by either free radical or ionic processes, can exist in which stereosequences are not generated by the simple probability laws outlined above. The probability of a given placement could be affected by the nature of the preceding placements and in particular of the last placement in the growing chain.

When this situation exists, the different conditional probabilities that are involved become important. By considering only the effect of the last placement, the following scheme is evolved.[38] If the last two units in the chain are in isotactic placement with one another, α_i is defined as the conditional probability that the addition of the next unit will also result in an isotactic placement, while β_i represents the conditional probability that a syndiotactic placement will result. Similarly, α_s represents the conditional probability that a syndiotactic placement will be followed by an isotactic one, while β_s represents a syndiotactic placement following a syndiotactic one. Then

$$\alpha_i + \beta_i = 1$$
$$\alpha_s + \beta_s = 1 \tag{4-24}$$

The unconditional probability α that two adjacent monomer units selected at random are in isotactic placement with one another is obtained by summing over all the possible outcomes of the previous placement. Thus

$$\alpha = \alpha\alpha_i + \beta\alpha_s$$
$$\beta = \beta\beta_s + \alpha\beta_i \tag{4-25}$$

When stereosequences are generated by this process, X_A can be identified with α, and p with α_i, when only units in isotactic placement crystallize. By applying the necessary and sufficient conditions for the crystallization of copolymers, Eq. (4-14) can be written as

$$\alpha\alpha_i^{\zeta-1} > \frac{1}{D} e^{-\zeta\theta} \tag{4-26}$$

When a favorable correlation exists in the stereosequence generation so that $\alpha > \alpha_i$, the limiting temperature at which crystallization can occur (the melting temperature) is expressed as

$$\frac{1}{T_m} - \frac{1}{T_m^\circ} = -\frac{R}{\Delta H_u} \ln \alpha_i \tag{4-27}$$

Hence it does not suffice to specify solely the compositional variable α in order to express the melting point–composition relation. The conditional probability α_i is also needed. However, if there is no correlation ($\alpha = \alpha_i$) or unfavorable correlation ($\alpha < \alpha_i$) a melting point relation similar to Eq. (4-16) is obtained, with p replaced by α. Similar results are obviously also obtained if only units in syndiotactic placement are capable of crystallizing.

A careful distinction must again be made between polymers that are completely regular, i.e., contain units in only isotactic or syndiotactic placement wherein homopolymer crystallization will be expected, and those polymers that are not completely regular, even though only units in a given type of placement crystallize. In the latter case, copolymer-type crystallization and melting will be expected. Thus, although a polymer may be termed isotactic or syndiotactic, its completely regular structure cannot be inferred. The presence of chain irregularities must always be anticipated. Although it is not mandatory that stereosequences be generated by the probability schemes outlined, it is clear that both the concentration of crystallizable units and their sequence distribution are the important factors governing their crystallization behavior.

Experimental results indicate that polymers in this category do, indeed, behave as copolymers. Although quantitative comparison is difficult, substantial qualitative evidence for this conclusion is available. By utilizing anionic polymerization methods and varying the polymerization conditions, particularly the nature of the catalyst, Natta[39] has prepared from propylene a series of crystalline polymers whose melting temperatures range from 176°C (presumed to be characteristic of the pure completely isotactic polymer) to 106°. Concomitantly, the degree of crystallinity that could be attained ranged from 85 to about 20 per cent. This is substantial evidence for the copolymeric character of these polymers and the fact that the crystallizable units are arranged in a random type of sequence distribution. As expected, the specific volume–temperature curves for these polymers possess the major characteristics of the theoretical curves for the melting of copolymers.[40] Newman[41] has examined in detail the specific volume–temperature relations for different soluble portions of polypropylene. These results are given in Fig. 4-9. The increasing stereoirregularity of the fractions manifests itself in lowered melting temperatures and an increased diffuseness of melting. The nature of the fusion curves illustrated is essentially identical to that for random copolymers containing repeating units that are chemically different. However, since the principles governing crystallization and fusion are the same in both cases, similar results are obtained.

In the homogeneous free radical polymerization of vinyl monomers such as methyl methacrylate,[33] vinyl acetate,[35] vinyl chloride,[36] and isopropyl and cyclohexyl acrylates,[34] stereocontrol can be achieved by varying the temperature of polymerization. As the temperature of polymerization is lowered, the crystallization of the resulting polymer becomes more easily discernible. This can be attributed to differences in the values of k_α and k_β and the favoring of units adding in one configuration over the other as the polymerization temperature is lowered.

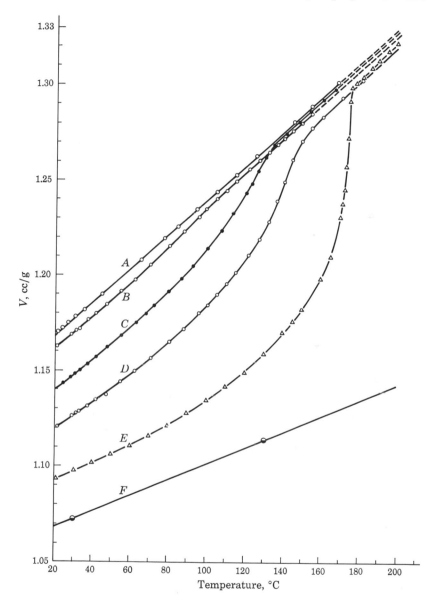

Fig. 4-9 Plot of specific volume against temperature for a polypropylene sample and four soluble extracts from it. *A*: ether extract, quenched; *B*: pentane extract, annealed; *C*: hexane fraction, annealed; *D*: trimethyl pentane fraction, annealed; *E*: experimental whole polymer annealed; *F*: pure crystalline polymer. [*From Newman* (41).]

For the cases studied in detail, the preferential development of sequences in syndiotactic form is favored as the polymerization temperature is lowered.[35,36,42]

A major problem for polymers in general and stereoirregular polymers in particular is whether, even if a polymer is not obviously crystalline as prepared, it is potentially crystallizable. This problem is frequently encountered in dealing with copolymers of various types, and the answer resides in a consideration of crystallization mechanisms and kinetics to be discussed in a subsequent chapter. It is observed that certain of the stereoirregular polymers, as, for example, polystyrene synthesized by means of olefin catalysts[43] and polymethyl methacrylate[33,44,45] prepared by free radical or ionic methods, are not obviously crystalline as prepared. However, by treatment with particular solvents or diluents at elevated temperatures, crystallinity can be developed in these polymers.[33,43–45]

The initial difficulties in inducing crystallization can be attributed to the large depressions of the melting temperature that are easily achieved by the presence of even a modest quantity of chain irregularities. In the cases cited, it is highly probable that because of the irregular chain structure the melting temperature of the polymer has been substantially reduced from that of the perfectly regular homopolymer so as to bring it into close proximity to the temperature of glass formation. The crystallization process would then become very difficult because of the kinetics of the transformation, although it would still be thermodynamically favored. This situation could be alleviated by treatment with or by addition of diluents that would depress the glass temperature a relatively greater amount than the melting temperature. According to Eq. (3-8), the addition of a diluent of large molar volume with poor solvent power (positive χ_1) results in a further minimum depression of the melting temperature for a given polymer concentration. The depression of the glass temperatures of the undiluted polymer depends primarily on composition and not on the nature of the diluent. By utilizing the appropriate type of diluent, therefore, the temperature interval between the melting temperature and glass temperature can be substantially increased over that of the undiluted system. In terms of the kinetic processes involved, crystallization should now become more favored. Diluents of the aforementioned type have, in fact, been most successful in inducing crystallinity. Thus, although polymer chains may possess sufficient structural regularity to crystallize, crystallinity will not develop unless kinetically favorable conditions are available. The noncrystallizability of a polymer, particularly a copolymer, cannot be definitely or categorically stated, unless the optimum conditions for crystallization have been satisfied.

The more obvious observation of crystallinity in the stereo-irregular polymers, i.e., being crystalline when actually prepared, must depend on the polymerization conditions. Before the advent of detailed studies of the polymerization processes leading to stereo-regular polymers, it was known that certain polymers, such as poly-vinyl chloride, polyacrylonitrile, polychlorotrifluoroethylene, and poly-vinyl alcohol, were crystalline as usually prepared, despite the strong possibility of the occurrence of stereochemical irregularities. In many instances, X-ray diffraction patterns, when used as a criterion, did not definitely support the contention of crystallinity. However, par-ticularly in the case of polyvinyl chloride[46,47] and polyacrylonitrile,[48] solution properties and mechanical properties gave substantial evi-dence of the existence of crystallinity. Subsequent preparation of these polymers by methods designed to impart a greater amount of chain regularity has confirmed these observations.[36,49]

4-7 Branching

Another type of chain irregularity that influences the melting and crystallization processes is branching, since the branch points are, in general, structurally different from the other chain units. An example of the introduction of short branches of regular length into a chain has already been given for the case of polyethylene copolymers. An assessment of this effect can be achieved by comparing the fusion of a linear and branched polymer comprised of the same type of repeating unit. Polyethylene, which can be prepared in either type of structure, is convenient to study from this point of view.

Heat capacity[50,51] and specific volume–temperature measure-ments[52,53] indicate that branched polyethylene melts very broadly; approximately half of the crystallinity disappears over a 40° tempera-ture interval. This can be contrasted rather sharply with the linear analog previously discussed (see Chap. 2). A comparison of the two polymer types is given in Fig. 4-10. The broad melting of the branched polymer (curve *B*) is again characteristic of the fusion of a polymer containing chain irregularities. On the other hand, the melting of the linear polymer is typically that of a homopolymer. The melting process for the polymer illustrated is very sharp, with about 70 per cent of the crystallinity disappearing in only a 3 to 4° interval. As has already been indicated, even sharper melting can be attained subsequent to more stringent crystallization conditions. Other

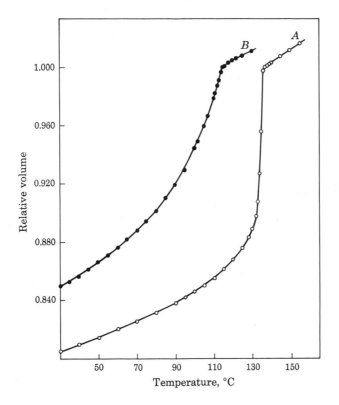

Fig. 4-10 Plot of relative volume against temperature.
Curve *A*, for linear polyethylene (polymethylene); curve *B*,
branched polyethylene (53).

branched crystalline polymers would be expected to show similar
fusion behavior when compared with their linear counterparts.

4-8 Ordered Copolymers

The discussion of the crystallization and fusion of copolymers has heretofore been limited to cases of crystallizable units with either random
sequence distribution or distributions closely approaching random
sequence. Copolymers can also be prepared when other types of
sequence distributions prevail. Two extreme cases are of interest.
One is the ordered or block copolymer in which, in contradistinction
to the random copolymer, the crystallizable units are arranged in very
long uninterrupted sequences. The other is the case in which there is
a strong tendency for the crystallizable and noncrystallizable units to

alternate. Since the relations between the sequence propagation parameter p and the composition are not the same, quite different behavior is anticipated for the various types of copolymers.

When strict alternation between two structural units occurs, there is a distinct possibility that a new crystal lattice will be formed. For example, for an ethylene–carbon monoxide copolymer in 1:1 mole ratio the repeating unit becomes $(CH_2—CH_2—CO)_n$. Such a polymer has been prepared[54] and possesses a crystal structure different from that of polyethylene, particularly in the c-axis direction. The melting point of the polymer is approximately 180°, which is substantially greater than that of polyethylene. This structure persists even if the ratio of ethylene to carbon monoxide is increased to 1.1:1. Further increases in the relative ethylene content leads to a repeat distance in the unit cell characteristic of polyethylene.

For an ordered copolymer the sequence propagation probability parameter p greatly exceeds the mole fraction of crystallizable units X_A. The melting temperature therefore is not depressed as much as for a random copolymer of the same composition, and according to Eq. (4-21) the fusion process itself becomes appreciably sharper. These conclusions are in accord with the observations of Coffey and Meyrick[55] who studied the melting temperature–composition relations for a series of ordered copolyesters of polyethylene adipate/polyethylene sebacate. In contrast to the results for the random-type copolymers of the same constituents, which follow the pattern of Fig. 4-5, the melting temperature of the ordered copolymer remains essentially invariant with added coingredient. These results are illustrated in Fig. 4-11. For these copolymers the melting of only the major component is observed, and the melting temperature is unaffected by compositional variations. A step-shaped melting temperature–composition curve thus results. The introduction of different repeating units in definite blocks into the chain allows for chemical variations to be built into the polymer molecule without losing the advantage of the physical and mechanical properties associated with high melting temperatures and high levels of crystallinity. The retention of these properties has been reported for ordered copolymers of polyethylene terephthalate and polyoxyethylene glycol.[56] In this case the incorporation of 30 per cent of the second component in an ordered manner results in only a slight depression of the melting temperature. This is in marked contrast to what would be expected for a random-type copolymer of the same composition. The preparation of ordered copolymers is not restricted to copolyesters or copolyamides. A block copolymer of isotactic and syndiotactic methyl methacrylate has been reported[44] as have stereoblock polymers of polypropylene[39] and ordered copolymers of ethylene and propylene.[57]

   There is a distinct possibility that the ordered type of copolymer, admittedly more complex chemically than discussed above, may occur naturally in the fibrous proteins and possibly in the nucleic acids. Although the fibrous proteins are composed of many chemically differ-ent amino acid residues, it appears that many of them can enter into

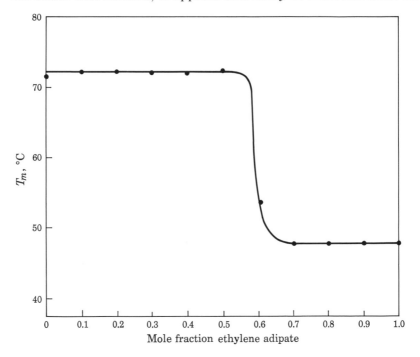

Fig. 4-11   Plot of melting temperature against composition for ordered ethylene adipate–ethylene sebacate copolymers. [*Redrawn from data of Coffey and Meyrick* (55).]

the same crystal lattice.   If all the repeating units participated in the crystallization process, melting typical of a homopolymer would be expected despite the heterogeneous chemical character of the chain. If, however, certain units were restricted from crystallizing for stereo-chemical reasons, then a fusion process typical of a copolymer would result.   Therefore, it is not required a priori that a stoichiometric identity be maintained between the over-all composition of the protein or nucleic acid and those chain units involved in crystallization.   This concept has an important bearing on the interpretation of physical-chemical processes involving the crystal-liquid transformation in such systems. In addition, it is an important factor in interpreting the X-ray diffraction patterns of fibrous proteins since only those units that crystallize contribute to the diffraction. Hence only those structures are ultimately determined by this technique. Thus, for this relatively complex type of polymer, the nature and concentration of the chemical units that actually partake in the crystallization and their sequence distribution need to be specified in order properly to understand properties and phenomena related to crystallization.

For the fibrous proteins one could envisage the case where those amino acid residues that crystallize (comparable to the A units) are arranged in one block while those that do not crystallize are present in another block. The two stereochemically differing blocks would then alternate along the chain. This arrangement would be schematically equivalent to that of the ordered copolyesters. It would also be possible to have a random sequence distribution between the crystallizable and noncrystallizable units. Distinction between these possibilities involves structural determinations, thermodynamic studies, and an assessment of physical and mechanical properties. Silk fibroin possesses an arrangement of amino acid residues along the polypeptide chain that appears to be characteristic of an ordered copolymer, despite the fact that a crystallographic structure has been presented[58] that could accommodate all the chemically differing repeating units. Analyses[59] of the small peptide fragments found in partial hydrolyzates of silk fibroin are not in accord with the concept of a regular chemical repeating sequence throughout the molecule. Rather, a structure in which certain types of residues occur in particular portions of the chain is suggested. Specific fissions of the polypeptide chain at the tyrosine residues utilizing the enzyme chymotrypsin have allowed for the isolation of two major portions.[60] Sixty per cent of the chain contains only glycine, alanine, and serine residues and gives a powder X-ray diffraction pattern similar to native fibroin. The other portion contains all the bulky amino acid residues as well as glycine, alanine, and serine in small concentration. It is doubtful whether the latter portion participates in the crystallization. These analytical results are in accord with the suggestion of Meyer,[61] that the glycine, serine, and alanine residues form the crystalline regions of the polymer, with the other residues being relegated to the amorphous or noncrystalline regions.

The concept of a partially crystalline structure for silk fibroin is further enhanced by studies of mechanical properties. The elastic properties of fibers, derived from different species of silk moths, that contain varying proportions of amino acid residues with long or bulky side chains have been studied.[62] Fibers containing 90 per cent glycine and alanine are relatively inextensible, as would be expected if they are essentially completely crystalline. On the other hand, as the amino acid content of the more bulky side groups increases, the fibers become more extensible. This result is compatible with the presence of a significant amorphous content. The mechanical properties, taken together with the information for the sequence distribution of amino acid residues, strongly suggest that silk fibroin can be considered an ordered copolymer. Other fibrous proteins, particularly those of the keratin and collagen class, may very well be categorized in the same manner.

4-9   Cocrystallization and Isomorphic Replacement

The fibrous and globular proteins as well as the nucleic acids possess crystal structures that allow different chemical repeating units of the same general type to enter into the lattice. Crystallographic analysis indicates a stereochemical identity among many of the amino acid residues and among the nucleotides. Under favorable circumstances, the simpler synthetic copolymers exhibit the same phenomena. The units are said to cocrystallize, and X-ray diffraction studies indicate the presence of only one crystal structure characteristic of the principal component present. The melting point–composition relations for such systems are different from those for random or ordered copolymers.

Several examples of isomorphic replacement in copolyamides have been reported.[63-67] Definitive rules for the pertinent structural factors of comonomers that favor cocrystallization have not, however, been developed as yet. For example, Edgar and Hill[63] noted, from calculations based on normal bond lengths and angles, that the distance between the carboxyl groups in terephthalic and adipic acid is almost identical. On this basis, partial substitution in the crystal lattice of these two diacids was anticipated. This is found to be the case for poly(hexamethylene adipamide/terephthalamide) copolymers. The melting points of these copolymers increase monotonically with increasing terephthalic acid concentration. No minimum in the melting point curve is observed, as would be expected if only one of the comonomers crystallized. It can thus be concluded that cocrystallization of the two units has occurred. Other such systems have been reported,[64,66,67] but more definite guiding rules are required. Having comonomeric units of identical length is not a sufficient requirement for cocrystallization. This is evident from the observation that copolyesters corresponding to the copolyamides cited above do not cocrystallize.

Cocrystallization is also observed among vinyl copolymers.[68] The random introduction of isomorphous units causes a continuous variation of the melting point which assumes values intermediate between those of the pure individual homopolymers.   Copolymers of

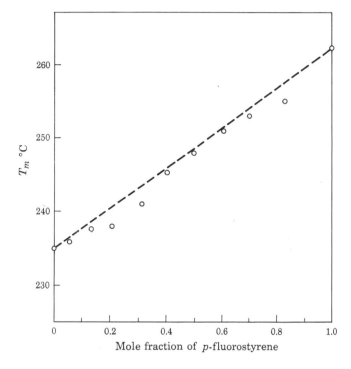

Fig. 4-12   Plot of melting temperatures of styrene–*p*-fluorostyrene copolymers as a function of mole fraction of *p*-fluorostyrene.   [*From Natta* (68).]

o-fluorostyrene and styrene exhibit the same crystal structure and practically the same lattice constants.   Isomorphism is observed over the complete composition range.   The formation of mixed crystals in this system can be attributed to the same identity period for each of the homopolymers and the very small differences in the sizes of the fluorine and hydrogen atoms.   However, cocrystallization has also been observed when the corresponding homopolymers possess different crystalline structures.   For example, the stable crystalline modifications of polystyrene and poly-*p*-fluorostyrene have different symmetries, the former being a threefold helix and the latter a fourfold one. Nevertheless, the copolymers are crystalline over the complete composition range.[68]   The melting point is essentially a linear function of composition in this instance, as is illustrated in Fig. 4-12.   This in itself provides substantial evidence of cocrystallization.   The evidence for the formation of solid solutions in polymethylene copolymers containing methyl side groups has already been given.

4-10   Copolymer-Diluent Mixtures

The crystallization of a copolymer from its mixture with a low molecular weight diluent occurs over the complete concentration range, as in the analogous situation for homopolymers.   The relation between the melting point and polymer composition is similar to that given by Eq. (3-8),[69] when the melting point of the undiluted copolymer is used in place of $T_m°$.   Experimentally this relation has been verified for a variety of stereoirregular polymers such as polychlorotrifluoroethylene,[70] polyacrylonitrile,[71] and polypropylene.[72]

The crystallization of a homopolymer from dilute solution results in the appearance of two distinct phases which are easily separable by mechanical means.   This phenomenon has been previously discussed, and the unusual morphology observed has been illustrated in Figs. 1-10 and 1-11.   On the other hand, when a random-type copolymer crystallizes from dilute solution, a mechanical separation of the two phases very often cannot be made.   However, more careful and systematic experimentation is required to delineate quantitatively the details of total polymer concentration, the thermodynamic nature of the solvent, and the copolymer composition at which this phenomenon occurs. The polymer molecules pervade the whole volume of the system, and the dilute solution with very high fluidity is converted to a rigid medium of high viscosity.   This process is popularly termed gelation and is a manifestation of the crystallization process.

This drastic change in mechanical properties upon crystallization from dilute solutions has been observed in such diverse systems as polyvinyl chloride in dioctyl phthalate,[47] polyacrylonitrile in dimethyl formamide,[48] nitrocellulose in ethyl alcohol,[73] and methyl cellulose in water.[74]   Polyvinyl chloride and polyacrylonitrile possess copolymeric character because of stereoirregularities, while in the noncompletely substituted cellulosics cocrystallization of the chain units is probably not complete.   Crystallization of these systems in dilute solution can occur upon either raising or lowering the temperature, the solubility being governed by the magnitude and sign of the free energy of dilution relative to that of fusion. The two cellulosic systems are examples of crystallization, accompanied by gelation, that results when the temperature is raised.[73,74] It appears to be a general rule that all polymer systems displaying this type of gelation crystallize as copolymers. However, it should also be noted that all the polymers cited possess or are suspected of possessing very extended configurations.

The copolymeric character of the molecules is conducive for gel formation, for even if the equilibrium requirements were fulfilled not all the chain units would participate in the crystallization, so that only a small fraction of them would be transformed. Consequently, since the large number of chain elements that do not crystallize are interconnected by means of the crystalline regions, they pervade the entire volume and impart to the system its characteristic rigidity and high viscosity. For copolymers, particularly in crystallizing from dilute solution, the accretion of chains in the lateral direction is severely restricted since the irregular chain structure does not permit any significant reentry of a chain once it emerges from a crystallite. Without this reentry, lateral growth cannot be very extensive. (This subject is discussed in greater detail in Chap. 9.) This effect, accompanied by retardations in longitudinal development, must necessarily limit the number of chain elements participating in the crystallization.

The gelation process that has been discussed must be clearly distinguished from the other types of gel formation that can be induced in polymer systems. In particular, distinction should be made between gelation caused by crystallization and gels caused by network formation without a phase change. The latter type of gels or three-dimensional networks can be formed by the introduction of a sufficient number of intermolecular cross-links into a collection of polymer chains or by the polymerization of multifunctional comonomers.[75] Considerable confusion exists since gel formation can occur by these diverse mechanisms. When immersed in diluent, gels of the latter type display mechanical properties similar to those formed by the crystallization of copolymers, although the polymer itself is amorphous. Gels formed as a consequence of crystallization can be melted to form a sol or homogeneous solution. On this basis, a distinction can be made between the different types of gels. Flory and Garrett[76] have shown that the classical gelation system, that of gelatin in water, occurs as a consequence of a crystal-liquid transformation and the gelation or solation process can be treated as a first-order phase transition.

According to the works of Marsland,[77] a similar type of sol-gel transformation appears in certain problems of biological interest such as amoeba movement and in the development of the furrow just preceding cell division in the mitotic cycle. Crystallizable protein molecules appear to be involved, and studies of the effect of pressure and temperature on the cessation of amoeba movement or the impediment of furrow development indicate that a relation similar to that of the Clausius-Clapeyron equation is obeyed. This gives evidence that the sol-gel transformations identified with these processes involve the transition between two distinct phases, most likely the crystal and the liquid phases.

REFERENCES

1. Flory, P. J.: *Trans. Faraday Soc.*, **51**: 848 (1955).
2. Richardson, M. J., P. J. Flory, and J. B. Jackson: *Polymer*, **4**: 221 (1963).
3. Ke, B.: *J. Polymer Sci.*, **61**: 47 (1962).
4. Mandelkern, L.: *Rubber Chem. Technol.*, **32**: 1392 (1959).
5. Eichorn, R. M.: *J. Polymer Sci.*, **31**: 197 (1958).
6. Swan, P. R.: *J. Polymer Sci.*, **56**: 409 (1962).
7. Flory, P. J., L. Mandelkern, and H. K. Hall: *J. Am. Chem. Soc.*, **73**: 2532 (1951).
8. Evans, R. D., H. R. Mighton, and P. J. Flory: *J. Am. Chem. Soc.*, **72**: 2018 (1951).
9. Edgar, O. B., and E. Ellery: *J. Chem. Soc.*, 2633 (1952).
10. Sonnerskog, S.: *Acta Chem. Scand.*, **10**: 113 (1956).
11. Izard, E. F.: *J. Polymer Sci.*, **8**: 503 (1952).
12. Mandelkern, L., R. R. Garrett, and P. J. Flory: *J. Am. Chem. Soc.*, **74**: 3939 (1952).
13. Flory, P. J., H. D. Bedon, and E. H. Keefer: *J. Polymer Sci.*, **28**: 151 (1958).
14. Maynard, J. T., and W. E. Mochel: *J. Polymer Sci.*, **13**: 235 (1954).
15. Mandelkern, L., M. Tryon, and F. A. Quinn, Jr.: *J. Polymer Sci.*, **19**: 77 (1956).
16. Hart, E. J., and A. W. Meyer: *J. Am. Chem. Soc.*, **71**: 1980 (1949).
17. Condon, F. E.: *J. Polymer Sci.*, **11**: 139 (1953).
18. Binder, J. L.: *Ind. Eng. Chem.*, **46**: 1727 (1954).
19. Lanzavecchih, G.: *Ind. Chim. Belge*, Suppl. 2, 347 (1959).
20. Natta, G., and P. Corradini: *Angew Chem.*, **68**: 615 (1956).
21. Stavely, F. W., and coworkers: *Ind. Eng. Chem.*, **48**: 778 (1956).
22. Horne, S. E., Jr., J. P. Kiehl, J. J. Shipman, V. L. Folt, C. F. Gibbs, E. A. Wilson, E. B. Newton, and M. A. Reihart: *Ind. Eng. Chem.*, **48**: 784 (1956).
23. Adams, H. E., R. S. Stearns, W. A. Smith, and J. L. Binder: *Ind. Eng. Chem.*, **50**: 1508 (1958).
24. Natta, G., and P. Corradini: *Atti Accad. Naz. Lincei*, **19**: 230 (1953).

25. Cuneen, J. I., and F. W. Shipley: *J. Polymer Sci.*, **36**: 77 (1959).
26. Cuneen, J. I., and W. F. Watson: *J. Polymer Sci.*, **38**: 521 (1959).
27. Golub, M.: *J. Polymer Sci.*, **25**: 373 (1957).
28. Cuneen, J. I., G. M. C. Higgins, and W. F. Watson: *J. Polymer Sci.*, **40**: 1 (1959).
29. Pauling, L., R. B. Corey, and H. R. Branson: *Proc. Natl. Acad. Sci. U.S.*, **37**: 205 (1951).
30. Mizushima, S.: *Advances in Protein Chem.*, **9**: 299 (1954).
31. Natta, G.: *J. Polymer Sci.*, **16**: 143 (1955); G. Natta, P. Pino, P. Corradini, F. Danusso, E. Mantica, G. Mazzanti, and G. Moraglio: *J. Am. Chem. Soc.*, **77**: 1708 (1955).
32. Huggins, M. L.: *J. Am. Chem. Soc.*, **66**: 1991 (1944).
33. Fox, T. G., W. E. Goode, S. Gratch, C. M. Huggett, J. F. Kincaid, A. Spell, and J. D. Stroupe: *J. Polymer Sci.*, **31**: 173 (1958).
34. Garrett, B. S., W. E. Goode, S. Gratch, J. F. Kincaid, C. L. Levesque, A. Spell, J. D. Stroupe, and W. H. Watnabe: *J. Am. Chem. Soc.*, **81**: 1007 (1959).
35. Fordham, J. W. L., G. H. McCain, and L. E. Alexander: *J. Polymer Sci.*, **39**: 335 (1959).
36. Fordham, J. W. L., P. H. Burleigh, and C. L. Sturm: *J. Polymer Sci.*, **41**: 73 (1959).
37. Fordham, J. W. L.: *J. Polymer Sci.*, **39**: 321 (1959).
38. Coleman, B. D.: *J. Polymer Sci.*, **31**: 155 (1958).
39. Natta, G.: *J. Polymer Sci.*, **34**: 531 (1959).
40. Danusso, F., G. Moraglio, W. Ghiglia, L. Motta, and G. Talamini: *Chim. Ind.* (Milan), **41**: 748 (1959).
41. Newman, S.: *J. Polymer Sci.*, **47**: 111 (1960).
42. Stroupe, J. D., and R. E. Hughes: *J. Am. Chem. Soc.*, **80**: 2341 (1958).
43. Williams, J. L. R., J. Van Den Berghe, W. J. Dulmage, and K. R. Dunham: *J. Am. Chem. Soc.*, **78**: 1260 (1956); J. L. R. Williams, J. Van Den Berghe, K. R. Dunham, and W. J. Dulmage: *J. Am. Chem. Soc.*, **79**: 1716 (1957).
44. Fox, T. G., B. S. Garrett, W. E. Goode, S. Gratch, J. F. Kincaid, A. Spell, J. D. Stroupe: *J. Am. Chem. Soc.*, **80**: 1768 (1958).
45. Korotkov, A. A., S. P. Mitsengendlev, U. N. Krasulinc, and L. A. Volkova: *High Molecular Weight Compounds*, **1**: 1319 (1959).
46. Doty, P. M., H. L. Wagner, and S. F. Singer: *J. Phys. Colloid Chem.*, **55**: 32 (1947).
47. Walter, A. T.: *J. Polymer Sci.*, **13**: 207 (1954).
48. Bisschops, J.: *J. Polymer Sci.*, **12**: 583 (1954); **17**: 89 (1955).
49. Etlis, V. S., K. S. Minskev, E. E. Rylov, and D. N. Bort: *High Molecular Weight Compounds*, **1**: 1403 (1959).
50. Raine, H. C., R. B. Richards, and H. Ryder: *Trans. Faraday Soc.*, **41**: 56 (1945).
51. Dole, M., W. P. Hellingen, N. R. Larson, and J. A. Wethington: *J. Chem. Phys.*, **20**: 781 (1952).

52. Hunter, E., and W. G. Oakes: *Trans. Faraday Soc.*, **41**: 49 (1945).
53. Mandelkern, L., M. Hellman, D. W. Brown, D. E. Roberts, and F. A. Quinn, Jr.: *J. Am. Chem. Soc.*, **75**: 4093 (1953).
54. Chatani, Y., T. Takizawa, S. Murahashi, Y. Sakata, and Y. Nishimura: *J. Polymer Sci.*, **55**: 811 (1961).
55. Coffey, D. H., and T. J. Meyrick: *Proc. Rubber Technol. Conf.*, 2nd, 1954, p. 170.
56. Coleman, D.: *J. Polymer Sci.*, **14**: 15 (1954).
57. Kontos, E. G., E. K. Easterbrook, and R. D. Gilbert: *J. Polymer Sci.*, **61**: 69 (1962).
58. Marsh, R. E., R. B. Corey, and L. Pauling: *Biochim. Biophys. Acta*, **16**: 1 (1955).
59. Lucas, F., J. T. B. Shaw, and S. G. Smith: *Advan. Protein Chem.*, **13**: 107 (1958).
60. Lucas, F., J. T. B. Shaw, and S. G. Smith: *Nature*, **178**: 861 (1956); *Biochem. J.*, **66**: 468 (1957).
61. Meyer, K. H., and H. Mark: *Chem. Ber.*, **61**: 1932 (1928).
62. Lucas, F., J. T. B. Shaw, and S. G. Smith: *J. Textile Inst.*, **46**: T-440 (1955).
63. Edgar, O. B., and R. Hill: *J. Polymer Sci.*, **8**: 1 (1952).
64. Tu, A. J., and R. D. Evans: *J. Polymer Sci.*, **20**: 5361 (1959).
65. Carmer, F. B., and R. G. Beaman: *J. Polymer Sci.*, **21**: 237 (1956).
66. Thomas, P. R., T. C. Trauter, and G. J. Tyler: paper presented before International Union of Pure and Applied Chemistry, Symposium on Macromolecules, Wiesbaden, Germany, 1959.
67. Levine, M., and S. C. Temin: *J. Polymer Sci.*, **49**: 241 (1961).
68. Natta, G.: *Makromol. Chem.*, **35**: 94 (1960).
69. Flory, P. J.: *J. Chem. Phys.*, **17**: 223 (1949).
70. Beuche, A. M.: *J. Am. Chem. Soc.*, **74**: 65 (1952).
71. Krigbaum, W. R., and N. Tokita: *J. Polymer Sci.*, **43**: 467 (1950).
72. Danusso, F.: *Atti Accad. Naz. Lincei*, **25**: 520 (1958).
73. Newman, S., W. R. Krigbaum, and D. K. Carpenter: *J. Phys. Chem.*, **60**: 648 (1956).
74. Heyman, E.: *Trans. Faraday Soc.*, **31**: 846 (1935).
75. Flory, P. J.: "Principles of Polymer Chemistry," pp. 347ff., 454ff., Cornell University Press, Ithaca, N.Y., 1953.
76. Garrett, R. R., and P. J. Flory: *Nature*, **177**: 176 (1956); P. J. Flory and R. R. Garrett: *J. Am. Chem. Soc.*, **80**: 4836 (1958).
77. Marsland, D. A., and D. E. S. Brown: *J. Cellular Comp. Physiol.*, **20**: 295 (1942); J. V. Landan, A. M. Zimmerman, and D. A. Marsland: *J. Cellular Comp. Physiol.*, **44**: 211 (1954); D. A. Marsland and J. V. Landan: *J. Exptl. Zool.*, **125**: 507 (1954).

THERMODYNAMIC QUANTITIES

5-1 Introduction

Since the fusion of polymeric systems can be classified as a first-order phase transition, the equilibrium melting temperature of a polymer is a well-defined quantity. It is therefore a matter of interest to assess how the melting temperature of a homopolymer depends on the chemical and structural properties of the chain repeating unit. Since the melting temperature is uniquely described by the ratio of the heat to entropy of fusion, per chain repeating unit, attention must be focused on these two quantities. They have been determined experimentally for a variety of polymers so that attention can be given to the problem of a molecular interpretation of the melting points of macromolecules. However, it is premature to expect that quantitative laws concerning this problem can be formulated at present. This is particularly true in light of the sparsity of generalizations describing how the melting temperatures of the simpler monomeric substances depend on their chemical constitution. On the other hand, an examination of the data that are available for various polymers is instructive, and certain salient features of the problem can be developed.

Caution must be exercised in examining the melting points of polymers to ensure that the values employed represent the equilibrium quantities. This requires the measurement of changes in a thermodynamic property on a well-annealed specimen or on one crystallized at a temperature close to the melting temperature. The changes in mechanical properties or in structural characteristics, which inevitably accompany fusion, can be used only as a qualitative guide in locating the melting temperature and serve best in distinguishing between large differences in melting temperature. The equilibrium melting temperature must reflect the disappearance of the most perfect crystals. The optimum crystallization procedures must be adopted so that these conditions can be approached. As more care has been given to the measurements and more effective annealing treatments have been developed, significant increases in the melting temperature of a variety of polymers have been observed. Melting temperatures have been increased by the adoption of slow heating rates subsequent to crystallization. An additional augmentation of this quantity is achieved when the initial crystallization is conducted very close to the melting point.

5-2   Melting Temperatures, Heats, and Entropies of Fusion

The pertinent thermodynamic quantities characterizing the fusion of homopolymers are summarized in Tables 5-1 to 5-3. In Table 5-1 are the data obtained from an analysis of the melting point depression caused by monomeric diluents, utilizing the procedures developed in the preceding chapter. The melting points of the polymer and the polymer-diluent mixture were obtained by employing slow heating rates following the crystallization. To allow for the different sizes of the repeating units, when comparing the value of ΔH_u for the various polymers, this quantity has been divided by M_0, the molecular weight of the chemical repeating unit. Thus, the heat of fusion per gram of crystalline polymer is given in the fourth column of the table. Dividing ΔH_u by the absolute melting temperature yields the entropy of fusion per repeating unit, ΔS_u. In an attempt to develop a rational basis for comparing the entropy of fusion of polymers whose repeating units contain different numbers of chain atoms, ΔS_u has been divided by the number of single bonds connecting the chain atoms of the repeating unit. This quantity is given in the last column of Table 5-1.

The heats of fusion, ΔH_u^*, can also be obtained calorimetrically for various polymers. From an estimate of the degree of crystallinity of the system before fusion, the more fundamental quantity ΔH_u can be approximated. Results obtained for those polymers when data are

TABLE 5-1

Thermodynamic quantities characterizing the fusion of polymers

(ΔH_u determined from the depression of the melting temperature by monomeric diluents)

Polymer	T_m, °C	ΔH_u, cal/mole	$\Delta H_u/M_0$, cal/g	ΔS_u, cal deg^{-1} mol^{-1}	ΔS_u/bond, cal/deg
Polyethylene[1]	137.5†	960	68.5	2.34	2.34
Polypropylene[2]	176	2,600	62.0	5.78	2.9
Poly(isoprene), 1,4-*cis* (natural rubber)[3]	28	1,050	15.3	3.46	1.15
Poly(isoprene), 1,4-*trans* (gutta-percha)[4]‡	74	3,040	45.1	8.75	2.92
Poly(styrene)[5]	239	2,000	19.2	3.9	1.95
Poly(chloroprene)1,4-*trans*[6]¶	80	2,000	22.6	5.68	1.89
Poly(chlorotrifluoroethylene)[7]	210	1,200	10.3	2.49	1.25
Polyvinyl fluoride[8]	197	1,800	39	3.87	1.9
Poly(decamethylene adipate)[9]	79.5	10,200	36	29	1.60
Poly(decamethylene sebacate)[10]	80	12,000	35	34	1.55
Poly(decamethylene azelate)[11]	69	10,000	31	29	1.39
Poly(nonmethylene azelate)[11]	65	10,300	33	30.5	1.52
Poly(decamethylene terephthalate)[11]	138	11,000	36	27	1.91
Poly(hexamethylene terephthalate)[11]	160.5	8,500	34	19.5	1.95
Poly(tetramethylene terephthalate)[12]	230	7,600	33	15.1	1.9
Poly(tetramethylene isophthalate)[12]	152.5	10,100	45	23.7	3.0
Poly(*N,N'*-sebacoyl piperazine)[13]	180	6,200	24.5	13.7	1.25
Poly(decamethylene sebacamide)[11]	216	8,300	24.5	17	0.77
Poly(decamethylene azelamide)[11]	214	8,800	27	18	0.86
Cellulose tributyrate[14]	207	3,000	8.1	6.2	3.1
Cellulose trinitrate[15]	>700	900–1500	3.0–5.0	1.5	0.75
Cellulose (2.44)nitrate[16]	617	1,350	5.2	1.51	0.76
Cellulose tricaprylate[17]	116	3,100	5.7	8.0	4.0
Polyethylene oxide[18]	66	1,980	45	5.35	2.68
Polymethylene oxide[19]	180	1,590	53	3.5	3.5
Polyacrylonitrile[20]	317	1,200	23	2.0	1.0
Collagen[21]	145§	2,250	24	5.85	1.95

† The melting point of a high molecular weight fraction has been directly determined as 138.5°C.[22]

‡ For the higher melting polymorph.

¶ Extrapolated to the all-1,4-trans polymer.

§ Extrapolated from the melting point of ethylene glycol mixtures.

not available from more exacting analyses are given in Table 5-2. It should be noted that measurements of this type have usually been carried out using rapid heating schedules on polymers crystallized well below the melting temperature. Consequently, the values given for $T_m°$ and ΔH_u must be treated as approximate only.

The variation of the melting temperature with applied hydrostatic pressure p obeys the Clausius-Clapeyron equation

$$\frac{dT_m{}^\circ}{dp} = T_m{}^\circ \frac{\Delta V_u}{\Delta H_u} \tag{5-1}$$

where ΔV_u represents the latent volume change per unit that occurs on melting. If both ΔV_u and the degree of crystallinity are known, ΔH_u can be estimated from appropriate experiment. Estimates of this

TABLE 5-2
Thermodynamic quantities characterizing the fusion of polymers
(ΔH_u estimated from calorimetric measurements of the pure polymer)

Polymer	$T_m{}^\circ$, °C	ΔH_u, cal/mol	$\Delta H_u/M_0$, cal/g	ΔS_u, cal deg^{-1} mol^{-1}	ΔS_u/bond, cal/deg
Poly(ethylene terephthalate)[23]	267	5,500	28.1	10.2	1.7
Poly(ethylene sebacate)[24]	76	8,000	30.5	23.	1.65
Poly(hexamethylene adipamide)[25]	267	10,300	45	19.1	1.36
Poly(hexamethylene sebacamide)[25]	226	12,000	43	24.	1.32
Poly(caproamide)[26]	225	5,100	45	10.3	1.46
Polymethylene oxide[27,28]	180	1,780	59.2	3.94	3.94

TABLE 5-3
Thermodynamic quantities characterizing the fusion of polymers
(ΔH_u estimated from variation of melting temperature with applied hydrostatic pressure)

Polymer	T_m, °C	ΔH_u, cal/mol	$\Delta H_u/M_0$, cal/g	ΔS_u, cal deg^{-1} mol^{-1}	ΔS_u/bond, cal/deg
Poly(tetrafluoroethylene)[29]	327 (1 atm) 335 (69 atm)	1460	14.6	2.9	1.45

quantity, when the aforementioned procedure is the sole source of information for a given polymer, are listed in Table 5-3. The analysis of the melting temperature of copolymers, which in principle can yield the quantity ΔH_u, has not been utilized in this compilation because of the complications discussed in Chap. 4.

From the data in these tables it is apparent that no simple or obvious correlation exists between the melting temperatures and the heats of fusion. The heats of fusion for the different polymers listed fall into two general classes. In one of these, the values of ΔH_u are of the order of several thousand calories per mole of repeating unit, and in the other category they are about 10,000 cal/mole. Many of the high melting polymers are characterized by lower heats of fusion; conversely, a large number of the low melting polymers possess relatively large heats of fusion. In discussing the location of T_m°, it should be emphasized that ΔH_u and ΔS_u represent the difference in the enthalpy and entropy, respectively, between the liquid and crystalline states. Therefore it is the changes occurring on fusion that are of importance. Consequently proper attention must be given to these properties in both states.

The thermodynamic data accumulated for the hydrocarbon polymers show that the values of T_m° and ΔH_u determined for linear polyethylene are in reasonable accord with the corresponding values for a high molecular weight n-paraffin extrapolated from analysis of the fusion of its low molecular weight homologs.[1,30-36] The melting temperature of 137.5° given in Table 5-1 for the whole polymer has been increased to 138.5° as a result of the more nearly perfect development of the crystalline state in a high molecular weight fraction.[22] The melting temperature of 176°, given for polypropylene, should be taken as a lower limit for the completely isotactic polymer. On a molar basis the heat of fusion is slightly greater than that of polyethylene but slightly less when calculated on a weight basis. Syndiotactic polypropylene of unspecified stereoregularity has been reported to have a slightly higher T_m than its isotactic counterpart.[37] The respective differences in the heats and entropies of fusion of these two stereoisomeric polymers remain to be elucidated. Isotactic polystyrene is an example of a relatively high melting polymer with a low heat of fusion. On a weight basis, its heat of fusion is comparable to the much lower melting natural rubber. Clearly, for these polymers the entropies of fusion must play a significant role in the location of T_m.

The melting of the diene-type polymers follows certain generalizations observed for their monomeric analogs. It is well known, for example, that cis isomers of ethylene derivatives are lower melting than the corresponding trans isomers. Hence it is not surprising that 1,4-*trans*-polyisoprene is higher melting than the 1,4-cis polymer. Similarly, 1,4-*cis*-polybutadiene has a melting temperature of +1°,[37] while that of the 1,4-trans polymer is 148°. Among polyesters and polyurethanes containing the CH=CH group in the main chain, the cis isomer has a lower melting temperature than the trans.[38] The melting temperature of the cis isomer of the polyurethane prepared from 1,4-cyclohexanediol and methylene bis(4-phenyl isocyanate) is substantially less than the corresponding trans isomer. However, when 1,4-cyclohexanedimethanol is used as the glycol, comparable melting temperatures are observed for the two isomers.[39]

Isotactic 1,2-polybutadiene has a melting temperature of 120°,[40] while T_m for the syndiotactic isomer is reported to be 154°.[41]   A higher melting temperature for the syndiotactic polymer relative to the isotactic one, previously noted for polypropylene, is also observed for polymethyl methacrylate.[42]   The general observation can therefore be made that syndiotactic polymers are higher melting than their isotactic counterparts.   The basis for this remains obscure since appropriate values of ΔH_u and ΔS_u are not available for comparison.

Many of the polymers prepared from the branched 1-olefins, such as 4,4-dimethyl-1-hexene and 3-phenyl-1-butene, possess melting temperatures of the order of 350°;[43] the melting temperature of poly-p-xylene is reported as 412°.[44]   From the values of ΔH_u generally expected and observed for hydrocarbons, the extremely high melting temperatures for these polymers must be attributed to a very low entropy of fusion.

Polymers commonly considered to be elastomers must have very low glass temperatures and either be noncrystalline or, if crystallizable, have low melting temperatures.   Three polymers in this category are natural rubber, polyisobutylene, and polydimethyl siloxane, which possess melting temperatures of 28°,[3] 5°,[45] and about −40°,[46] respectively.   The heat of fusion of polyisobutylene would be expected to be typical of the hydrocarbon polymers while the corresponding quantity for the dimethyl siloxane polymer would not be expected to be any lower.   Hence the basis for the relatively low melting temperatures of these polymers and their classification as elastomers must reside in a relatively large entropic contribution to the fusion process.

The halocarbon polymers are examples of a class of polymers that have high melting temperatures but possess low heats of fusion, as evidenced by the thermodynamic quantities assigned to poly(chlorotrifluoroethylene) and poly(vinyl fluoride).   The melting temperature of poly(tetrafluoroethylene) is reported to be in the vicinity of 330°. Estimates of the heat of fusion for this polymer, based on studies of the variation of the melting temperature with hydrostatic pressure, yield a value substantially less than that for polyethylene.   The high melting temperatures observed for this class of polymers must again be attributed to a significant role played by the entropy of fusion.

The aliphatic polyesters melt at a lower temperature than polyethylene, in analogy with the melting temperature of the monomeric chain esters as compared with the corresponding hydrocarbons.   A general decrease in T_m is noted as the proportion of ester groups in the chain increases.[47] This is contrary to what would be expected if in the crystalline state there was an increased intensity of intermolecular interactions attributable to the polar ester groups. However, the two polyesters containing the greatest concentration of ester groups along the chain are anomalous in this respect. Polyethylene succinate melts at 108° while polyethylene malonate is a liquid at room temperature.[48] Polyesters that contain an odd number of CH_2 sequences melt at a lower temperature than those containing an even number of sequences. ΔH_u for polyesters containing an odd number of units is slightly less than for the even-numbered polymers. This may be the explanation for the difference in melting temperatures between the two types.

The introduction of ring structures into the chain gives rise to substantially higher melting temperatures when compared with the corresponding aliphatic polymers. This is particularly exemplified by the polyesters[49] and polyanhydrides.[50] For example, polysebacic anhydride melts at 83°, while for polymers derived from dibasic aromatic acids T_m's range from 150 to over 300°. The data in Table 5-1 show that the aromatic polyesters are much higher melting than their aliphatic counterparts. However, both types of polyesters have comparable values for ΔH_u. The significantly higher melting temperatures of the aromatic polymers must be a result of a lowered entropy of fusion. On the basis of the entropy of fusion per single bond, however, the values for the aromatic polyesters are slightly greater. Hence when the chain backbone contains ring structures, the method suggested for comparing the entropy of fusion of different polymers is not quantitative. Among the aromatic polyesters, poly-(tetramethylene terephthalate) melts at a much higher temperature than its isomer poly(tetramethylene isophthalate). This can be attributed to the higher entropy of fusion of the isophthalate polymer. A similarity to the melting behavior of monomeric substances is again indicated since it is known that the para di-derivatives of benzene are higher melting than the other isomeric compounds.

The aliphatic polyamides are much higher melting than poly-ethylene, and in contradistinction to the polyesters there is a general increase of T_m as the proportion of polar groups in the chain increases. This can be explained by the hydrogen bonding capacity of the amide groups. The melting temperatures follow the accepted generaliza-tion[47,49] according to which chains containing even-numbered units are higher melting than those containing odd-numbered units. Those with mixed odd-even sequences melt at temperatures somewhere in between. This difference between odd and even polymers is com-parable to the alternation of melting points of similarly constituted chain monomers.   This alternation in T_m is observed, for example, in the low molecular weight n-paraffins but the difference in melting temperatures disappears with increasing chain length.   In the case of the polyesters, where accurate melting temperatures have been obtained, an 11° difference exists between the melting of poly(decamethylene sebacate) and poly(decamethylene azelate).   The corresponding polyamides possess only a 2° difference in melting temperatures.   Many of the melting points in the literature,[47–49] which serve as a basis for the aforementioned generalizations in polymeric systems, have been determined by rapid heating.   Comparisons of such melting temperatures are subject to errors, which could be as large as 20° in some cases.

The replacement of the H atom of the NH group by an alkyl group leads to a large reduction in the melting temperature.   For example, the polymer of N-methyl undecanoic acid $[N—CH_3—(CH_2)_{10}CO]_n$ melts at 60° while the unsubstituted polymer melts at 182°.[51]   The reduction in T_m has been ascribed to the decreased capacity for hydrogen bond formation when the H atom is replaced by an alkyl group.

A comparison of the data in Table 5-1 for the aliphatic polyamides with the corresponding polyesters indicates that, despite the much higher melting temperatures of the former, their heats of fusion are substantially less, the potentially greater hydrogen bonding capacity of the polyamides notwithstanding.   Attention is again focused on the importance of the entropy of fusion, and one can assert that the aliphatic polyamides are higher melting because they possess a lower entropy of fusion.   Two of the three polyamides, for which data are available, are capable of forming intermolecular hydrogen bonds while poly-N,N'-sebacoyl piperazine cannot.   Despite the differences in melting temperature for these three polymers, the heats of fusion on a weight basis are comparable.   Any significance that is to be applied to the role of hydrogen bond formation in causing higher melting temperatures must be reflected in its influencing the entropy of fusion. The estimates of ΔH_u from calorimetric measurements for three polyamides are similar and substantially greater than the values deduced for two similar polymers by analysis of melting point depression data. Although the basis for this discrepancy is not clear, an uncertainty exists in calorimetric studies in ascertaining the level of crystallinity.

The polyurethane polymers contain the functional group

$$—(O—CO—NH)$$

They are similar to polyamides in that hydrogen bond formation is possible between the polar groups but the O—CH$_2$ bonds typical of polyesters are also present. It is, therefore, not surprising that the melting temperatures of the polyurethanes fall between those of the polyesters and polyamides.[47] It again appears that those polymers with an even number of CH$_2$ sequences melt at higher temperatures than those containing an odd number of such sequences.

Cellulose and its derivatives are very polar polymers characterized by high melting temperatures. One notes, however, that this class of polymers possesses extremely low heats of fusion. For example, cellulose trinitrate has the highest reported melting temperature of any polymer but it also has the smallest heat of fusion. Thus, effects of polarity and chain structure in influencing T_m must again be reflected in the entropy of fusion. The low heats of fusion given in Table 5-1 are for the completely crystalline polymer. For the usual situation, where only partial crystallinity prevails, the enthalpy of fusion that would be directly measured must be significantly less. Thus, it is not surprising that cooling curves show no flat or "halt" in the vicinity of the melting temperature for cellulose tributyrate,[52] nor that similar heats of solution, independent of the state of the polymer, are obtained[53-55] for cellulose and its derivatives. The latter observations cannot be construed to mean that these polymers are not crystalline or that the crystal-liquid transformation does not occur, as has been inferred.

The decreased melting temperature of cellulose tricaprylate with respect to cellulose tributyrate is accompanied by an increase in the entropy of fusion. This can be attributed to an additional gain in the configurational entropy of the ester side groups. As the length of the side group of the tri-substituted derivatives increases, the melting points initially decrease, reach a minimum value, and then increase with further increase in the side-group length.[56] This is typical of the melting behavior of linear polymers with long pendant alkyl groups and is also observed in polymers prepared from 1-olefins.[57]

The melting temperature of polyethylene oxide is much less than that of polyethylene. The larger entropy of fusion of polyethylene oxide could be a result of a greater flexibility in the liquid state because of the periodic introduction of ether linkages along the chain. Polypropylene oxide possesses a melting temperature almost identical with that for polyethylene oxide. Either the introduction of the methyl side group does not affect ΔS_u and ΔH_u or, if alterations occur in these quantities, they do so in the same proportion. The relative concentration of methylene groups to oxygen atoms would appear to be of importance. However, the melting temperature of polyisobutylene oxide is 156° [58]   The melting point of polymethylene oxide is increased by more than 100° over that for polyethylene oxide.   The heat of fusion for this polymer, on a weight basis, is slightly greater than that for polyethylene oxide while the entropy of fusion per single bond is also slightly greater.   The importance of the proportion of ether linkage per repeating unit in influencing the location of the melting point is perhaps illustrated for the polythioethers.[47]   From an initial melting point of 145° for the polymer containing the repeating unit $(CH_2)_2S$ the melting point drops to about 65° as the number of CH_2 groups in the repeating unit is increased.   For polymers containing the disulfide link along the chain, melting points are substantially less than the corresponding thioethers, indicating that the polarity of the sulfur atoms is not a major factor in controlling the melting temperature.

Polyacrylonitrile is another example of a polar, high melting polymer with a low heat of fusion.   The corresponding low entropy of fusion for this polymer indicates that very little configurational freedom is gained in the transfer of a repeating unit from the crystalline to the molten state.   Crystallizable polymers prepared from esters of acrylic and methacrylic acid are all relatively high melting.[42]   Little can be said in the way of comparing melting points within this class of polymers until the required thermodynamic quantities have been determined.

The fusion of the protein collagen has been analyzed in detail so as to yield the appropriate thermodynamic quantities.   The investigation of Flory and Garrett[21] has shown that the thermodynamic parameters deduced for this naturally occurring polymer are very similar to those characteristic of the simpler polymers.   Both the heat and entropy of fusion appear to be normal, the heat of fusion on a weight basis being similar to that of the synthetic polyamides.   Any enhanced stability endowed to the crystalline state of the polymer by virtue of hydrogen bond formation is not in evidence unless this contribution is much smaller than believed.

The repeating units present in major proportions in the collagen molecule are glycine, proline, and hydroxyproline.   Although the concentration of amino and imino acid residues varies among the different species, both in vertebrates and invertebrates the glycine content remains essentially constant and comprises about a third of the total residues.   Despite this compositional variation among the various collagens, correlations exist between the melting temperature (determined at fixed total polymer concentration) and the imino acid content.   Gustavson[59] noted that the melting temperature increased with increasing concentration of hydroxyproline.   The increased stability was attributed to hydrogen bond formation involving the hydroxyl groups of hydroxyproline. Thus, the increase in T_m is presumed to be due to an increase in ΔH_u, possible alterations in ΔS_u being ignored. However, it has been subsequently pointed out[60-62] that a more satisfying correlation exists between melting temperature and total concentration of imino acid residues. Garrett has suggested[54] that the reason for the increased melting temperature may be a decrease in ΔS_u which accompanies the increase in total proline and hydroxyproline content. The increasing concentration of pyrrolidine rings in the main chain would be expected to suppress the configurational freedom of the molecule in the molten state. A lower entropy of fusion would result if the crystalline phase were unaffected. Consequently the melting temperature would increase. In principle, increased stability can be obtained, even in a fibrous protein, by suitably altering the configurational properties of the melt. The development of thermodynamically more stable structures does not necessarily require or imply an increased concentration of hydrogen bonds in the crystalline state.

The melting temperatures of another class of macromolecules of biological interest, the synthetic polynucleotides and the naturally occurring nucleic acids, have been measured.[63-65] In the ordered state, molecules of deoxyribonucleic acid are composed of two interwoven chains in helical configuration. The crystallographic structure deduced by Watson and Crick[66] permits only specific type of pairing between heterocylic bases on each of the chains. Consistent with the analytical results that the concentration of purine bases is equal to the concentration of pyrimidine bases, base pairing through hydrogen bonding is, for steric reasons, permitted only between adenine (A) and thymine (T) and between guanine (G) and cytosine (C). Upon melting, the two chains separate and assume random configurations.

Melting temperatures, in dilute solution, for a variety of deoxyribonucleic acids of different compositions have been obtained.[63,65] The composition of the base pairs, expressed as the per cent guanine plus cytosine, varies from 0 to 65, and the melting temperatures increase in proportion with the concentration of this base pair. For a synthetically prepared nucleic acid containing only A-T, the melting temperature is 65°C; it increases to 95°C for a naturally occurring polymer containing about 65 per cent G-C. Since the two base pairs involve different numbers of hydrogen bonds,[67] the G-C pair being able to form three hydrogen bonds with each other while the A-T pair can form only two, it is concluded that they contributed differently to the stability of the helix.[63,64] The differences in melting temperature among the deoxyribonucleic acids are therefore attributed to the intensity of the hydrogen bonds between the two chains comprising the crystalline molecule. Formally, therefore, strong emphasis is given to the role of ΔH in governing the fusion. The influence of the entropy of fusion is tacitly ignored despite its important contribution to the melting process in simpler polymers. Whether significant configurational differences in the molten state exist among nucleic acids of varying composition is yet to be ascertained.

Multichain, ordered molecules can also form from the single stranded synthetic polyribonucleotides.[68,69] Allowance must be made in these cases for other types of base pairing (and their concomitant hydrogen bonds). The melting temperatures of four such complexes, determined under identical conditions, can be compared.[64] Two systems composed of complementary purine and pyrimidine bases of polyadenylic and polyuridylic acid and of polycytosinic and polyinosinic acids have melting temperatures of 75 and 90°, respectively. Triple-stranded helixes, composed of chains containing only purine bases as poly(I + I + I) and poly(A + I + I), have melting points of 40 and 60°, respectively. The differences in melting temperature have again been presumed to be due to dissimilar intensities of hydrogen bonding.

5-3   Entropy of Fusion

Attempts to correlate the melting temperatures of polymers with intermolecular interactions utilizing the cohesive energy density of the repeating units as a measure of these interactions have been notably unsuccessful.[47,48,70,71] These procedures focus attention solely on ΔH_u. Since no simple relation is observed between T_m and ΔH_u, it is not surprising that many polymers with low cohesive energy densities are high melting while conversely many low melting polymers possess relatively high cohesive energy densities. From a survey of the melting temperature of a wide variety of polymers and the thermodynamic quantities governing fusion, it is evident that the entropy of fusion is of prime importance in establishing the value of the melting temperature.[70] This is particularly striking for the very high melting polymers where a relatively low value of ΔS_u is invariably observed. ΔS_u is a measure of the entropy difference for a chain repeating unit between the crystalline and liquid states. Any molecular interpretation must consider both these states.

Crystals can be disordered so that the extent of departure from regularity in the crystalline state will alter the entropy of this state. The amount of disorder increases with increasing temperature, which in turn leads to a decreased entropy of fusion with increasing melting temperature. For example, it has been observed[25,72,73] that certain polyamides undergo a polymorphic transition from triclinic to hexagonal form at elevated temperatures. Hexagonal packing allows a greater amount of rotational freedom about the chain axis and thus an increased entropy in the crystalline state. The suggestion has been made that this phenomenon accounts in part for the higher melting temperatures of the aliphatic polyamides as compared with the corresponding polyesters,[11] the latter not existing in the hexagonal form. An assessment of the validity of the generalization that increased configurational disorder in the crystalline state is characteristic of the higher melting polymers must await a more detailed structural analysis in the vicinity of the melting temperature for other polymers.

The distinctly different structural characteristics of a polymer molecule in the crystalline and liquid states must manifest itself in an increase in the configurational entropy of the system upon melting. In the liquid state, polymer molecules can assume a wide array of configurations. Depending on the polymer, they can range from random coils to elongated rodlike molecules. The configuration assumed depends on the specific nature of the chain repeating unit and their mutual interactions. The potentials that hinder the rotation of one chain unit relative to another are governed by steric repulsions and the interactions between neighboring chain substituents. The configurational entropy of the liquid state depends, therefore, on the configuration and relative extension of the individual polymer molecules. The entropy of fusion therefore reflects, in part, the configurational properties of the chain in the molten state. Hence a large variation in the entropy of fusion among diverse classes of polymers can be expected on the basis of their known differences in configuration.

Information with respect to the average configuration of individual polymer molecules can be obtained from appropriate dilute solution measurements. From such measurements it is known, for example, that natural rubber,[74] polyisobutylene,[75] and polydimethyl siloxane[76] exist in a highly coiled form, as evidenced by the relatively low values of the ratio $(\langle r^2{}_0 \rangle / \langle r^2 \rangle_{fo})^{1/2}$ (see Table 1-1). Thermodynamic analyses show that these polymers are relatively low melting primarily as a result of entropy effects. The highly coiled form allows the assumption of a relatively large number of configurations in the melt and consequently a high entropy of fusion. In contrast, dilute solution data indicate that other classes of polymers such as cellulose derivatives[77-80] and polyacrylonitrile[20] are highly extended in the molten state. The halocarbon polymers can be assumed to be in the same category. Polymers that are highly extended in the liquid state do not experience as large an increase in configurational entropy upon melting. Consequently a decrease in the entropy of fusion from this cause is to be expected. All things being equal, such polymers are high melting solely because of their chain configuration. High heats of fusion are thus not necessarily required for high melting temperatures. Other polymers assume configurations between these two extremes with a concomitant influence on the entropy of fusion.

To evaluate the configurational entropy that is actually gained on fusion, the contribution of the change in volume that occurs on melting must be separated from the observed entropy of fusion, ΔS_u. Formally[81,82]

$$\left(\frac{\partial S}{\partial V}\right)_T = \left(\frac{\partial P}{\partial T}\right)_V = -\frac{\alpha}{\beta} \qquad (5\text{-}2)$$

where α is the volume-temperature coefficient at constant pressure and β is the volume-pressure coefficient at constant temperature. Thus at $T_m°$, the equilibrium melting temperature at 1 atm, the change in entropy caused by the volume change can be expressed as

$$\Delta S_V = \Delta V_u \left(\frac{\partial P}{\partial T}\right)_V = -\frac{\alpha}{\beta}\Delta V_u \qquad (5\text{-}3)$$

If the assumption is made that

$$\Delta S_u = \Delta S_V + (\Delta S_u)_V \qquad (5\text{-}4)$$

one can obtain $(\Delta S_u)_V$, the entropy change on melting at constant volume at $T_m°$. The thermodynamic data necessary to evaluate ΔS_V are available for several different polymers. Estimates of $(\Delta S_u)_V$, based on these data and the assumption of Eq. (5-4), are given in Table 5-4.

TABLE 5-4
Estimates of the entropy of fusion at constant volume for various polymers (units cal/mole)

Polymer	ΔS_u	ΔS_v	$(\Delta S_u)_v$	Ref.
Polyethylene	2.29	0.52	1.77	(1)
	2.34	.46	1.84	(27)
Natural rubber	3.46	1.8	1.7	(3)
Gutta-percha†	8.75	3.7	5.1	(4)
Polymethylene oxide	3.5	2.1	1.4	(27)
Polyethylene oxide	5.35	1.13	4.22	(83)
Polystyrene	3.9	1.3	2.6	(5)
Polytetrafluoroethylene	1.14	0.38	0.76	(27)

† For the higher melting polymorph.

The data in Table 5-4 show quite forcibly that the volume change that occurs on melting, in general, makes a substantial contribution to the observed entropy of fusion. For natural rubber, for example, approximately half of the entropy change can be attributed solely to the volume change. For any quantitative analysis of the influence of molecular configuration on melting, it thus becomes mandatory that the entropy of fusion at constant volume be calculated.

5-4 Chain Configuration and Crystallization

The previous analysis has directed attention to the importance of the chain configuration in the molten state in governing fusion. A method for quantitatively assessing the stability of the ordered polymer phase in terms of the chain configuration has been given by Flory.[84,85] In this calculation a lattice treatment for the mixing of polymer and diluent molecules is utilized. The partition function developed for a single chain takes cognizance of the rotational isomeric character of a polymer molecule.

By the methods of Volkenstein and coworkers[86-88] and Lifson,[89] each bond in the chain is considered to be in one of the available minima in the potential function describing the hindrance to rotation. Each of these preferred bond orientations is treated as a discrete state, and the chain configuration is described by assigning each bond to one of these states. However, the state of a given bond is not independent of that of its immediate neighbors. The problem is therefore virtually identical to that of a one-dimensional Ising lattice. Well-known methods for treating this problem have been developed,[90,91] so that the dependence of a given bond orientation on that of its predecessor can be accounted for.

To calculate the chain portion function, one defines a matrix $U = \|u_{ij}\|$. An element of this matrix, u_{ij}, represents the transitional probability or statistical weight that rotational state j succeeds i. All possible succession of states, appropriately weighted, are included in the matrix. By following the methods previously developed, the partition function for a long chain molecule, representing all the configurations of an isolated polymer chain, can be expressed as

$$Z \cong \text{trace } (U^{x-2}) \cong \omega^{x-2} \tag{5-5}$$

where ω is the largest eigenvalue of the matrix U. This eigenvalue may be interpreted as representing the effective number of states available to a bond; hence it is a measure of the relative diversity of configurational forms that a chain can assume. In this sense, it can be utilized to describe the "flexibility" of the chain.

The partition function for a system comprised of n_2 chains, characterized by the partition function of Eq. (5-5), and n_1 solvent molecules, with the molar volume ratio of polymer to diluent being equated to x, can be given as[84,85]

$$Q_M = q_1{}^{n_1} q_2{}^{n_2} \frac{(n_1 + n_2)!(n_1 + xn_2)^{-n_2(x-1)}}{n_1! n_2!} \left(\frac{z}{2}\right)^{n_2} \omega^{n_2(x-2)}$$

$$\times \exp \frac{-\chi_1 x n_1 n_2}{n_1 + x n_2} \quad (5\text{-}6)$$

In Eq. (5-6) q_1 and q_2 represent the internal partition functions for the diluent and polymer molecules, respectively; z is the lattice coordination number representing the number of directions available to the first bond of the chain, and the symmetry number of the polymer molecule is taken as 2†. Upon introducing Stirling's approximation, the free energy of mixing pure solvent and ordered polymer becomes

$$\Delta F_m = RT[n_1 \ln v_1 + n_2 \ln v_2 + \chi_1 x n_2 v_1]$$

$$- n_2 RT \left[\ln \frac{xz}{2e} + (x - 2) \ln \frac{\omega}{e} \right] \quad (5\text{-}7)$$

n_1 and n_2 are now the number of moles of the respective components. Equation (5-7) can be written as

$$\Delta F_m = \Delta F_m^* + \Delta F_D \quad (5\text{-}8)$$

Thus the free energy of mixing can be separated into two terms, one of which depends on the composition and is independent of ω. The other is dependent solely on ω and hence on the configurational properties of the chain. ΔF_m^*, the first bracketed term in Eq. (5-7), represents the free energy of mixing chain molecules without altering their internal structure; that is, ω is the same in both the initial and final states. It is recognized as the Flory-Huggins mixing expression.[92,93] The remaining term, ΔF_D, represents the free energy change that occurs when perfectly ordered polymer molecules (all bonds in the preferred orientation) are converted to a state of random disorder in which directions of neighboring chains are uncorrelated with one another and the partition function of an individual chain is given by ω^{x-2}. This separation of the free energy of mixing into two terms, one depending

† The equivalence between Eq. (5-6) and the partition function originally formulated[84] is obtained by noting that $\omega^{-1} = 1 - f$. In the original treatment, f is defined as the fraction of bonds in nonenergetically favored orientations.

solely on composition and the other on the intramolecular configuration, has very important consequences.

For a pure polymer, $v_2 = 1$ so that $\Delta F_m = \Delta F_D$. The disordered state will be stable only if $\Delta F_D < 0$. According to Eq. (5-7), the inequality

$$\frac{\omega}{e} > \left(\frac{xz}{2e}\right)^{1/(x-2)} \qquad (5\text{-}9)$$

must be satisfied. For large values of x this reduces to

$$\omega > e > 2.72 \qquad (5\text{-}10)$$

Thus if the above condition is not fulfilled, the ordered state, wherein the polymer molecules lie parallel to one another, will be more stable. For a chain whose configurational freedom is restricted, any attempt to fill a large fraction of the volume with the chains in disordered arrangement will meet the obvious difficulty of insufficient space. A suitable sequence of contiguous sites for the location of an additional molecule will not exist. Hence the requisite polymer concentration in a given volume can be achieved only by the development of an ordered system. The limitation on the intramolecular chain structure that leads to this situation is specified by Eq. (5-10). The transformation from the disordered state to one of parallel order is a cooperative process since the full advantage to be gained from ordering can be realized only if all the chains in a given neighborhood simultaneously become parallel.

The criterion for the stability of a phase resides in the value of the partition function for the individual chain. This partition function is, in general, a monotonically decreasing function of the temperature. It possesses its greatest value at high temperature and approaches unity as an asymptotic limit as the temperature approaches absolute zero. There is the distinct possibility, therefore, that there is a temperature at which the condition $\omega = e$ will be satisfied. At this temperature the transition from the ordered form, stable at low temperature, to the disordered form should occur spontaneously. This transformation will take place solely as a consequence of intramolecular interactions. The influence or role of intermolecular forces has not as yet been invoked. The existence of a transition of this type for a real chain depends on the value of ω and its temperature coefficient. From this point of view, the melting temperature of a polymer and its configurational properties in the molten state are intimately related through ω.

Crystallization, or the development of a three-dimensional ordered structure, can be envisaged as a two-step process. The first step involves the cooperative ordering of the chains in parallel array by the intramolecular process outlined above. For homopolymers, or polymers possessing sufficient regularity of structural units, only small adjustments in the relative positions of the rodlike molecules are required to bring neighboring substituents into juxtaposition (the development of longitudinal order) in order to complete the crystallization process. The latter step could occur by means of intermolecular interactions with a concomitant decrease in free energy. Hence the intermediate parallel state will be less stable than the three-dimensionally ordered state and transformation to the latter, barring any kinetic impediments, should occur spontaneously.† There is therefore the general expectation of both intramolecular and intermolecular contributions to the free energy of fusion. The theory outlined provides the basis for a significant contribution to fusion from intramolecular interactions. However, in contrast to transitions in dilute solution, intermolecular effects must also play an important role in the crystallization and melting of bulk polymers. Consequently, the transition is much sharper than if the process were restricted to one-dimensional ordering.

As diluent is added to the system, the competition for space between chain elements becomes less severe, so that the disordered amorphous phase gains an advantage in comparison with the pure polymer system. It can be shown that for a high molecular weight polymer-diluent mixture, which is athermal ($\chi_1 = 0$), the condition for the disordered phase to be stable is

$$\omega > e^{v_2} \tag{5-11}$$

Thus as v_2 is decreased, the value of ω required for the stability of the amorphous phase can be appreciably diminished. Therefore melting can, in principle, be accomplished merely by dilution.

The influence of the restrictions in chain configuration on the crystallization-melting process depends on the partition function assuming the required critical value in an accessible temperature range.

---

† Evidence has been presented that certain polymers, such as polyacrylonitrile and polyvinyl trifluoroacetate, are only laterally ordered in the crystalline state.[94] Either kinetic difficulties or the stereoisomeric nature of the chain repeating units would account for the lack of development of three-dimensional order. However, because of the extended nature of the chain configuration for these polymers a regularity in the chain-to-chain packing would still be required when ω is less than e.

The assessment of this possibility for a real polymer chain involves the evaluation of ω through the stipulation of the potential function hindering rotation about the chain bonds. As a convenient starting point, it has become customary to utilize a potential function of the form applicable to n-butane which has three preferred rotational isomers. In this case the trans position is energetically favored over the two gauche positions which occur at rotation angles $+120°$ and $-120°$, respectively. If the trans state is taken as the reference state, and the free energy difference between the trans and the gauche states is ϵ, then

$$\omega = 2g + 1 \tag{5-12}$$

where $g = \exp(-\epsilon/kT)$. In the convention being adopted, $\epsilon > 0$ signifies that the trans state is energetically favored, while if $\epsilon < 0$ either of the two gauche states is preferred. For a polyethylene chain, however, the succession of two gauche states of different sense (i.e., $+120°$, $-120°$) is suppressed because of severe steric interactions of carbon atoms, the so-called "pentane interference." A zero weighting factor is therefore assigned to this probability of succession.[27,85] With this restriction,[75]

$$\omega = \frac{g+1}{2}\left[1 + \sqrt{1 + \frac{4g}{(1+g)^2}}\right] \tag{5-13}$$

Equation (5-13) in conjunction with Eq. (5-5) describes the partition function for an isolated polyethylene chain in the molten state. As an illustrative example, we can also examine a potential energy function hindering rotation which contains but two energetically favored positions. For this case

$$\omega = g + 1 \tag{5-14}$$

A plot of the variation of ω with temperature for these three cases is given in Fig. 5-1. The horizontal dashed line represents the critical condition $\omega = e$. When the trans configuration is favored ($\epsilon > 0$), ω never exceeds e for either the two-minima potential or the three-minima potential with pentane interference, irrespective of the temperature or the energy difference between rotational isomers. For the potential function possessing three minima, with no restrictions on the succession of states, ω exceeds e for small values of the variable ϵ/kT. If Eq. (5-13) is indeed an adequate representation for the polyethylene chain and the trans isomer is favored by about 500 cal/mole, as is supposed,[95] then the crystal-liquid phase transition could not occur without invoking the action of intermolecular forces.

If for a given chain, however, the gauche states are energetically favored, a situation that has been postulated for polymethylene oxide,[27,96] then ω can easily exceed the critical value. The examples cited, which perhaps may bear some resemblance to the appropriate function for real polymer chains, serve to show that the critical values required are realizable. However, as the case for polyethylene illus-

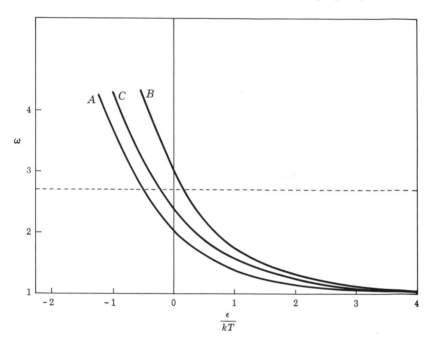

Fig. 5-1 Plot of quantity ω against ϵ/kT for various preferred states of rotational isomerism. Curve A, two preferred rotational states of equal energy; curve B, three preferred rotational states, two of which are of equal energy; curve C, similar situation to that of B but with "pentane interference." Horizontal dashed line represents $\omega = e$.

trates, it does not imply that crystallization in bulk systems, even in favorable cases, usually occurs solely as a consequence of intramolecular interactions.

From Eq. (5-7) and the definition of ΔF_D, the free energy of fusion per bond resulting from the intramolecular configurational change that occurs on ordering the polymer chains can be expressed as

$$\Delta F_{u,I} = -RT \ln \frac{\omega}{e} \qquad (5\text{-}15)$$

for a polymer of high molecular weight.   Accordingly,

$$\Delta S_{u,I} = R \ln\left(\frac{\omega}{e}\right) + RT\frac{d\ln\omega}{dT} \tag{5-16}$$

and
$$\Delta H_{u,I} = -\frac{Rd\ln\omega}{d(1/T)} \tag{5-17}$$

Equations (5-16) and (5-17) express the latent entropy and enthalpy of fusion resulting from the intramolecular ordering process.   These equations are based on a lattice calculation with the inherent assumption that the system is maintained at constant volume.   The thermodynamic quantities under study must be consistent with this stipulation.   The melting temperature of the pure polymer system, T'_m, consistent with the model, is thus defined as that observed at constant volume.   It is not identical with T_m, the melting temperature at 1 atm.   The latter temperature is usually significantly lower than T'_m.

At T'_m the critical conditions are satisfied when $\omega = e$ so that $\Delta F_{u,I} = 0$.   Thus

$$(\Delta S_{u,I})_{T'_m} = \left(\frac{RTd\ln\omega}{dT}\right)_{T=T'_m} \tag{5-18}$$

If all the weighting factors in the matrix **U** are of the form zero, unity or $g = \exp(-\epsilon/RT)$, then

$$(\Delta S_{u,I})_{T'_m} = RT\left(\frac{d\ln\omega}{d\ln g}\frac{d\ln g}{dT}\right)_{T=T'_m} = \left(\frac{d\ln\omega}{d\ln g}\frac{\epsilon}{T}\frac{d\epsilon}{dT}\right)_{T=T'_m} \tag{5-19}$$

and
$$(\Delta H_{u,I})_{T'_m} = \left[\frac{d\ln\omega}{d\ln g}\left(\epsilon - \frac{T\,d\epsilon}{dT}\right)\right]_{T=T'_m} \tag{5-20}$$

Since $\epsilon = \epsilon_h - T\epsilon_S$, if ϵ_h and ϵ_S are assumed independent of temperature, the latent entropy change at T'_m due to intramolecular effects is

$$(\Delta S_{u,I})_{T'_m} = \left(\frac{\epsilon_h}{T'_m}\right)\left(\frac{d\ln\omega}{d\ln g}\right)_{T=T'_m} \tag{5-21}$$

while correspondingly

$$(\Delta H_{u,I})_{T'_m} = (\epsilon_h)\left(\frac{d\ln\omega}{d\ln g}\right)_{T=T'_m} \tag{5-22}$$

Since the first factor on the right of Eq. (5-21) is the entropic difference between two bond orientations, the quantity $(d\ln\omega/d\ln g)_{T=T'_m}$ must represent the fraction of bonds that isomerize to the preferred configuration during the ordering process.   When intramolecular processes make a substantial contribution to fusion, an inverse relation between the entropy of fusion and the melting temperature will exist. If $\omega = ng + 1$, an expression that results from most potential functions hindering rotation, when no restrictions are placed on the succession of states,

$$(\Delta H_{u,I})_{T'_m} = \epsilon_h \left(1 - \frac{1}{e}\right)$$

$$(\Delta S_{u,I})_{T'_m} = \frac{\epsilon_h}{T'_m} \left(1 - \frac{1}{e}\right)$$

(5-23)

These relations have been previously derived.[84]   When there is an interdependence between successive rotational states, the term $(d \ln \omega / d \ln g)$ depends in detail on the restrictions imposed.   Theoretically when ω is independently defined, T'_m, $(\Delta S_{u,I})_{T'_m}$, and $(\Delta H_{u,I})_{T'_m}$ can be calculated. A comparison of these quantities with experimental results, computed at constant volume, will allow for an assessment of the intramolecular contributions to the fusion process.

The configurational properties of real chains and the difficulty experienced in filling a given space with extended chains, randomly arranged relative to one another, provide a basis for the molecular interpretation of crystallization and melting.   From the point of view of intramolecular contributions, the entropy of fusion must have an important influence in determining the melting temperature.   The observation that many high melting polymers with low entropies of fusion are relatively highly extended in the molten state (as deduced from dilute solution measurements) can be given a rational explanation.

5-5 Polymorphism

Polymers can crystallize in different structural modifications and hence display polymorphic behavior similar to that exhibited by monomeric substances.   For example, the trans hydrocarbon polymers gutta-percha and polybutadiene possess different crystallographic structures, in close analogy to the polymorphism of the monomeric trans hydrocarbons.   From studies of its stereochemistry, Bunn[97] has predicted the possibility of four different crystalline modifications of gutta-percha (1,4-*trans*-polyisoprene).   Three of these polymorphs have been observed and identified;[97,98] two of them are formed solely by cooling the polymer to an appropriate temperature, while the third form crystallizes only upon stretching.   Polymorphism is not limited to the simpler polymers but is also observed in proteins[99] and synthetic polypeptides.[100]

The polymorphism observed in polymers can be divided into two broad categories. In one of these the chain can assume distinctly different ordered configurations in the crystalline state. This gives rise to different repeat distances in the unit cell. This class is exemplified by the trans poly hydrocarbons and the α and β structures observed in the polypeptides and the fibrous proteins. In the other type of polymorphism the chain configuration and the repeat distance along the chain axis remain unaltered but the manner in which the crystalline sequences are packed in the unit cell differs. This situation is frequently observed in the polyamides. For example, for polyhexamethylene adipamide[72] and polyhexamethylene sebacamide[73] the asymmetric packing in the basal plane of the triclinic cell shifts to hexagonal packing as the temperature is increased, although the planar zigzag chain structure is maintained. For isotactic polymers, where the chains are in a helical configuration in the crystal, the packing of right- and left-handed helices in the same lattice must be considered. This can lead to a modification in the crystal structure. This is presumed to be the case for polypropylene.[37] A polymorphic situation can also develop if the crystals are composed of only right- or left-handed helices.

The polymorphic modification observed is a result of the crystallization conditions and is governed to a large extent by kinetic factors. Changes in the temperature, pressure, stress, or composition can affect the conversion of one crystalline form to another. This can occur either by direct conversion or by the melting of one polymorph and the subsequent recrystallization of the other from the melt. The latter process, however, may not be easily distinguishable from the former in terms of direct experimental observation. A determination of the free energy of fusion for each of the forms allows for a decision in respect to their relative stabilities and for a thermodynamic description of the transformation.

Figure 5-2 is a schematic diagram of two possible modes of the transformation of one polymorph to another. Since the temperature is taken as the only intensive variable in this example, the free energy of each of the phases can be represented by curves in the planar diagram. The liquid phase is designated by L and the two crystalline phases by C_I and C_{II}, respectively. In Fig. 5-2a, form II is higher melting than form I (as evidenced by the intersections of their free energy curves with that for the liquid phase) and has the lower free energy at all temperatures below its melting temperature. Hence, it is the thermodynamically more stable polymer at all temperatures. Form I must, therefore, be a metastable variety; it will melt below

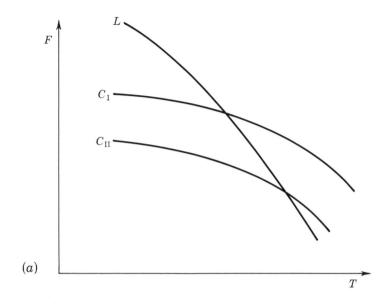

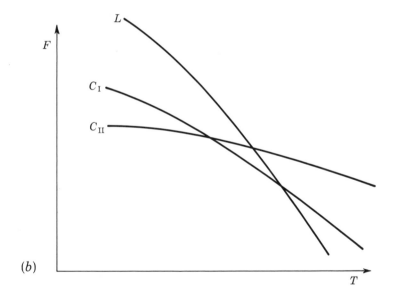

Fig. 5-2   Schematic diagram of the free energy (at constant pressure) as a function of temperature for two crystalline modifications and the liquid state of the same polymer.

form II. Figure 5-2*b* depicts a different situation. Although form I is now the higher melting polymorph, the inverse situation of Fig. 5-2*a* does not exist. Rather, at low temperatures, form II is most stable (now the lower melting form). As the temperature is increased, its free energy curve first intersects that for form I so that a crystal-crystal transformation occurs. At intermediate temperatures form I becomes the more stable crystalline species until its melting temperature is reached. For systems containing more than one intensive variable, as the pressure or the force, the free energy surfaces of the individual phases are treated in a similar manner. The addition of diluent to the liquid phase results in a decrease in its free energy at all temperatures and a concomitant alteration of the stability conditions of each of the crystalline phases.

The stability of each polymorph is therefore quantitatively described by its free energy per repeating unit. The crystal form that has the lowest free energy relative to a standard state at a given temperature is the more stable one. If the completely liquid polymer is taken as the standard state, the crystalline modification having the greatest free energy of fusion is the more stable one. Thus, thermodynamic criteria for stability can be established without recourse to kinetic observations. The latter type of observation, which depends upon the ease with which a particular form develops, could lead to erroneous and misleading conclusions. Since the free energy of fusion can be deduced by studying the melting point depression with added diluent, the necessary methods are available by which formally to treat polymorphism in macromolecular systems.

The only polymeric system that has been quantitatively treated in this manner is gutta-percha, the naturally occurring 1,4-*trans*-polyisoprene.[4] The heats of fusion of the two polymorphs that crystallize without the application of any external stress has been determined. It was concluded that the lower melting modification is metastable at all temperatures at which it exists. This method of analysis seems to be particularly appropriate for the study of the $\alpha \rightarrow \beta$ transformation of the synthetic polypeptides and fibrous proteins. For these systems the crystalline modification that develops with the greatest facility in a given solvent and state of deformation does not necessarily reflect that which is most stable.[101,102] When deformation is involved prior to crystallization, the free energy of the liquid state is increased. One modification may now become more stable over another, or the crystallization kinetics of a metastable variety may be favored by the deformation process. These questions can again be resolved by determining the free energy of fusion of each of the forms. It is interesting to contemplate whether the naturally occurring crystalline macromolecules are found in their thermodynamically most favored modification.

REFERENCES

1. Quinn, F. A., Jr., and L. Mandelkern: *J. Am. Chem. Soc.*, **80**: 3178 (1958).
2. Danusso, F., G. Moraglio, and E. Flores: *Atti Accad. Naz. Lincei*, **25**: 520 (1958).
3. Roberts, D. E., and L. Mandelkern: *J. Am. Chem. Soc.*, **77**: 781 (1955).
4. Mandelkern, L., F. A. Quinn, Jr., and D. E. Roberts: *J. Am. Chem. Soc.*, **78**: 926 (1956).
5. Dedeurwaerder, R., and J. F. M. Oth: *J. Chim. Phys.*, **56**: 940 (1959).
6. Mochel, W. E., and J. T. Maynard: *J. Polymer Sci.*, **13**: 235 (1954).
7. Bueche, A. M.: *J. Am. Chem. Soc.*, **74**: 65 (1952).
8. Sapper, D. I.: *J. Polymer Sci.*, **43**: 383 (1960).
9. Mandelkern, L., R. R. Garrett, and P. J. Flory: *J. Am. Chem. Soc.*, **74**: 3939 (1952).
10. Evans, R. D., H. R. Mighton, and P. J. Flory: *J. Am. Chem. Soc.*, **72**: 2018 (1950).
11. Flory, P. J., H. D. Bedon, and E. H. Keefer: *J. Polymer Sci.*, **28**: 151 (1958).
12. Conix, A., and R. Van Kerpel: *J. Polymer Sci.*, **40**: 521 (1959).
13. Flory, P. J., L. Mandelkern, and H. K. Hall: *J. Am. Chem. Soc.*, **73**: 2532 (1951).
14. Mandelkern, L., and P. J. Flory: *J. Am. Chem. Soc.*, **73**: 3026 (1951).
15. Flory, P. J., R. R. Garrett, S. Newman, and L. Mandelkern: *J. Polymer Sci.*, **12**: 97 (1954).
16. Newman, S.: *J. Polymer Sci.*, **13**: 179 (1954).
17. Goodman, P.: *J. Polymer Sci.*, **24**: 307 (1957).
18. Mandelkern, L.: *J. Appl. Phys.*, **26**: 443 (1955).
19. Inoue, M.: *J. Polymer Sci.*, **51**: 518 (1961).
20. Krigbaum, W. R., and N. Takita: *J. Polymer Sci.*, **43**: 467 (1960).
21. Flory, P. J., and R. R. Garrett: *J. Am. Chem. Soc.*, **80**: 4836 (1958).
22. Chiang, R. F., and P. J. Flory: *J. Am. Chem. Soc.*, **83**: 2857 (1961).
23. Smith, C. W., and M. Dole: *J. Polymer Sci.*, **20**: 37 (1956).
24. Wunderlich, B., and M. Dole: *J. Polymer Sci.*, **24**: 201 (1957).
25. Wilhoit, R. C., and M. Dole: *J. Phys. Chem.*, **57**: 14 (1953).
26. Dole, M., and B. Wunderlich: *Makromol. Chem.*, **34**: 29 (1959).
27. Starkweather, H. W., Jr., and R. H. Boyd: *J. Phys. Chem.*, **64**: 410 (1960).
28. Linton, W. H., and H. H. Goodman: *J. Appl. Polymer Sci.*, **1**: 179 (1959); C. F. Hammer, T. A. Koch, and J. F. Whitney: *J. Appl. Polymer Sci.*, **1**: 169 (1959).
29. McGear, P. L., and H. C. Duus: *J. Chem. Phys.*, **20**: 1813 (1952).
30. Etessani, A. H., and M. F. Saurger: *J. Inst. Petrol.*, **25**: 253 (1939).

31. Van Nes, K., and H. A. Van Westen: "Aspects of the Constitution of Mineral Oils," p. 105, Elsevier Publishing Company, New York, 1951.
32. Garner, W. E., K. van Bibber, and A. M. King: *J. Chem. Soc.*, 1533 (1931).
33. Meyer, K. H., and A. J. A. van der Wyk: *Helv. Chim. Acta*, **20**: 83 (1937).
34. Dole, M., W. P. Hettinger, Jr., N. R. Larson, and J. A. Wethington, Jr.: *J. Chem. Phys.*, **21**: 731 (1952).
35. Billmeyer, F. W.: *J. Appl. Phys.*, **28**: 1114 (1957).
36. Broadhurst, M.: *J. Chem. Phys.*, **36**: 2578 (1962).
37. Natta, G.: *Makromol. Chem.*, **35**: 94 (1960).
38. Marvel, C. S., and C. H. Young: *J. Am. Chem. Soc.*, **73**: 1066 (1951).
39. Lyman, D. J.: *J. Polymer Sci.*, **55**: 507 (1961).
40. Natta, G., L. Porri, P. Corradini, and D. Morero: *Atti Acad. Naz. Lincei, Mem., Classe Sci.*, **20**: 560 (1956).
41. Natta, G., and P. Corradini, *Atti Acad. Naz. Lincei, Mem., Classe Sci.*, **19**: 229 (1955).
42. Fox, T. G., B. S. Garrett, W. E. Goode, S. Gratch, J. F. Kincaid, A. Spell, and J. D. Stroupe: *J. Am. Chem. Soc.*, **80**: 1768 (1958); T. G. Fox, W. E. Goode, S. Gratch, C. M. Huggett, J. F. Kincaid, A. Spell, and J. D. Stroupe: *J. Polymer Sci.*, **31**: 173 (1958).
43. Campbell, T. W., and A. C. Haven, Jr.: *J. Appl. Polymer Sci.*, **1**: 73 (1959).
44. Kaufman, M. H., H. F. Mark, and R. B. Mesrobian: *J. Polymer Sci.*, **13**: 3 (1954).
45. Kell, R. M., B. Bennett, and P. B. Stickney: *Rubber Chem. Technol.*, **31**: 499 (1958).
46. Weir, C. E., W. H. Leser, and L. A. Wood: *J. Res. Natl. Bur. Std.*, **44**: 367 (1950).
47. Bunn, C. W.: *J. Polymer Sci.*, **16**: 323 (1955).
48. Bunn, C. W., in R. E. Hill (ed.): "Fibers from Synthetic Polymers," p. 310, Elsevier Publishing Company, Amsterdam, 1953.
49. Hill, R., and E. E. Walker: *J. Polymer Sci.*, **3**: 609 (1948).
50. Conix, A.: *J. Polymer Sci.*, **29**: 343 (1958).
51. Aelion, R.: *Ann. Chim. (Paris)*, **3**: 5 (1948).
52. Baker, W. O., and C. S. Fuller: *Ind. Eng. Chem.*, **38**: 272 (1946).
53. Kargin, V. A., and G. L. Slonimskii: *Usp. Khim.*, **24**: 785 (1955).
54. Kargin, V. A.: *J. Polymer Sci.*, **30**: 247 (1958).
55. Kargin, V. A.: *High Molecular Weight Compounds*, **2**: 466 (1960).
56. Malm, C. J., J. W. Mench, D. C. Kendall, and G. D. Hiatt: *Ind. Eng. Chem.*, **43**: 684, 688 (1951).
57. Reding, F. P.: *J. Polymer Sci.*, **21**: 547 (1956).
58. Kambara, S., and A. Takahadi: *Makromol. Chem.*, **58**: 226 (1962).
59. Gustavson, K. H.: "The Chemistry and Reactivity of Collagen," chap. 9, Academic Press Inc., New York, 1956.
60. Piez, K. A.: *J. Am. Chem. Soc.*, **82**: 247 (1960).
61. Burge, R. E., and R. D. Hynes: *J. Mol. Biol.*, **1**: 155 (1959)
62. Garrett, R. R.: See P. J. Flory in Discussion, *Brookhaven Symp. Biol.* No. 13, "Protein Structure and Function," p. 229, 1960.

63. Marmur, J., and P. Doty: *Nature*, **183**: 1427 (1959).
64. Doty, P., H. Boedtker, J. R. Fresco, R. Haselkorn, and M. Litt: *Proc. Natl. Acad. Sci. U.S.*, **45**: 482 (1959).
65. Marmur, J., and P. Doty: *J. Mol. Biol.*, **5**: 109, (1962).
66. Watson, J. D., and F. H. C. Crick: *Nature*, **171**: 737 (1953).
67. Pauling, L., and R. B. Corey: *Arch. Biochem. Biophys.*, **65**: 164 (1956).
68. Warner, R. C.: *J. Biol. Chem.*, **229**: 711 (1957).
69. Davies, D. R., and A. Rich: *J. Am. Chem. Soc.*, **78**: 3548 (1956); A. Rich: *Nature*, **181**: 521 (1958); A. Rich: *Biochim. Biophys. Acta*, **29**: 502 (1958); D. R. Davies and A. Rich: *J. Am. Chem. Soc.*, **80**: 1003 (1958).
70. Mandelkern, L.: *Chem. Rev.*, **56**: 903 (1956).
71. Dole, M.: *Advan. Polymer Sci.*, **2**: 221 (1960).
72. Brill, R.: *J. Prakt. Chem.*, **161**: 49 (1942).
73. Slichter, W. P.: *J. Polymer Sci.*, **35**: 82 (1959).
74. Wagner, H. L., and P. J. Flory: *J. Am. Chem. Soc.*, **74**: 195 (1952).
75. Fox, T. G., Jr., and P. J. Flory: *J. Am. Chem. Soc.*, **73**: 1909 (1951).
76. Flory, P. J., L. Mandelkern, J. Kinsinger, and W. B. Shultz: *J. Am. Chem. Soc.*, **74**: 3364 (1952).
77. Mandelkern, L., and P. J. Flory: *J. Am. Chem. Soc.*, **74**: 2517 (1952).
78. Hunt, M. L., S. Newman, H. A. Scheraga, and P. J. Flory: *J. Phys. Chem.*, **60**: 1278 (1956).
79. Holzer, A. M., H. Benoit, and P. Doty: *J. Phys. Chem.*, **58**: 624 (1954).
80. Flory, P. J., O. K. Spurr, and D. K. Carpenter: *J. Polymer Sci.*, **27**: 231 (1958).
81. Oriani, R. A.: *J. Chem. Phys.*, **19**: 93 (1951).
82. Slater, J. C.: "Introduction to Chemical Physics," McGraw-Hill Book Company, Inc., New York, 1939.
83. Malcolm, G. N., and G. L. D. Ritchie: *J. Phys. Chem.*, **66**: 852 (1962).
84. Flory, P. J.: *Proc. Roy. Soc. (London), Ser. A*, **234**: 60 (1956).
85. Flory, P. J.: *J. Polymer Sci.*, **49**: 105 (1961).
86. Volkenstein, M. V., and O. B. Ptitsyn: *Dokl. Akad. Nauk SSSR.*, **78**: 657 (1951).
87. Volkenstein, M. V.: *J. Polymer Sci.*, **29**: 441 (1958).
88. Ptitsyn, O. B., and I. A. Sharonov: *Zh. Tekhn. Fiz.*, **27**: 2744, 2762 (1957).
89. Lifson, S.: *J. Chem. Phys.*, **29**: 80 (1958); **30**: 964 (1959).
90. Kramers, H. A., and G. H. Wannier: *Phys. Rev.*, **60**: 252 (1941).
91. Newell, G. F., and E. W. Montroll: *Rev. Mod. Phys.*, **25**: 353 (1953).
92. Huggins, M. L.: *J. Phys. Chem.*, **46**: 151 (1942); *Ann. N.Y. Acad. Sci.*, **43**: 1 (1942).
93. Flory, P. J.: *J. Chem. Phys.*, **10**: 51 (1942).
94. Bohn, C. R., J. R. Schaefgen, and W. O. Statton: *J. Polymer Sci.*, **55**: 531 (1961).
95. Flory, P. J., C. A. Hoeve, and A. Ciferri: *J. Polymer Sci.*, **34**: 337 (1959).
96. Uchida, T., Y. Kurita, and M. Kubo: *J. Polymer Sci.*, **19**: 365 (1956).
97. Bunn, C. W.: *Proc. Roy. Soc. (London), Ser. A*, **180**: 40 (1942).
98. Fisher, D.: *Proc. Phys. Soc. (London), Ser. B*, **46**: 7 (1953).

99. Astbury, W. T., and H. J. Woods: *Phil. Trans. Roy. Soc. London, Ser. A,* **232**: 333 (1934).

100. Bamford, C. H., W. E. Hanby, and F. Happey: *Proc. Roy. Soc. (London), Ser. A,* **205**: 30 (1951).

101. Blout, E. R., C. de Loze, S. M. Bloom, and G. D. Fasman: *J. Am. Chem. Soc.,* **82**: 3787 (1960).

102. Diorio, A. F., L. Mandelkern, and E. R. Lippincott: *J. Phys. Chem.,* **66**: 2096 (1962).

FUSION OF
CROSS-LINKED POLYMERS

chapter
6

6-1 Introduction

One type of chain irregularity requiring special attention is that in
which units are involved in intermolecular cross-links.   When an adequate number of intermolecular cross-links are imposed on a collection
of linear polymer chains, a three-dimensional network structure reach-
ing macroscopic dimensions is developed.   Such structures are termed
infinite networks.   According to theory[1,2] the initial formation of a
network occurs when the fraction of cross-linked units ρ exceeds a
critical value:

$$\rho_c = \frac{1}{\bar{y}_w - 1} \cong \frac{1}{\bar{y}_w} \qquad (6\text{-}1)$$

where $\bar{y}_w$ is the weight-average degree of polymerization of the initial
molecules.   At this point, called the gel point, not all the polymer
chains are attached to the insoluble network.   Depending on details
of the initial molecular weight distribution, the further introduction
of cross-links into the system results in the incorporation of the remain-

ing chains into the network.[3]   In the usual cases of interest, complete network formation requires that only a few per cent of the chain units be involved in intermolecular cross-linkages.   If the sole effect, as far as crystallization behavior is concerned, of the cross-linkages were their concentration, the previous discussion of copolymers would be applicable.   However, this conclusion is not justified on the basis of further theoretical thought and experimental observation.

In contrast to other types of chain irregularities, units involved in intermolecular cross-linkages act in a unique manner since they actually join together portions of different chains.   Besides the possibility that these units could be restricted from participating in the crystallization for steric reasons, the fact that a network structure has now been evolved could lead to alterations of the crystallization pattern when contrasted with the crystallization of a collection of individual polymer chains.

In the theoretical treatment for the formation of networks it is customary to assume that the points of cross-linkage are randomly distributed over the volume of the specimen.   It is not necessary, however, to make any restrictive assumptions in regard to the disposition of the polymer chains at the time of network formation. Although networks are commonly formed from randomly coiled polymer chains, this represents only a special case among many possibilities. Networks can also be formed from deformed systems or systems where the chains are in ordered or partially ordered array when the cross-links are introduced.   The cross-linkages themselves are always assumed to be randomly distributed in space.   Theory has shown[4] that many of the resulting properties are expected to be strongly influenced by the nature of the chain arrangement at the time of network formation. Therefore, in discussing the properties of networks in general and their crystallization behavior in particular, careful distinction must be made as to their mode of generation.

Intermolecular cross-linkages can be introduced into a collection of polymer chains by chemical reaction, as, for example, the vulcanization of natural rubber,[5] or in favorable cases by the action of high-energy ionizing radiation.[6]   Many naturally occurring macromolecular systems develop, in the course of their synthesis, a sufficient number of intermolecular cross-links so that in the molten state they display the major characteristics of an infinite network.   For purposes of simplification, we shall limit the discussion to an idealized perfect network which contains no free chain ends and from which all soluble molecules have been removed.

A network in the liquid or amorphous state can be given a quantitative description[4,7,8] by defining a chain as that portion of the molecule which traverses from one cross-linked unit to a succeeding one. It is convenient to characterize each chain by a vector **r** which connects the average position of its terminal units, namely, the cross-linked units. The number of chains ν must be equal to the number of intermolecularly cross-linked units. If N_0 is the total number of chain units in the network, then ρ is equal to ν/N_0. The network is then characterized by the number of chains and their vector distribution. When the network is deformed, it is assumed that the chain vector distribution is altered directly as the macroscopic dimensions so that an affine transformation of the average position of the coordinates of the cross-links occurs. It is also further assumed that the individual chains obey Gaussian statistics.

A reference state for the network is conveniently taken as one which represents the isotropic network with mean square vector components, $\overline{x_0^2} = \overline{y_0^2} = \overline{z_0^2} = \overline{r_0^2}/3$. In the reference state so chosen the mean-square chain vector length $\overline{r_0^2}$ is identical with the corresponding unperturbed length of the free chain. For any given state of the network, where $\overline{x^2}$, $\overline{y^2}$, and $\overline{z^2}$ are the average squares of the cartesian components of the chains, the entropy of the network contains a term

$$\frac{k\nu}{2}\left[-\frac{3}{\overline{r_0^2}}\left(\overline{x^2} + \overline{y^2} + \overline{z^2}\right)\right]$$

for the internal configurations of the chains.[4,7] The contribution to the total entropy of the random distribution of cross-linkages over the volume V of the sample is[4,9]

$$\frac{k\nu}{2}\ln V + \text{const}$$

for tetrafunctional cross-links (cross-linkages between two molecules). Therefore, the entropy difference between a given specified state and the reference state can be expressed as

$$\Delta S = \frac{3k\nu}{2}\left[-\frac{\left(\overline{x^2} + \overline{y^2} + \overline{z^2}\right)}{\overline{r_0^2}} + 1 + \ln\langle\alpha\rangle\right] \tag{6-2}$$

where $\langle\alpha\rangle = (\overline{x^2}\,\overline{y^2}\,\overline{z^2}/\overline{x_0^2}\,\overline{y_0^2}\,\overline{z_0^2})^{1/6}$. The parameter $\langle\alpha\rangle$ measures the geometric mean of the linear dilation in the actual state relative to the reference state. It is not necessary that the volume of the reference state and the state under consideration be identical.

For a network formed from polymer chains in the isotropic

randomly coiled state, $\langle\alpha\rangle$ equals unity at the same temperature and network volume as prevailed during cross-linking. On the other hand, for a network formed by the cross-linking of nonrandomly disposed chains the value of $\langle\alpha\rangle$ depends on details of the dimensions of the molecules and their arrangement; for the network at its initial volume and temperature, $\langle\alpha\rangle$ may be either less than or greater than unity. With this brief description of the formation and characterization of networks, attention can be given to the melting of crystallizable networks.

6-2 Theory of the Melting of Isotropic Networks

The melting temperature of an unstressed isotropic network, $T_m{}^i$, can be expressed quite generally as the ratio of the enthalpy of fusion to the entropy of fusion. The entropy of fusion can conveniently be treated as the additive contribution of three terms. These are $\Delta S°$, the entropy of fusion in the absence of the constraints imposed on the chain configurations by cross-linkages; $\Delta S_x°$, the alteration of the chain configurational entropy in the reference state, $\langle\alpha\rangle = 1$, which results from the presence of the cross-linkages; and $\Delta S_{el}{}^i$, the entropy change that occurs in going from the reference state to the real isotropic state. In the latter, $\langle\alpha\rangle$ assumes a value characteristic of the network structure. The melting temperature of the isotropic network can therefore be expressed as

$$\frac{1}{T_m{}^i} = \frac{\Delta S° + \Delta S_x° + \Delta S_{el}{}^i}{\Delta H} \qquad (6\text{-}3)$$

and depends on the network constitution and mode of its generation.

If the network structure is such that the crystallization of the cross-linked units is not restricted, ΔH and $\Delta S°$ can be taken to be independent of the fraction of units cross-linked. Under these conditions, $\Delta S°$ is identified with the entropy of fusion of the pure non-cross-linked polymer, and the ratio of $\Delta S°$ to ΔH is identified with the equilibrium melting temperature $T_m°$ of the pure polymer. If, however, steric requirements are such that cross-linked units are excluded from the crystalline regions, an alteration of these quantities will occur. The presence of cross-linked units in the molten phase and not in the crystalline phase results in an increase in $\Delta S°$ (when compared with the non-cross-linked polymer) of an amount $R\rho$ per mole of chain units. The melting temperature must accordingly be depressed for this reason, if ΔH is unaffected by the presence of cross-links.

For networks formed from randomly coiled chains, $\Delta S_x°$ must be essentially zero since the units cross-linked are selected at random. This type of cross-linking process does not influence the configurational entropy characteristic of random non-cross-linked chains. For this case $\Delta S_{el}{}^i$ must also be zero. However, if polymer chains initially arranged in parallel array are cross-linked to form a network, the above factors must be greatly modified. If $\langle \alpha \rangle$ is known, $\Delta S_{el}{}^i$ can be calculated from theory.[4] Its contribution to Eq. (6-3) is shown to be small. However, because of the nature of the chain disposition at the time of network formation, a certain element of the high degree of order that is initially present will be imposed on the network. This element of order will be maintained throughout any subsequent transformations that the network may undergo as long as the initially imposed cross-links are not severed.

When cross-linking occurs in this initial state of axial order, it is required that the unit of one molecule that is being cross-linked be joined to a neighboring predetermined unit. Thus, even though the cross-links are randomly distributed in space, units to be paired can no longer be selected at random. Since this pairing of units is maintained even in the liquid state, a decrease in the configurational entropy of the liquid occurs as a consequence of the introduction of cross-links in the prescribed manner. This stands in marked contrast to the random cross-linking of random chains. This decrease in the configurational entropy of the liquid manifests itself in a decrease in the total entropy of fusion, which is embodied in the term $\Delta S_x{}^\circ$.

To calculate $\Delta S_x{}^\circ$ for networks formed from perfectly axially ordered chains, it is necessary to compute the probability that the units involved in cross-linkages will occur in suitable juxtaposition relative to one another. The results of such a calculation can be expressed as[4]

$$\Delta S_x{}^\circ = k\nu \left(\frac{\ln C}{2} - \frac{9}{4} + \frac{3}{4} \ln \frac{\nu}{N_s} \right) \tag{6-4}$$

where C is a dimensionless quantity of the order of unity and N_s is the number of statistical elements in the network.† A similar expression has been derived by Schellman[10] for the effect of intramolecular cross-linkages in stabilizing ordered polypeptide chains.

From the foregoing, quantitative expressions can be developed for the isotropic melting temperature of various types of crystallizable networks. For networks formed from random chains, if the cross-

---

† A statistical element of the network bears the same relation to a chain unit as the statistical element of an "equivalent statistical chain" does to the repeating unit of a real chain. See Ref. 7, p. 410ff.

linked units participate in an unrestricted manner in the crystallization, i.e., if the cross-linked and non-cross-linked units are indistinguishable, then no change in the melting temperature in comparison
with the non-cross-linked polymer should be observed. On the other
hand, if the cross-linked units do not enter the crystal lattice, then

$$\frac{1}{T_m{}^i} - \frac{1}{T_m{}^\circ} = \frac{R}{\Delta H_u}\rho \qquad (6\text{-}5)$$

and a decrease in the melting temperature should occur. Equation
(6-5) can be recognized as the limiting form of Eq. (4-18), which
describes the melting temperature of a random copolymer containing ρ
noncrystallizing chain units.

When a network is formed from perfectly axially ordered chains and
the cross-linked units participate as equals in the crystallization process

$$\frac{1}{T_m{}^\circ} - \frac{1}{T_m{}^i} = \frac{R\rho}{\Delta H_u}\left(\frac{9}{4} - \frac{3}{4}\ln \rho k\right) \qquad (6\text{-}6)$$

to a good approximation. Here k is the number of chemical repeating
units that can be identified with a statistical element. According to
Eq. (6-6), the isotropic melting temperature of such a network should
increase when compared with the melting temperature of the initially
non-cross-linked system. If the cross-linked units are restricted from
participating in the crystallization, however, this effect would be
partially offset by the necessity of introducing into Eq. (6-6) a term
equivalent to the right-hand side of Eq. (6-5). Experimentally determined melting temperatures for networks formed under different
conditions can now be examined in terms of the analysis set forth.

6-3 The Melting Temperature of Networks Formed from Random Chains

The random cross-linking of randomly arranged polymer chains corresponds to the usual vulcanization of natural rubber by chemical
means, the cross-linking of natural rubber at room temperature by
means of high-energy ionizing radiation, and the irradiation cross-
linking of polyethylene at temperatures above its melting temperature,
to cite a few examples. Such networks can be crystallized from the
melt merely by cooling and the isotropic melting temperature subsequently determined. A summary of results for some typical networks in this category is given in Fig. 6-1. The networks were formed
by irradiating polyethylene above its melting temperature[11] and by

cross-linking natural rubber chemically by reaction with either sulfur or with di-*t*-butyl peroxide.[12]   Melting temperatures in all cases were determined, utilizing slow heating rates subsequent to crystallization. The depression of the melting temperature relative to that of the non-cross-linked polymer is plotted as a function of the fraction of units cross-linked.

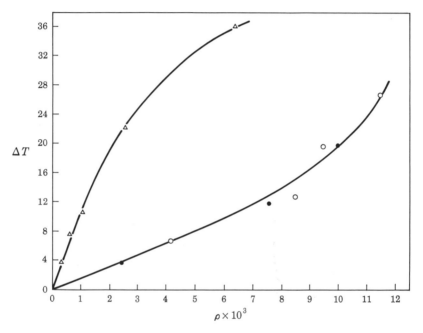

Fig. 6-1 Plot of melting point depression (ΔT) as a function of fraction of units cross-linked (ρ) for polymer networks formed from random chains.   Triangles, molten polyethylene cross-linked by ionizing radiation; open circles, natural rubber cross-linked with sulfur; solid circles, natural rubber cross-linked with di-*t*-butyl peroxide.   (*Data from Refs.* 11 *and* 12.)

For the two different natural rubber networks the melting point depression depends only on the fraction of units cross-linked and not on the chemical processes by which the cross-links were introduced.   The most significant observation is the fact that a substantial depression of the melting temperature is achieved when only a very small number of units are cross-linked.   For the natural rubber networks the melting temperature is depressed 20° when 1 per cent of the units are involved in cross-linkages.   Similarly, for the polyethylene networks a melting point depression of 30° is observed when about 0.5 per cent of the chain units are cross-linked.   Comparable results have been reported for the melting temperatures of chemically formed networks of *cis*-polybutadiene.[14]   Large melting point depressions in networks of this type appear to be general phenomena.

If the depression of the melting temperature results solely from the fact that cross-linked units are excluded from the crystalline phase, then Eq. (6-5) should be applicable to the data of Fig. 6-1.   According to this equation, when values of ΔH_u for natural rubber and polyethylene are utilized, a melting point depression of only about 2 to 3°, at most, is expected.   This theoretical expectation is clearly not in harmony with the experimental observations, and the applicability of Eq. (6-4) can be seriously questioned.   In deriving this equation, the inherent assumption was made that equilibrium conditions prevail. This implies that the development of crystallinity in the chain direction is impeded solely by the random distribution of the noncrystallizing units along the molecule, and the lateral development of crystallinity is unrestricted.   If these conditions are not fulfilled, so that a less perfect crystalline state is generated, Eq. (6-5) cannot be applied and a more severe melting point depression results.   Several lines of evidence indicate that the crystallization of the type of networks under discussion results in a state that does not adhere to the rigid specifications set forth.

Wide-angle X-ray diffraction studies[11,12] of crystalline networks of polyethylene and natural rubber show that with increasing cross-linking density a progressive broadening of the reflections from various crystalline planes occurs.   This can be attributed to decreasing crystallite size, to the development of further imperfections in the crystals, or to strain.   Irrespective of which of these effects causes the broadening of the X-ray diffraction lines, they each can make a contribution to the melting point depression.   Therefore, the major reason for the large depression of the melting points of polymer networks is that the perfection of the crystallinity that can be developed, even after careful annealing procedures are adopted, is severely restricted.   This restriction can be presumed to be caused by the presence of cross-links. Permanent types of cross-links act to prevent the lateral accretion of polymer chains, which is a necessary step in the formation of the larger crystallites.   Nearest-neighbor units to those cross-linked may also be prevented from crystallizing so that the longitudinal development of crystallinity is restricted to a greater extent than would be expected solely from a consideration of the concentration of cross-linked units.

Kuhn and Majer[14] have shown that for a swollen polymeric network the freezing point of the monomeric liquid component is significantly depressed when compared with that of the pure liquid.   For natural rubber networks swollen with benzene or for polyacrylic acid–polyvinyl alcohol networks swollen in water, the magnitude of the depression is related to the fraction of units cross-linked.   The freezing point depression progressively increases as the cross-linking density of the network increases, as much as a 21° depression having been observed.   The freezing point depression results from the limited size of the crystals formed.   The restriction on crystal size is attributable to the network structure and the presence of cross-linked units.   Thus, not only does the presence of cross-links in relatively small concentration retard crystallization of the network itself, but the crystallization of the diluent present in a swollen gel is also severely hampered.

6-4   The Melting Temperature of Networks Formed from Axially Ordered Chains

Networks can be prepared from polymer chains initially in the axially oriented or fibrous state, as contrasted to the type of network discussed in the previous section.   A network of the former type is obtained, for example, by subjecting fibrous natural rubber to the action of ionizing radiation.[12,15]   Prior to fusion and the determination of the isotropic melting temperature, the sample is retracted or relaxed and then crystallized merely by cooling.   A comparison can then be made with the melting temperature of networks formed from the same polymer by the same process, with the polymer chains initially being in the randomly coiled state.   The dependence of the melting temperature on the fraction of units cross-linked for these two extreme types of natural rubber networks is given in Fig. 6-2.   The lower curve, which represents the results for the networks formed from random chains, displays a melting point depression very similar to that previously indicated for the chemically cross-linked natural rubber systems.   The upper curve shows, however, that only a very small depression of the melting temperature is observed, over an appreciable cross-linking range, for networks formed from axially oriented chains.   Consequently, at any cross-linking level, $T_m{}^i$ is greater for networks of the latter type in comparison with those formed from random chains.   Moreover, the difference in melting temperature between the two networks becomes greater as the cross-linking level is increased.   We therefore have a definitive example of the greater stability that is ultimately imparted to the system by imposing the cross-links on ordered chains.   The fundamental basis for this is the decreased configura-

tional entropy in the liquid state that accompanies this mode of network formation.

According to Eq. (6-6), if the cross-linked units participate in the
crystallization, a progressive increase in the isotropic melting temperature should result. This is not observed, so that it can be concluded that even in this instance cross-linkages still impede the
crystallization process. However, if it is assumed that the non-
configurational effects of the cross-links are the same for the two types
of networks, a quantitative comparison of the differences in observed

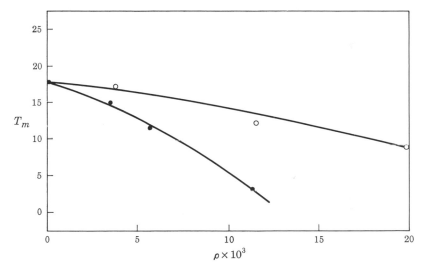

Fig. 6-2 Plot of isotropic melting temperature of natural rubber networks
formed by irradiation. Solid circles, random chain; open circles, chains
axially oriented at time of network formation (12).

melting temperature can still be made by invoking Eq. (6-6). With
this assumption, the differences in expected melting temperatures can
be calculated for different values of ρ. The results of such a calculation are given in Table 6-1 for networks formed from random and
oriented chains, respectively. A value of $\Delta H_u = 1050$ cal/mole was
used, and the parameter k was assigned values of 1 and 3. When
comparison is made at the same values of ρ, the differences in melting
temperature observed are in good accord with theoretical expectations
over the cross-linking range in which crystallizable networks can be
prepared. Excellent agreement is obtained when 1 per cent or less of
the units are cross-linked. The slight deviations that occur for the
higher values of ρ can be attributed to the very large depression of the

melting point observed for networks formed from random chains in this range. Quantitative support can therefore be given to the concept that a significant decrease in the configurational entropy of the liquid state occurs when networks are formed from axially oriented chains. A partially ordered liquid can be said to have been developed. It could be surmised that other interesting changes in liquid state properties could be accomplished by these methods.

TABLE 6-1
Comparison of isotropic melting temperatures for natural rubber networks

$\rho \times 10^3$	$(1/T^i_{m,r} - 1/T^i_{m,o}) \times 10^3$†		
	Observed	Theoretical	
		$k = 1$	$k = 3$
5.0	0.049	0.062	0.052
7.5	0.080	0.084	0.073
10.0	0.110	0.109	0.093
12.5	0.163	0.133	0.113
15.0	0.180	0.155	0.131

† $T^i_{m,r}$ is the isotropic melting temperature for networks formed from random chains. $T^i_{m,o}$ is the corresponding temperature for networks formed from ordered chains. SOURCE: Ref. 12.

6-5 The Melting Temperature of Networks Formed from Crystalline Nonoriented Chains

Since a network with rather unique properties is developed as a result of cross-linking highly axially oriented polymer chains, the question naturally arises as to the kind or degree of intermolecular order required for these effects. In particular, partially crystalline undeformed polymers possess a large amount of intermolecular order, since portions of the polymer molecules are constrained to lie parallel with one another in three-dimensional array. This order is present only on a microscopic scale since the crystalline regions are randomly arranged relative to one another. The question whether the possession of such order affects the properties of the resultant isotropic network is a matter to be decided by experiment.

Investigations have shown that the isotropic melting temperatures of networks formed from crystalline but nonoriented linear polyethylene differ significantly from those of networks of the same polymer formed when the chains are in the molten state. For the latter type of network a continuous decrease in $T_m{}^i$ is observed with cross-linking,

TABLE 6-2
Properties of polyethylene networks
formed at 17° by the action of
high-energy ionizing radiation

(a)		(b)	
v_1 (130°)	$T_m{}^\circ$	T'_m	v_1 (at T_M^*)
0.97	131	102	0.88
0.95	131	104	0.83
0.83	131	105.3	0.77
0.74	131	106.2	0.69
0.61	131	110	0.58
0.39	131	114	0.36
0.28	132		

TABLE 6-3
Properties of polyethylene networks
formed at 175°C by the action of
high-energy ionizing radiation

(a)		(b)	
v_1 (130°)	T_m	T_m	v_1 (at T_m^*)
0.93	134	101	0.84
0.91	132.5	100.2	0.85
0.87	130	100	0.80
0.76	128	100.6	0.71
0.70	115.5	94	0.68
0.49	107.5		
	101		

as was demonstrated in Fig. 6-1. On the other hand, for the networks formed from the crystalline polymer the melting temperature is depressed only 6.5° and remains independent of the fraction of units cross-linked up to relatively high cross-linking levels.[11] These melting temperatures are determined after melting and recrystallizing the network after the initial introduction of cross-links. These observations are summarized in columns *a* of Tables 6-2 and 6-3. The networks are characterized by the volume fraction of xylene inbibed at swelling equilibrium at 130° [v_1 (130°) in Tables 6-2 and 6-3]. Decreasing values of v_1 indicate a progressively increasing value of ρ. For the least swollen network formed at 17° (in the highly crystalline state), it is estimated that approximately 2.5 per cent of the units are involved in cross-linkages.[11] Despite this significant variation in ρ, $T_m{}^i$ does not change after the slight initial decrease from the value of the pure polymer.

The greater stability of the crystalline state of networks formed from unoriented but crystalline chains, as compared with networks formed from the amorphous polymer, can be qualitatively explained on the same basis as that for networks formed from fibrous natural rubber. Although prior to network formation the crystallites are randomly arranged relative to one another, portions of chains are still constrained to lie in parallel array. The cross-linking of the predominantly crystalline polymer cannot, therefore, involve the random selection of pairs of units. The units that can be paired are limited by the local chain orientation imposed by the crystallization process. An increase in the isotropic melting temperature of such networks would therefore be expected. It can be concluded that orientation on a macroscopic scale is not required for partial order in the liquid state to develop. Concomitantly a decrease in the entropy of fusion will result.

This manifestation of molecular order in the liquid state is further substantiated by direct microscopic observation of the polymer melt.[11,16] As illustrated in Fig. 6-3, intense birefringence in a spherulitic pattern persists at temperatures above the melting temperature for such systems. In contrast, for polyethylene cross-linked when molten, no birefringence is observed above $T_m{}^i$. The presence of birefringence in the former case can be directly attributed to the unique liquid structure that has been developed.

The intensity of the electron beam utilized in electron microscopic examination of thin crystalline polymer films is usually of sufficient intensity to induce cross-linking. Therefore, from the results given above, it is not surprising that, after initial examination in the crystalline state, thin films of polyamides and polyethylene display ordered structures when subsequently examined in the molten state by this technique. These observations are to be expected. They cannot be construed as evidence that, in general, the liquid state in polymers is an ordered one.[17] For the reasons discussed, the partially ordered liquid represents a very interesting but unique case, resulting from the nature of the chain arrangement at the time of network formation.

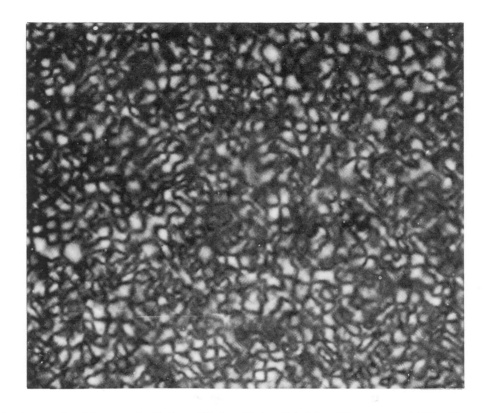

Fig. 6-3 Photomicrograph of linear polyethylene (Marlex-50) irradiated for 120 megarad at 25°.   Photograph taken at 150° after ½ hr at that temperature (11).

6-6   The Melting of Network-Diluent Mixtures

The crystallization of a polymer network can also occur when the network is in contact with a monomeric liquid or diluent. The simplest case to treat is that of a crystalline network in contact with a large excess of a one-component liquid phase. This corresponds to a thermodynamic open system. Upon melting, the network in the amorphous state imbibes large quantities of the surrounding fluid; the amount of swelling that occurs depends on the network structure, the temperature, and the polymer-diluent thermodynamic interaction parameter. Conversely, on crystallization, diluent is exuded from the network. It is completely excluded if it cannot enter the crystal lattice.

At the melting temperature, the crystalline polymer phase is in equilibrium with a mixed phase composed of amorphous polymer and imbibed liquid. The latter phase, in turn, must be in equilibrium with the pure solvent phase. Three distinct phases must coexist in equilibrium at the melting temperature. Therefore the requirements for equilibrium are

$$\mu_u^c - \mu_u^\circ = \mu_u^m - \mu_u^\circ \tag{6-7}$$
$$\mu_1^l - \mu_1^\circ = 0 \tag{6-8}$$

for the components common to each of the phases. μ_u^c and μ_u^m represent the chemical potentials of the polymer unit in the crystalline and mixed phases, while μ_m° represents the chemical potential of the pure molten polymer unit. Equation (6-8) specifies the equality of chemical potential of the solvent component in the mixed and supernatant phases.†

The free energy change ΔF for the formation of the mixed phase from its pure components, the pure solvent and the pure isotropic amorphous network, consists of two parts. One is the free energy of mixing ΔF_M and the other is the elastic free energy ΔF_{el} which results from the expansion of the network structure because of swelling (Refs. 4 and 7, p. 578).

From the Flory-Huggins theory[18,19] of polymer solutions

$$\Delta F_M = kT(n_1 \ln v_1 + \chi_1 n_1 v_2) \tag{6-9}$$

where n_1 is the number of solvent molecules. Utilizing an idealized but conventional theory for rubber elasticity wherein it is assumed

† The treatment can, of course, be generalized to include a multicomponent supernatant phase and a partitioning of components between it and the mixed phase. The situation where diluent enters the crystalline phase can also be included.

that the deformation process accompanying the swelling involves no internal energy change attributable to interactions between chains, ΔF_{el} can be written as[4]

$$\Delta F_{el} = \frac{kT\nu}{2}\left[(3\langle\alpha\rangle^2\alpha_s^2 - \ln\alpha_s^3 - 3 - 3\ln\langle\alpha\rangle)\right] \tag{6-10}$$

where α_s represents the linear swelling factor for the network-diluent mixture. From the sum of Eqs. (6-9) and (6-10),

$$\frac{\mu_u^m - \mu_u^{\circ}}{RT} = -\frac{V_u}{V_0}(v_1 - \chi_1 v_1^2)$$

$$+ \frac{\rho}{2}[1 - v_2 + 2\langle\alpha\rangle(v_2^{\frac{1}{3}} - v_2^{-\frac{2}{3}})] \tag{6-11}$$

since $\alpha_s^3 = v_2^{-1}$. As in the nonnetwork case, $\mu_u^c - \mu_u^{\circ}$ can be expressed as

$$\mu_u^c - \mu_u^{\circ} = -\Delta H_u\left(1 - \frac{T}{T_m}\right) \tag{6-12}$$

where T_m is now identified with the equilibrium melting temperature of a given network. At equilibrium, $T = T_m^*$ so that

$$\frac{1}{T_m^*} - \frac{1}{T_m^{\circ}} = \frac{R}{\Delta H_u}\frac{V_u}{V_1}(v_1 - \chi_1 v_1^2)$$

$$+ \frac{R\rho}{2\Delta H_u}\{2\langle\alpha\rangle[v_2^{-\frac{2}{3}} - v_2^{-\frac{1}{3}} - (1 - v_2)]\} \tag{6-13}$$

The first two terms on the right-hand side of Eq. (6-13) are identical to that obtained for the non-cross-linked polymer-diluent mixture at the same composition. The remaining terms represent the contribution of the elastic free energy of the mixed phase. For an open system, the composition of the mixed phase v_2 is determined from Eq. (6-8), which is a specification of the swelling equilibrium (Ref. 7, p. 578). Therefore v_2 is an equilibrium quantity and should be so designated. It can be identified with the reciprocal of the equilibrium swelling ratio at $T = T_m^*$. For a closed system, where the composition of the mixed phase is fixed and the supernatant phase is absent, Eqs. (6-6) and (6-12) suffice to specify the melting point relations.

A comparison of Eq. (6-13) with Eq. (3-8) indicates that a greater depression of the melting point should be observed for a network than for a collection of polymer chains of the same constitution at the same concentration because of the contribution from the elastic free energy. However, since the values of ρ usually encountered are of the order of 0.01 to 0.02 or less, this effect is quite small. It manifests itself only when v_2 of the mixed phase becomes less than 0.5.

The melting temperatures of polyethylene networks immersed in a large excess of xylene have been measured.[11] The results can be examined in terms of the equilibrium theory. For networks formed from either random chains or from nonoriented crystalline chains, a depression of the isotropic melting temperature relative to the undiluted system is naturally observed. However, as an examination of columns (*b*) in Tables 6-2 and 6-3 reveals, the melting temperatures T_m^* of the two different networks depend quite differently on the cross-linking density. When immersed in xylene, the networks formed in the crystalline state display a continuous and significant increase of melting temperature with increased cross-linking. However, the melting temperatures for the networks formed from random chains display a slight decrease in T_m^* with increased cross-linking. The results for the networks formed from the crystalline chains immersed in an excess of diluent are in sharp contrast with the melting points of the undiluted networks of natural rubber or polyethylene. Irrespective of the chain disposition prior to network formation in the latter cases, a decrease in T_m with cross-linking is invariably observed.

The melting temperatures of the network-diluent mixtures depend on the nature of the initial network and on the volume fraction of liquid that is imbibed subsequent to fusion. For the networks formed at 17°, T_m for the undiluted networks is constant with cross-linking. However, the equilibrium swelling at T_m^* (v_1 at T_m^*) in Tables 6-2 and 6-3 continuously decreases. The melting point depression must be progressively diminished, with the net result that T_m^* increases. However, for the networks formed from random chains, the rate of decrease of T_m is not compensated by the concentration changes in the mixed phase, so that a decrease in T_m^* results.

An attempt to examine quantitatively these observations in terms of theory is given in Fig. 6-4. The solid line in this plot is computed from Eq. (6-13) with $\chi_1 = 0$ and neglect of the elastic contribution. Detailed analysis of these data is hampered by the fact that χ_1 is not known for this system and the network parameters cannot be specified with sufficient accuracy for the purpose at hand. However, for the low values of v_1, where neither the thermodynamic interaction term nor the elastic term makes an appreciable contribution to the melting point depression, the data follow the simplest theoretical expectation. As the polymer concentration in the mixed phase decreases, a contribution to the melting point depression of these terms is expected and deviations from the simplified theory are observed. A positive value of χ_1 could be anticipated that would allow for the observed increased melting temperature above that calculated for the case $\chi_1 = 0$. Despite the obvious shortcomings of an exact quantitative comparison, it is perhaps noteworthy that the existing theory can encompass the apparently diverse manner in which the melting points of the two different types of network-diluent systems vary with

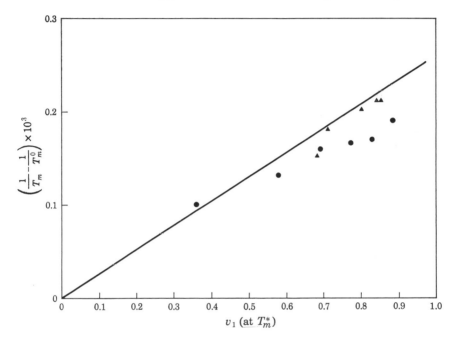

Fig. 6-4 Plot of $1/T_m - 1/T_m{}^\circ$ against volume fraction of xylene imbibed upon melting, v_1. Solid circles, networks from crystalline chains; triangles, networks from molten chains; solid line, theoretical plot according to Eq. (6-13) with $\chi_1 = 0$ and $\rho = 0$. (*Data from Ref.* 11.)

increasing amounts of cross-linking. The importance of accounting for the concentration of the mixed phase in an open system is strongly emphasized.

6-7 Fibrous Proteins

Certain of the fibrous proteins, such as collagen[20] and α-keratin from various layers of epidermis,[21] display an increased melting temperature as the number of cross-links are increased. For collagen, increases in melting temperature of up to 35° have been observed after the introduction of cross-links by means of specific tanning processes.[20] For various layers of the epidermis of cow's lip the melting temperature progressively decreases in going from the outer to inner layer, while the cystine content (which can presumably be related to the number of intermolecular cross-links) also decreases.

The fibrous proteins are naturally occurring axially ordered systems, with the cross-links imposed on the ordered structure. Therefore, according to theoretical concepts,[4] if the cross-linkages do not impede the crystallization, a continuous increase of melting temperature with cross-linking should be expected. However, the melting of the fibrous proteins is almost invariably determined when they are immersed in a suitable liquid medium. Consequently, at equilibrium the polymer concentration in the mixed phase must also increase with increasing cross-linking density. An elevation of the melting temperature is also expected from this cause in analogy with the previous results for the polyethylene network-diluent mixtures. Thus both an alteration of the entropy of fusion and a compositional change in the mixed phase result from the introduction of cross-links into a fibrous protein system. Both these effects act to raise the melting temperature and favor the stability of the crystalline phase. As would be anticipated, in experiments carried out in the presence of a large excess of liquid, a strong correlation has been shown to exist between the melting of collagen and the swelling capacity in the mixed phase.[22]

REFERENCES

1. Flory, P. J.: *J. Am. Chem. Soc.*, **63**: 3097 (1941).
2. Stockmayer, W. H.: *J. Chem. Phys.*, **12**: 125 (1944).
3. Flory, P. J.: *J. Am. Chem. Soc.*, **69**: 30 (1947).
4. Flory, P. J.: *J. Am. Chem. Soc.*, **78**: 5222 (1956).
5. Craig, D.: *Rubber Chem. Technol.*, **30**: 1291 (1957).
6. Charlesby, A.: "Atomic Radiation and Polymers," Pergamon Press, New York, 1960.
7. Flory, P. J.: "Principles of Polymer Chemistry," p. 464, Cornell University Press, Ithaca, N.Y., 1953.
8. Treloar, L. R. G.: "The Physics of Rubber Elasticity," Oxford University Press, New York, 1947.
9. Flory, P. J.: *J. Chem. Phys.*, **18**: 108 (1950).
10. Schellman, J. G.: *Compt. Rend. Trav. Lab. Carlsberg, Ser. Chim.*, **29**: 223 (1955).
11. Mandelkern, L., D. E. Roberts, J. C. Halpin, and F. P. Price: *J. Am. Chem. Soc.*, **82**: 46 (1960).
12. Roberts, D. E., and L. Mandelkern: *J. Am. Chem. Soc.*, **82**: 1091 (1960).

13. Trick, G. S.: *J. Polymer Sci.*, **41**: 213 (1959).
14. Kuhn, W., E. Peterli, and H. Majer: *Z. Elektrochem.*, **62**: 296 (1958); W. Kuhn and H. Majer: *Z. Physik. Chem. (Frankfurt)*, **3**: 330 (1955); W. Kuhn and H. Majer: *Angew Chem.*, **68**: 345 (1956); W. Kuhn and H. Majer: *Ric. Sci.*, *Suppl. A*, **3** (1955).
15. Roberts, D. E., and L. Mandelkern: *J. Am. Chem. Soc.*, **80**: 1289 (1958); D. E. Roberts, L. Mandelkern, and P. J. Flory: *J. Am. Chem. Soc.*, **79**: 1515 (1957).
16. Hammer, C. F., W. W. Brandt, and W. L. Peticolas: *J. Polymer Sci.*, **24**: 291 (1957).
17. Kargin, V. A.: *J. Polymer Sci.*, **30**: 247 (1958); V. A. Kargin and G. L. Slonimskii; *Usp. Khim.*, **24**: 785 (1955).
18. Huggins, M. L.: *J. Phys. Chem.*, **46**: 151 (1942); *Ann. N.Y. Acad. Sci.*, **41**: 1 (1942).
19. Flory, P. J.: *J. Chem. Phys.*, **10**: 51 (1942).
20. Gustavson, K. H.: "The Chemistry and Reactivity of Collagens," p. 227, Academic Press, Inc., New York, 1956.
21. Rudall, K. M.: "Symposium on Fibrous Proteins," *J. Soc. Dyers Colourists*, 15 (1946); *Advan. Protein Chem.* **7**: 253 (1952).
22. Theis, F. R.: *Trans. Faraday Soc.*, **42B**: 244 (1946).

ORIENTED
CRYSTALLIZATION
AND CONTRACTILITY

chapter

7

7-1 Introduction

A characteristic property of amorphous polymers is the ability to sustain large strains or deformations. For a cross-linked system that forms a three-dimensional network the strain is usually recoverable and the deformation process reversible. The tendency toward crystallization is greatly enhanced, however, by deformation, since chains between points of cross-linkages are distorted from their most probable configuration upon stretching. A decrease in configurational entropy consequently ensues. Hence, if the deformation is maintained, less entropy remains to be sacrificed in going over to the crystalline state. The decrease in the total entropy of fusion allows crystallization to occur at a higher temperature than would normally be observed for the same substance in the absence of any deformation. This increased tendency toward crystallization is exemplified by natural rubber and polyisobutylene which crystallize very slowly in the absence of an external stress but crystallize extremely rapidly upon stretching.

It is a widely observed experimental fact that crystallites produced by stretching usually occur with their chain direction preferentially oriented parallel to the axis of elongation.   This is particularly true for crystallizations conducted at large deformations.†   These observations are in contrast to the crystalline texture that results when the transformation is induced merely by cooling.   In the latter case the crystallites are, on an average, randomly arranged relative to one another.   When a portion of a deformed chain is incorporated into a crystallite, the average stress that it exerts at its end points is reduced.   This conclusion can be reached either by the application of Le Châtelier's principle or from a more detailed molecular analysis.[2,3] According to the molecular theory of rubber elasticity, the force exerted by the fixed chain ends is inversely proportional to the number of statistical elements contained in the chain and the magnitude of its end-to-end distance.[2,4]‡   Since only the remaining amorphous units contribute to the resulting retractive force, the former quantity is decreased somewhat as a result of oriented crystallization.   Moreover, the distance traversed by the remaining amorphous units is severely reduced because of the disproportionately greater distance taken up by the crystalline units.   Consequently, the retractive force exerted is diminished by the crystallization process.

The conclusion is reached that orientation imposed by stretching promotes crystallization and that crystallization in a previously oriented polymer diminishes the stress.   For any stress likely to be borne by amorphous chains, the length of the randomly coiled molecule projected on the fiber axis is considerably less than its length in the crystalline state.   This is in accord with the known crystal structures of polymers.   Hence for oriented systems, melting results in a contraction and crystallization in an elongation.   Macroscopic dimensional changes and changes in the stress exerted can therefore be coupled with and related to the crystal-liquid phase transition.   This behavior, which reflects one of the unique properties of polymer chains, results from their configurational versatility.   It is not limited to the simpler types of chain molecules but should apply equally well to the fibrous proteins and other macromolecules of biological interest.   Many polymers in the latter category are characterized by the prevalence of an ordered crystalline arrangement in the native state.   Cognizance must therefore be taken of the existence of this state when

---

† Certain exceptions to this generalization can be noted.   These usually result from nonisothermal crystallization at small deformations.   In these instances the chain axes are more preferentially oriented normal to the stretching directions.[1]

‡ For a further detailed discussion of rubber elasticity theory, see Ref. 5.

attention is given to such properties as thermoelastic behavior and to the mechanism by which major changes in length are incurred.

In order to analyze properly the melting of an oriented system, it must be ascertained whether the process is reversible, i.e., whether oriented crystallites are formed on subsequent recrystallization. This concern exists since it is possible that the original oriented crystalline state will not be regenerated. The possible nonequilibrium aspects of the melting of an oriented polymer and the complications that result have been discussed in connection with the melting of "stark" rubber.[6] When natural rubber is stored in temperate climates, it frequently becomes hard and inelastic because of the development of significant amounts of crystallinity. Upon initial heating, the melting point is significantly higher than that assigned to the equilibrium melting temperature of natural rubber (in the absence of any external force). This apparent contradiction is resolved when it is shown that for "stark" rubber the crystalline regions are preferentially oriented despite the absence of any external force. The maintenance of this orientation during fusion results in an elevated melting temperature. After the initial melting and subsequent recrystallization, melting points that are normal for natural rubber are observed since oriented crystallization does not redevelop.

Many polymers can be rendered fibrous, i.e., made to possess a high axial orientation of the crystallites, by suitable mechanical means. This condition can, in many cases, be maintained below the melting temperature without an application of external force. On melting, in addition to the usual changes in properties, an axial contraction is observed. This transformation temperature has therefore been designated as the shrinkage temperature. However, only under certain unique conditions (see following) can this temperature be identified with the equilibrium melting temperature. In general, in the absence of an equilibrium tensile force, the original crystalline state is not regenerated merely by reversing the melting process. Even if a tensile force is applied to the system, a distinction must be made between the shrinkage temperature T_s and the equilibrium melting temperature T_m. The latter temperature requires the coexistence of amorphous and crystalline phases along the fiber length, whereas in a well-oriented highly crystalline fiber a significant amount of superheating may be required to initiate melting and observe shrinkage. Hence serious error may arise, as is the case for collagen fibers,[7,8] by failure to discriminate between T_m and T_s. The shrinkage temperature, therefore, is not an appropriate quantity for thermodynamic analyses.

Although irreversible melting is commonly associated with

oriented crystalline polymers, the possibility of conducting the transformation under reversible conditions which approach equilibrium cannot be disregarded. In fact, the treatment of this problem from the point of view of phase equilibria leads to important relations between crystallization, deformation, and dimensional changes.[3,4]

7-2 One-component System Subject to a Tensile Force[4]

We consider a cross-linked fibrous system, comprised of highly axially oriented crystalline regions coexisting with amorphous zones, the latter regions being devoid of any vestiges of crystalline order. The fiber is subject to a uniform tensile force f acting in the direction of its axis. The fibers are assumed to be homogeneous and uniform with respect to chemical composition, structure, and cross section, apart from such differences as may exist in cross section as a result of the interspersion of crystalline and amorphous regions along its length.

According to the first law of thermodynamics, the change in internal energy E of any system can be written with complete generality as

$$dE = dQ - dW \qquad (7\text{-}1)$$

where dQ is the heat absorbed by the system and dW is the work performed by the system on its surroundings. If x_i represents the extensive variables characterizing the system and y_i the conjugate intensive variables,

$$dW = -\sum_i y_i \, dx_i \qquad (7\text{-}2)$$

and

$$dE = dQ - \sum_i y_i \, dx_i \qquad (7\text{-}3)$$

For a one-component system the intensive-extensive pairs of $-p$, V and f, L are those of interest. Here p and V are the pressure and volume, respectively, and L is the length of the fiber. For a process conducted reversibly, $dQ = T \, dS$, where S is the entropy, so that

$$dE = T \, dS - p \, dV + f \, dL \qquad (7\text{-}4)$$

Defining the Gibbs free energy by

$$F = E + pV - TS = H - TS \qquad (7\text{-}5)$$

where H is the enthalpy, there is obtained from Eqs. (7-4) and (7-5)

$$dF = -S \, dT + V \, dp + f \, dL \qquad (7\text{-}6)$$

For present purposes, it is more convenient to choose P, T, and f as the independent variables and hence advantageous to utilize the equivalent relation

$$d(F - fL) = -S\,dT + V\,dp - L\,df \qquad (7\text{-}7)$$

For the system to be in equilibrium at constant P, T, and f, the function $F - fL$ must be a minimum with respect to all permissible displacements.   In particular, it must be a minimum with respect to changes in the fraction of the fiber that is crystalline.   Thus

$$\left[\frac{\partial(F - fL)}{\partial\lambda}\right]_{P,T,f} = 0 \qquad (7\text{-}8)$$

if equilibrium is to be maintained between the two phases.   The total free energy of the fibrous system can be expressed as

$$F = \lambda F^a + (1 - \lambda)F^c \qquad (7\text{-}9)$$

where F^a and F^c are the free energies of the fiber when totally amorphous and totally crystalline, respectively, under the conditions specified by P, T, and f.   The other extensive properties can be expressed similarly.   Accordingly, the requirement for equilibrium becomes

$$F^a - fL^a = F^c - fL^c \qquad (7\text{-}10)$$

or
$$d(F^a - fL^a) = d(F^c - fL^c) \qquad (7\text{-}11)$$

From Eq. (7-7) it follows that

$$\left(\frac{\partial f}{\partial T}\right)_{p,eq} = \frac{-\Delta S}{\Delta L} \qquad (7\text{-}12)$$

at constant pressure.   Here ΔS and ΔL are the changes in entropy and length that occur upon fusion of the entire fiber at constant T, p, and f. For the reversible process being treated, the heat absorbed is expressed as

$$Q = T\,\Delta S = \Delta E + \Delta W = \Delta E + p\,\Delta V - f\,\Delta L \qquad (7\text{-}13)$$

so that
$$\Delta S = \frac{\Delta H - f\,\Delta L}{T} \qquad (7\text{-}14)$$

Combination of Eq. (7-14) with Eq. (7-12) yields

$$\left(\frac{\partial f}{\partial T}\right)_{p,eq} = \frac{f}{T} - \frac{\Delta H}{T\,\Delta L} \qquad (7\text{-}15)$$

or, in more compact form,

$$\left[\frac{\partial(f/T)}{\partial(1/T)}\right]_{p,\text{eq}} = \frac{\Delta H}{\Delta L} \tag{7-16}$$

which have been derived by Gee[9] and by Flory.[4] Equations (7-15) and (7-16) are obvious variants of the Clapeyron equation applicable to unidimensional systems of axially oriented crystalline and amorphous phases. The temperature T may be regarded as the melting temperature T_m under a force f and a pressure p. The analogy between this problem in phase equilibrium and the vapor-liquid or solid-liquid equilibrium of monomeric substances becomes apparent when it is realized that in Eqs. (7-15) and (7-16) $-f$ and L correspond to the pressure and volume in the more conventional formulation of the Clapeyron equation. At the temperature of vapor-liquid equilibrium for a one-component system, the pressure is independent of the volume of the system, i.e., independent of the relative abundance of each phase. In a similar manner, it is implicit in the above formulation that, for a one-component fibrous system with uniform properties throughout, the equilibrium force f must be independent of the length over the two-phase region at constant T and p. It will ordinarily be expected that $\Delta L < 0$, whereas $\Delta H > 0$. Therefore from Eq. (7-16), f/T will increase with T. In other words, the melting temperature increases with an increase in the applied tensile force at constant pressure.

The integration of Eq. (7-16) between specified limits leads to a relation between the equilibrium force f_{eq} and the melting temperature. This is analogous to integrating the Clausius-Clapeyron equation for vapor-liquid equilibrium. The dependence of the pressure on temperature is obtained, in this instance, if the equation of state relating the pressure to the volume of the liquid is known. For the present problem, the equation of state, relating the force acting on the amorphous network to its length, is required. This can be obtained from the theory of rubber elasticity.[4]

When a one-component amorphous network, composed of chains whose distribution of end-to-end distances is Gaussian, is subject to a simple tensile force, the relation between the force and length is given by

$$f = BTL_a\left(1 - \frac{L_i^3}{L_a^3}\right) \tag{7-17}$$

with

$$B = k\nu\left(\frac{\langle\alpha\rangle}{L_i}\right)^2 \tag{7-18}$$

L_i is the isotropic length of the amorphous network, i.e., the length under zero force, while L_a is the length in the amorphous state under the equilibrium tensile force f.† The relation between f and L_a is completely general and applies equally to networks formed from polymer molecules in random configuration and to those formed from highly oriented chains.

The macroscopic isotropic length of the sample can be related to the number of chains ν and their mean-square end-to-end distance by

$$L_i = \frac{\nu}{\sigma'} \left(\frac{\overline{r_0^2}}{3} \right)^{1/2} \langle \alpha \rangle \qquad (7\text{-}19)$$

where σ' is the number of chain vectors traversing a plane transverse to the axis of the sample. For networks formed from highly ordered chains, which are of particular interest in the present context, L_i increases as $\nu^{1/2}$. For such a system, σ can be identified with the number of chains in a cross section and hence is independent of ν. However, $\overline{r_0^2}$, which is proportional to the number of units in the chain, varies inversely as ν and consequently L_i varies as $\nu^{1/2}\langle\alpha\rangle$. Hence, from Eq. (7-18), B is independent of ν for networks formed in this manner. It is convenient to introduce the quantity L_m which represents the length of the amorphous fiber at maximum extension. Then[4]

$$B = \frac{3k\nu n'}{L_m^2} \qquad (7\text{-}20)$$

If L_a is sufficiently greater than L_i, the retractive force can be expressed as

$$f \cong 3kT\nu n' \frac{L_a}{L_m^2} \qquad (7\text{-}21)$$

Upon substitution of Eq. (7-17) into (7-16) there is obtained

$$(L^a - L^c)d\left[L^a - \frac{L_i^3}{(L^a)^2} \right] = \frac{\Delta H}{B} d\frac{1}{T} \qquad (7\text{-}22)$$

when it is recalled that $\Delta L = L^a - L^c$. Integration of this equation between the limits L_i and L_a and T_m and $T_m{}^i$ yields

$$2(L^a - L^c)\left[L^a - \frac{L_i^3}{(L^a)^2} \right] - \left[(L^a)^2 + \frac{2L_i^3}{L^a} - 3L_i^2 \right]$$

$$= \frac{2\Delta H}{B}\left(\frac{1}{T_m} - \frac{1}{T_m{}^i} \right) \qquad (7\text{-}23)$$

† Equation (7-17) is derived for a Gaussian network from the relation

$$f = (\partial \Delta F_{el}/\partial L)_{P,T\langle\alpha\rangle}$$

and the assumption $\Delta F_{el} = -T\,\Delta S_{el}$; the expression for ΔS_{el} is well known.[4]

where $T_m{}^i$ is the equilibrium melting temperature at zero force and T_m is the melting temperature at a force f such that the amorphous length is L^a. [The implicit relationship between T_m and the applied tensile force can also be obtained by utilizing Eqs. (7-17) and (7-18) to eliminate L^a in the above.] For networks formed from highly ordered chains, where B is given by Eq. (7-20),

$$2(L^a - L^c)\left[L^a - \frac{L_i{}^3}{(L^a)^2}\right] - \left[(L^a)^2 + \frac{2L_i{}^3}{L^a} - 3L_i{}^2\right]$$
$$= \frac{2L_m{}^2\,\Delta h'}{3R}\left(\frac{1}{T_m} - \frac{1}{T_m{}^i}\right) \quad (7\text{-}24)$$

where $\Delta h'$ is the heat of fusion per mole of equivalent statistical elements. For large deformations where $(L_i/L^a)^3 \ll 1$, so that Eq. (7-21) can be employed, the above simplifies to

$$\frac{(L^a)^2 - 2L^aL^c}{L_m{}^2} \cong \frac{2\Delta h'}{3R}\left(\frac{1}{T_m} - \frac{1}{T_m{}^i}\right) \quad (7\text{-}25)$$

Alternatively, the integration can be carried out between the limits L^c and L^a, with the result that

$$(L^c - L^a)^2\left[1 + \frac{2L_i{}^3}{L^c(L^a)^2}\right] = \frac{2\Delta H}{B}\left(\frac{1}{T_m} - \frac{1}{T_m{}^c}\right) \quad (7\text{-}26)$$

where $T_m{}^c$ is the melting point when $L^a = L^c$. Using the previous expression for B, there is obtained

$$\left(\frac{L^c - L^a}{L_m}\right)^2\left[1 + \frac{2L_i{}^3}{L^c(L^a)^2}\right] = \frac{2\Delta h'}{3R}\left(\frac{1}{T_m} - \frac{1}{T_m{}^c}\right) \quad (7\text{-}27)$$

For large deformations, this further simplifies to

$$\frac{(L^c - L^a)^2}{L_m{}^2} \cong \frac{2\Delta h'}{3R}\left(\frac{1}{T_m} - \frac{1}{T_m{}^c}\right) \quad (7\text{-}28)$$

When $T_m < T_m{}^c$, Eqs. (7-26) and (7-27) yield two solutions for L^a, one less than and the other greater than L^c. No real solutions exist when $T_m > T_m{}^c$. Thus, $T_m{}^c$ plays the role of a critical temperature above which the crystalline phase cannot exist.

If the deformation is sufficient so that (7-26) and (7-28) can be used, then L^a can be eliminated from each by means of Eq. (7-21). This manipulation leads to the results

$$\left(\frac{f}{T}\right)_{eq} \cong \frac{3k\nu n'}{L_m}\left[\frac{L^c}{L_m} \pm \sqrt{\frac{2\Delta h'}{3R}\left(\frac{1}{T_m} - \frac{1}{T_m{}^c}\right)}\right] \quad (7\text{-}29)$$

$$\left(\frac{f}{T}\right)_{eq} \cong \frac{3k\nu n'}{L_m}\left[\frac{L^c}{L_m} \pm \sqrt{\left(\frac{L^c}{L_m}\right)^2 + \frac{2\Delta h'}{3R}\left(\frac{1}{T_m} - \frac{1}{T_m{}^i}\right)}\right] \quad (7\text{-}30)$$

The approximate results, embodied in Eqs. (7-29) and (7-30), allow for a concise graphical representation of the phenomenon, as is illustrated in Fig. 7-1. If the deformation process is initiated at a temperature at which the network is in the amorphous state and if the equation of state is given by Eq. (7-21), f/T will increase linearly with L until crystallization sets in at point A. This point represents the melting temperature of the network under the specified force and elongation. As crystallinity develops, the length of the specimen

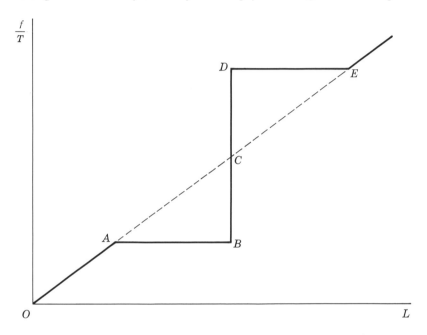

Fig. 7-1   Plot of f/T against length L for polymer networks undergoing a crystal-liquid transformation according to Eqs. (7-29) and (7-30). [*Flory* (4).]

increases along the line AB. For a one-component system the force must remain invariant until the transformation is complete at point B. The lesser of the two roots of Eqs. (7-29) and (7-30) is applicable to this equilibrium. The stress is then assumed to rise almost vertically in the inelastic highly rigid crystalline state developed at point B. If it is possible to attain a state in which $L^a > L^c$, the amorphous phase will be reconstituted along the line DE. The equilibrium force corresponds to the larger of the two roots in this case. With increasing temperature, the points A and E are displaced toward C and a temperature is reached where the equilibrium lines AB and DE vanish.

This temperature corresponds to $T_m{}^c$, the critical temperature above which crystallization cannot occur. The regeneration of the amorphous phase along the line DE seems scarcely to be a physically realizable situation. It is highly unlikely that a polymer chain could sustain the large deformation required for L^a to exceed L^c. Attention should therefore be focused primarily on the path $OABD$ for real systems. Utilization of the less restrictive equation of state [Eq. (7-17)] would still leave unaffected the salient features of Fig. 7-1. The linear stress-strain curve for the amorphous network that passes through the origin would be replaced by a curve starting at $L = L_i$ corresponding to $f/T = 0$ and which would be asymptotic to a line through the origin. The force-temperature-length relations expressed above in analytical and graphical form are quite general in concept. They do not depend on any details of the crystallographic structure of the ordered phase. Modification of these relations can be anticipated, however, with additional refinements in the statistical mechanical development of rubber elasticity theory.

The experimental investigations of Oth and Flory[10] substantiate the major conclusions of the theory outlined above. Their studies of the force-length-temperature relations for fibrous natural rubber, cross-linked in the oriented state, give strong support to the concept that this phenomenon can be treated as a classical problem in phase equilibria. The primary experiments performed involved the determination of the equilibrium force f_{eq} required to maintain the two coexisting phases in equilibrium at temperatures above the isotropic melting temperature. These intricate experiments were accomplished by initiating melting at a temperature above the shrinkage temperature. The completion of the transformation was prevented by increasing the force or by lowering the temperature or by performing both operations simultaneously. Equilibrium is approached from several directions in these experiments and f_{eq} thus established.

In accord with theory, it was found that, as long as the two phases coexist, f_{eq} is independent of the specimen length and increases with increasing temperature. The variation of the equilibrium force with the melting temperature is illustrated in Fig. 7-2 for a specific network. Even for the relatively small temperature interval in which equilibrium was established, substantial forces were required. Based on the cross section of the fiber, stresses of the order of 3 to 4 kg/cm² must be imposed to maintain the equilibrium. These stresses would be further increased if equilibrium were established at still higher temperatures. When the curve of Fig. 7-2 is extrapolated to zero force, the isotropic melting temperature $T_m{}^i$ is obtained. In this case, $T_m{}^i$

is found to be 6° lower than the shrinkage temperature observed in the absence of an external force and demonstrates the nonequilibrium character of the latter temperature.

In analogy with treatment of monomeric substances, where an analysis of the change in the transformation temperature with pressure yields the latent heat of vaporization or of fusion, the variation of the transformation temperature with force in the present case can be

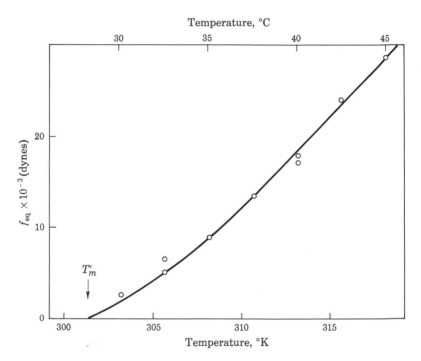

Fig. 7-2   Plot of force required for phase equilibrium against the temperature for cross-linked fibrous natural rubber. $\rho = 1.56 \times 10^{-2}$ and $T_m{}^i = 302°K$.   [*Oth and Flory* (10).]

analyzed to yield the heat of fusion involved in the transformation. The required quantity is obtained by the graphical integration of Eqs. (7-15) and (7-16).   The experimentally determined change in ΔL with temperature is utilized, and it is assumed that ΔS and ΔH are constant in the small temperature range of concern.   The latent changes ΔS and ΔH computed by this method can be ascribed entirely to the melting of that fraction of the polymer which is crystalline.   Hence, the changes on fusion for the hypothetically completely crystalline fiber are obtained by dividing the calculated quantity by the degree of

crystallinity. A comparison of the thermodynamic quantities governing the fusion as determined by this method and that obtained from
an analysis of the melting point depression of natural rubber by
monomeric diluents is given in Table 7-1. The results obtained from

TABLE 7-1
**Thermodynamic quantities governing the fusion of
natural rubber**

	From Eq. (7-16)[10]	From melting point depression[11]
T_m^i, °K	302	301
ΔH_u, cal/mole	1280 ± 150	1040 ± 60
ΔS_u, cal deg^{-1} mole^{-1}	4.2 ± 0.4	3.5 ± 0.2

the two methods compare quite favorably and give further substance
to the treatment of the phenomenon as a problem in phase equilibrium.

A compilation of the results for fibrous natural rubber can be
represented graphically as in Fig. 7-3. The equilibrium force as a
function of the length of the specimen is plotted at the various indicated temperatures above the isotropic melting temperature. For the
particular sample represented in Fig. 7-3 the latter temperature is
302°K. The horizontal solid lines represent the stresses necessary to
maintain the two phases in equilibrium. The length of the sample
upon the completion of melting, at the given force and temperature, is
indicated by the solid circles. The dashed lines represent the dependence of the force on length at each temperature in the amorphous state,
as calculated from rubber elasticity theory. The force-length relation
in the crystalline state at 303.2°K is indicated by the vertically rising
straight lines. A similar behavior would be expected at other temperatures as long as the observations are restricted to the crystalline
state. The set of isotherms in Fig. 7-3, which encompass the axially
oriented crystalline and the liquid states, corresponds to the isotherms
in a p-v diagram describing vapor-liquid condensation in monomeric
substances. It is to be noted in Fig. 7-3 that in the two-phase region
the force is independent of the length.

The increase in melting temperature that occurs with the applied
tensile force is readily discerned by the locus of the solid points in Fig.
7-3. The relations that exist between the force, length, and temperature when conditions are varied so that the fiber traverses the two-
phase region are also illustrated. Consider, for example, a network
maintained under conditions specified by point *A* in Fig. 7-30. This

corresponds to a sample 8 cm long in phase equilibrium at 303.2°K, under a tension slightly less than 4×10^5 dynes/cm². If a process is prescribed where the temperature is increased, while it is required that the length be maintained constant, a path described by a vertical line upward from point *A* will be followed. In order to maintain a constant length, it is clear that an external force must be applied to

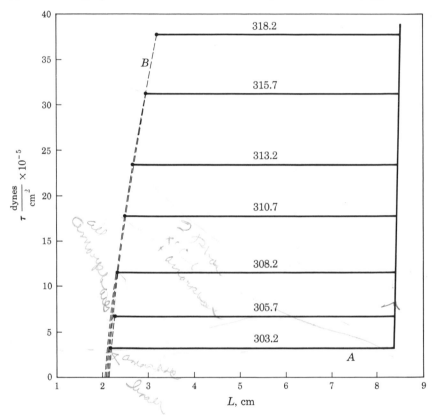

Fig. 7-3 Composite plot of tension-length relation at various temperatures for fibrous natural rubber. [*Data from Oth and Flory* (10).]

balance the retractive force developed by the crystalline network. This additional stress is needed to prevent melting, as the temperature is increased, for otherwise the original length would not be preserved. If the temperature is raised to 318.2°K during this process, a tension of 4 kg/cm² is developed. This tension is of the same order of magnitude as that developed by the muscle fiber system in tetanic contraction. For the fibrous natural rubber, still greater tension could be developed by merely increasing the temperature. The stress will continuously increase with temperature as long as the two-phase region is maintained, i.e., until the critical temperature $T_m{}^c$ is reached. The development of such large tensions with increasing temperature is obviously due to the separation of the horizontal portions of the isotherms in Fig. 7-3. This in turn is a reflection of the equation of state that characterizes the amorphous phase. The major contribution to the retractive force in the amorphous phase is usually a result of entropic changes. These changes are responsible for the separation of the isotherms in the two-phase region. We can conclude, therefore, that the large tensions developed are a consequence of the configurational versatility of the polymer chains. It should be noted, however, that the stress developed at constant length when the two-phase region is traversed is many times greater than the stress that can be obtained by increasing the temperature of a completely amorphous network whose length is fixed.

The preceding analysis demonstrates a fundamental mechanism by which large tensions can be developed in axially oriented crystalline macromolecular systems. This mechanism is an inherent property of polymers that possess these structural features and should find applicability irrespective of the crystallographic and chemical nature of the polymer chains and the methods used to induce melting.

One can also treat a network that is initially in the completely amorphous state as represented by point B in Fig. 7-3. If the temperature is lowered, while the stipulation of constant length is again made, a path vertically downward from point B must be traversed. As the two-phase region is entered, oriented crystallinity will develop and the equilibrium stress will concomitantly decrease. At 303.2°K the stress will have decreased about tenfold. A formal basis is thus provided for the experimental results of Smith and Saylor,[12] Tobolsky and Brown,[13] and Gent[14] who observed a relaxation of the stress during the oriented crystallization of natural rubber networks held at fixed length. The molecular basis for this decay of stress, which again resides in rubber elasticity theory, has already been discussed.†

---

† The decrease in stress expected and experimentally verified during the development of axially oriented crystallinity appears to be in contradiction to the widely observed stress-strain curves of natural rubber networks. The resolution of this apparent paradox lies in the different nature of the two processes. Crystallites formed during isothermal stretching, in the latter experiment, can act as additional points of cross-linkage. On further stretching, the chain segments in the amorphous regions are oriented much more than normal. A proportionately larger decrease in the entropy ensues which results in an increase in the retractive force. Since further crystallization will occur with subsequent elongation, this effect will be enhanced and the increase in tension accelerated.

Processes can also occur where the stress rather than the length is held constant as the temperature is varied. Consider the system (in the crystalline state) again at point A of Fig. 7-3. If the stress is now maintained constant while the temperature is raised, a horizontal path will be followed which will terminate at the appropriate dashed curve representing the completely amorphous state. Accompanying the transformation, in this example, there will be a fourfold diminution in length. This process is reversible as long as the equilibrium stress is maintained. Thus, by returning to the original temperature a spontaneous elongation will accompany the transformation from the amorphous to the crystalline state. A spontaneous increase in length during the crystallization of deformed natural rubber networks held at constant force has been reported.[12]

Anisotropic dimensional changes are also observed during the transformation of one oriented crystalline polymorph to another, as, for example, in polybutadiene[15] and α-keratin.[16] In these cases the dimensional changes are reflections of the different fiber repeat distances of the two polymorphs. The dimensional changes would thus be expected to be appreciably less than is observed during the crystal-liquid transformation. Moreover, since the elastic equations of state for the two forms should be similar, a large separation of the isotherms in the two-phase region (two crystal phases, in this instance) would not be expected. Hence the development of a large force of retraction would not be anticipated.

The melting-crystallization cycle of an oriented network conducted under equilibrium conditions results in a reversible contractile system when the force is held fixed. Alternatively, large changes in the tension are observed when the length is held constant. These two complementary observations are inherent properties of macromolecular systems. The foregoing analysis and description have been limited to a pure one-component homopolymer of uniform cross section. It can be extended, however, to include inhomogeneous fibers, copolymers, and polymer-diluent mixtures.[4]

Variations in either chemical structure or cross section along the fiber length result in a broadening of the transition between the crystalline and amorphous states. The primary effect of varying chemical structure, as, for example, in a copolymer, is manifested in a change of the melting point at a given force. Alterations in the cross section affect the stress, and since the equilibrium depends directly on the stress, different values of the critical stress occur in various cross sections. It is therefore possible for the transition to occur over a range in the tensile force at constant temperature and pressure in systems that, if homogeneous, would be invariant. More detailed analysis[4] indicates that relations similar to Eqs. (7-23) to (7-30) hold for inhomogeneous fibers, provided that they are interpreted to apply to the particular element of the fiber in phase equilibrium. Consequently, the lines AB and BD of Fig. 7-1 are replaced by sigmoidal curves.

Because of the two states available to a polymer network and the possibility of their coexistence in the macroscopic sample, unique thermoelastic coefficients can be observed. The coefficients of interest are those of force-temperature and of length-temperature which are

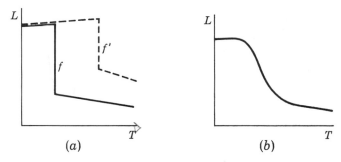

Fig. 7-4 (*a*) Schematic length-temperature relations for an idealized homogeneous fiber $f' > f$. (*b*) Same for an inhomogeneous fiber. [*After Flory* (3).]

related to each other by the identity

$$\left(\frac{\partial f}{\partial T}\right)_{P,L} = -\left(\frac{\partial f}{\partial L}\right)_{P,T}\left(\frac{\partial L}{\partial T}\right)_{P,f} \qquad (7\text{-}31)$$

Since $(\partial f/\partial L)_{P,T}$ is always positive, the sign of $(\partial f/\partial T)_{P,L}$ is opposite to that of $(\partial L/\partial T)_{P,f}$, and both coefficients are zero at the same length or force. The dependence of the length on the temperature at constant force is schematically illustrated in Fig. 7-4a for an idealized homogeneous fiber. At large L a small, positive thermal expansion coefficient typical of a crystalline solid is indicated. The melting point appears as a discontinuity in the diagram, and subsequently the molten fiber exhibits a moderate negative thermal expansion expected for a rubberlike substance. The melting point, of course, increases with increased force, as indicated by the dashed lines.

The melting range is broadened for fibers that are inhomogeneous with respect to chemical structure or cross-sectional area. The sharp discontinuity in length is now smoothed to a continuous curve, as indicated in Fig. 7-4b. The length-temperature coefficient is still slightly negative for shrunken fibers and positive at large extensions in the highly crystalline states.   At intermediate degrees of crystallinity, however, the coefficient is strongly negative.   It reaches a maximum negative value with increasing crystallinity and then assumes the normal positive values.   The force-temperature coefficients are similarly described by utilizing Eq. (7-31).   A wide variation in the behavior of the thermoelastic coefficients with extension can be expected as a consequence of the phase change that occurs and the diffuse melting of inhomogeneous fibers.   Thermoelastic behavior of the type described has, in fact, been observed for many of the fibrous proteins.[17,18,19]

7-3   Multicomponent Systems Subject to a Tensile Force

Melting and crystallization of oriented systems are also observed when such systems are placed in contact with diluent or with a solution containing monomeric solutes.   The introduction of additional components and phases causes some complications in the theoretical and experimental analyses, without, however, changing the fundamental physical processes involved.   Although these complexities must be recognized, they should not obscure or vitiate the understanding of the molecular mechanisms involved.   This is particularly true of the fibrous proteins for which the necessary experiments can be carried out only in the presence of diluent or appropriate chemical reactants.

Corresponding to Eq. (7-7) for a multicomponent system, we have

$$d(F - fL) = -S\,dT + v\,dp - L\,df + \sum_i \mu_i\,dn_i \qquad (7\text{-}32)$$

For equilibrium between the crystalline and amorphous phases it is now required that the function $F - fL$ be a minimum when δn_i moles of component i are transferred from one phase to another at constant P, T, f.   Hence

$$\delta(F - fL) = \delta n_i \mu_i{}^a - \delta n_i \mu_i{}^c = 0 \qquad (7\text{-}33)$$

or
$$\mu_i{}^a = \mu_i{}^c \qquad (7\text{-}34)$$

for each of the components present in both polymer phases.   When the simplifying assumption is made that the crystalline phase is a pure phase, Eq. (7-34) becomes

$$\mu_u{}^c = \mu_u{}^a \qquad (7\text{-}35)$$

Similarly, when a supernatant phase (designated by the superscript s) comprised of monomeric components is present, then for the amorphous portion of the fiber to be in equilibrium with this phase,

$$\mu_i{}^a = \mu_i{}^s \tag{7-36}$$

for each of the monomeric components present in the amorphous or mixed phase.

In the two polymer phases, the chemical potential of the polymer unit is a function of T, p, f, and composition. The crystalline phase being assumed pure,

$$d\mu_u{}^c = -S_u{}^c \, dT - V_u{}^c \, dp - L_u{}^c \, df \tag{7-37}$$

while for the amorphous phase containing r components

$$d\mu^a = -\bar{S}_u{}^a \, dT + \bar{V}_u{}^a \, dp - \bar{L}_u{}^a \, df + \sum_{i=1}^{r-1} \left(\frac{\partial \mu_u}{\partial x_i}\right)_{T,P,f} dx_i \tag{7-38}$$

where $\bar{S}_u{}^a$, $\bar{V}_u{}^a$, and $\bar{L}_u{}^a$ are the respective partial molar quantities of the polymer unit in this phase and x_i is the mole fraction of the ith component. For the two phases in equilibrium at constant p,

$$d\mu_u{}^a = d\mu_u{}^c \tag{7-39}$$

and

$$(\bar{L}_u{}^a - L_u{}^c) \, df = -(\bar{S}_u{}^a - S_u{}^c) \, dT + \sum_{i=1}^{r-1} \left(\frac{\partial \mu_i}{\partial x_i}\right)_{T,P,f} dx_i \tag{7-40}$$

When the composition of the amorphous phase is held fixed,

$$\left(\frac{\partial f}{\partial T}\right)_{p,n} = -\frac{\bar{S}_u{}^a - S_u{}^c}{\bar{L}_u{}^a - L_u{}^c} \tag{7-41}$$

where the subscript n denotes the constant concentration of all components. The invariance in composition required by Eq. (7-41) implies not only a fixed polymer concentration but also an unchanging concentration of the monomeric constituents present in this phase. The entropy change per polymer unit that occurs on melting at constant p, T, and n is given by

$$\bar{S}_u{}^a - S_u{}^c = \frac{(\bar{H}_u{}^a - H_u{}^c) - f(\bar{L}_u{}^a - L_u{}^c)}{T} \tag{7-42}$$

so that

$$\left[\frac{\partial f/T}{\partial (1/T)}\right]_{p,n} = \frac{\bar{H}_u{}^a - H_u{}^c}{\bar{L}_u{}^a - L_u{}^c} \tag{7-43}$$

It is convenient to multiply the numerator and denominator of the right-hand side of Eq. (7-43) by n_u, the total number of structural units in the fiber. Equation (7-43) then becomes

$$\left[\frac{\partial(f/T)}{\partial(1/T)}\right]_{p,n} = \frac{\Delta\bar{H}}{\Delta\bar{L}} \tag{7-44}$$

where $\Delta\bar{H} = \bar{H}^a - H^c$ and $\Delta\bar{L} = \bar{L}^a - L^c$. H^c and L^c are the enthalpy and length of the totally crystalline fiber at p, T, and f, and $\bar{H}^a$ and $\bar{L}^a$ are the partial derivatives of the total entropy and length, respectively, of the amorphous phase with respect to the fraction λ of the polymer in that phase. Thus, $\Delta\bar{H}$ consists of the heat of fusion plus the differential heat of dilution; the quantity $\Delta\bar{L}$ is similarly defined.

Two general situations must now be distinguished. In one case the total quantity of nonpolymeric components is fixed. In the other, the amorphous portion of the fiber is in equilibrium with a supernatant phase containing a large excess of the monomeric species. In the former case the fiber and its contents operate as a closed system. If only a one-component diluent is present, the system is bivariant at constant pressure. As melting progresses, the length of the fiber decreases. The composition of the amorphous phase changes since the polymer concentration increases while that of the diluent is fixed. The differential coefficient of Eq. (7-44) is for constant composition, a condition that can be identified with the constancy of λ. Hence

$$\left[\frac{\partial(f/T)}{\partial(1/T)}\right]_{p,n} = \left[\frac{\partial(f/T)}{\partial(1/T)}\right]_{p,\lambda} = \frac{\Delta\bar{H}}{\Delta\bar{L}} \tag{7-45}$$

In contrast to the pure one-component polymer system, $\Delta\bar{S}$, $\Delta\bar{L}$, and $\Delta\bar{H}$ are dependent on composition so that the force-temperature derivative depends on λ. Thus, the force in this instance is not uniquely determined by the temperature. Total melting does not occur at constant force for this case.

When a supernatant phase is present, the fiber and its contents operate as an open system since there can now be an exchange of matter between the supernatant and amorphous phases. If the supernatant consists of a single component, the system is univariant at constant pressure. The equilibrium force is thus uniquely determined by the temperature. Total melting occurs at constant force independent of the length of the specimen as in the case of the pure one-component system. Since an excess of diluent is present in the supernatant phase, equilibrium swelling in the amorphous phase can be established at the given f and T for all values of L. Thus as melting proceeds the composition of the mixed phase remains constant so that

$$\left(\frac{\partial f}{\partial T}\right)_{p,n} \equiv \left(\frac{\partial f}{\partial T}\right)_{p,\lambda} \equiv \left(\frac{\partial f}{\partial T}\right)_{p,L} = -\frac{\Delta\bar{\bar{S}}}{\Delta\bar{\bar{L}}} \tag{7-46}$$

and

$$\left(\frac{\partial(f/T)}{\partial(1/T)}\right)_{p,L} = \frac{\Delta\bar{\bar{H}}}{\Delta\bar{\bar{L}}} \tag{7-47}$$

The double-barred quantities represent the latent change that occurs on fusion of the polymeric component plus the integral change for mixing the required amounts of each component to arrive at the equilibrium composition of the amorphous phase.

When the supernatant phase is multicomponent, the system is no longer univariant. Although the conditions of Eq. (7-36) must still be satisfied, it does not ensure that the composition of the amorphous phase will remain fixed with changes in λ. At constant pressure the equilibrium force need no longer depend solely on the temperature. Consequently, total melting does not have to occur at constant force, in analogy to the behavior of a closed system.

Since the crystal-liquid equilibrium can also be regulated by chemical processes, the latter reactions will influence the force-length-temperature relations of axially oriented crystalline systems. The formal analysis of the problem is similar to that for a nonreacting system with

$$\left(\frac{\partial f}{\partial T}\right)_{p,n} = -\frac{[\partial(\mu_u{}^a - \mu_u{}^c)/\partial T]_{p,f,n}}{[\partial(\mu_u{}^a - \mu_u{}^c)/\partial f]_{p,T,n}} \tag{7-48}$$

Attention must now be given to the changes in the chemical potential of the polymer unit caused by the specific chemical reaction and to the phase(s) in which the reaction occurs. When these conditions are specified, the differential coefficient $(\partial f/\partial T)_{p,n}$ can be evaluated.

For purposes of illustration and for simplification, we shall assume that the chemical reaction is restricted to the amorphous polymer phase while the crystalline phase remains pure. Furthermore, we shall assume that the composition of the amorphous phase is invariant with λ even if the supernatant phase is multicomponent. This is equivalent to treating the supernatant as a single component. Then

$$\left(\frac{\partial f}{\partial T}\right)_{p,n} = \frac{-S_u{}^a - S_u{}^c}{\bar{L}_u{}^a - L_u{}^c} = \frac{-\Delta\bar{\bar{S}}}{\Delta\bar{\bar{L}}} \tag{7-49}$$

and

$$\left[\frac{\partial(f/T)}{\partial(1/T)}\right]_{p,n} = \frac{\Delta\bar{\bar{H}}}{\Delta\bar{\bar{L}}} \tag{7-50}$$

The triple-barred quantities represent the sum of three terms: the fusion of the pure polymer, the integral mixing of components to the composition specified by n, and the change in the quantity resulting from the change in the chemical potential of the structural unit caused by the chemical reaction.   Thus, for example, under the assumption of the constancy of composition of the amorphous phase with L, $\Delta\overline{\overline{H}}$ can be written as

$$\Delta\overline{\overline{H}} = \Delta H + \Delta H_M + \Delta H_R \qquad (7\text{-}51)$$

where ΔH is the heat of fusion, ΔH_M the integral heat of mixing, and ΔH_R the enthalpic change per structural unit caused by the chemical reaction at the total composition specified by n.

For a simple complexing reaction, of the type discussed in Chap. 3, the change in chemical potential can be expressed as[20]

$$\mu_u - \mu_u{}^\circ = -RT \ln (1 + Ka) \qquad (7\text{-}52)$$

Hence

$$\Delta H_R = RT^2 \frac{a}{1 + Ka}\left(\frac{\partial K}{\partial T}\right)_{p,f} = T \frac{a}{1 + Ka} \Delta H^\circ \qquad (7\text{-}53)$$

where ΔH° is the standard-state enthalpic change for the complexing reaction.   Whether the corresponding term ΔL_R differs from zero depends on whether the equilibrium constant for the reaction is a function of the applied stress.   Other possible chemical reactions can be treated in a similar manner[21] as long as the changes that occur in the chemical potential of the polymer unit can be specified.

When Eqs. (7-46) and (7-47) are integrated, relations similar to those for the one-component system are obtained.   The term $\Delta h'$ now includes the additive contributions of the heats of dilution and of reaction.   The integration must, of course, be carried out at constant composition of the amorphous phase so that the equation of state used must take cognizance of the polymer concentration in this phase.   The integration constants L_i and $T_m{}^i$ or L^c and $T_m{}^c$ refer to this fixed composition.   Thus, not only are the enthalpy and length terms affected by the compositional changes but the isotropic length and melting temperature are as well.

The tension required to maintain equilibrium between the crystalline and amorphous phases of cross-linked collagen has been determined.[8]   In these experiments the fiber is immersed either in a large excess of pure water or in an aqueous KCNS solution.   The experiments were conducted over a wide temperature range.   The value of the equilibrium force at a given temperature was found to be approximately independent of the total sample length and consequently the extent of the transformation.   When the supernatant phase consists solely of pure water, the system is univariant and the aforementioned result is to be expected.   However, the results obtained when the supernatant phase contains two components are indicative that the single-liquid approximation is valid in this instance.

Some typical results for the dependence of the equilibrium stress on the temperature for this fiber are illustrated in Fig. 7-5.   The change with temperature in the required stress is quite substantial.

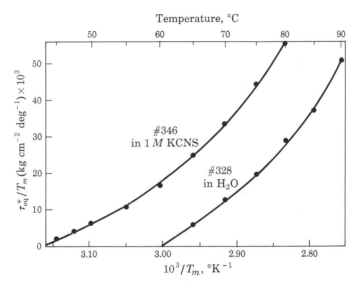

Fig. 7-5   Equilibrium stress τ_{eq}^{*} divided by T_m plotted against $1/T_m$ for collagen fibers immersed in pure water and in 1 M KCNS.   [*Flory and Spurr* (8).]

Extremely large stresses can be developed by this process, as has been previously noted from studies with fibrous natural rubber.   This is in marked contrast to the changes in the stress with temperature that are observed during the deformation of the completely amorphous collagen fiber.[8]   When the length of the amorphous fiber is kept constant, only relatively small increases in the stress are observed with increasing temperature.   It might be noted in this connection that a collagen fiber immersed in a $2M$ mercury-potassium iodide solution (a medium known to promote the melting of fibrous proteins) develops a tension of 100 kg/cm² when a constant length is maintained.[22]   Besides the changes in stress incurred in raising the temperature, Fig. 7-5 also demonstrates the changes that occur at fixed temperature as the composition of the supernatant phase is varied. For example, in pure water at 70° a stress of 4.4 kg/cm² is required to keep the two phases in equilibrium. However, if the supernatant phase is made $1M$ in KCNS, the stress required is increased to about 11.5 kg/cm². Thus substantial changes in the tension are developed by changing the composition of the supernatant phase. Since the slopes of the two curves in Fig. 7-5 are approximately the same at all temperatures, the major reason for the increase in the equilibrium stress resides in the change in $T_m{}^i$ from 60° in pure water to 43° in 1 M KCNS. These changes in $T_m{}^i$ result from the specific chemical processes involved.

According to Eqs. (7-49) and (7-53), the quantity $\Delta\bar{\bar{H}}/\Delta\bar{L}$ can be obtained from the slopes of the curves given in Fig. 7-5. If L^c is treated as a constant, $\Delta\bar{\bar{H}}$ can be calculated. Proper decomposition of $\Delta\bar{\bar{H}}$ into its constituent parts allows for an evaluation of ΔH_u, the heat of fusion of the polymer. This involves calculation of the integral heat of solution ΔH_{sol} and an estimation of ΔH_R, the contribution from the chemical reaction. With neglect of the latter term, the results of Flory and Spurr[8] are summarized in Table 7-2.

TABLE 7-2
Thermodynamic parameters for the fusion of collagen

Supernatant phase	$T_m{}^i$, °C	$\Delta\bar{\bar{H}}_u,$ kcal/mole	$\Delta H_{sol},$ kcal/mole	$\Delta H_u,$ kcal/mole	$\Delta S_u,$ cal deg^{-1} mole^{-1}
Water	60	1.2	−0.15	1.35	4.1
1 M KCNS	43	0.87	0.10	0.97	3.1
3 M KCNS	14	0.43	0.03	0.46	1.6

SOURCE: Ref. 8.

The observed reduction in the enthalpy of fusion as the KCNS concentration is increased may be more apparent than real since any contribution to $\Delta\bar{\bar{H}}$ from the chemical reaction has not been taken into account. The enthalpy changes cited in Table 7-2 refer to changes per mole of peptide units present in the native fiber rather than per mole of peptide units that are crystalline. Flory and Garrett,[7] utilizing the diluent method, found that for the system collagen–ethylene glycol $\Delta H_u = 2.25$ kcal/mole crystalline units. The smaller value found in water for this quantity by the method described above could be attributed to an appreciable amorphous content of the native collagen fiber. Alternatively, in the case of water at least, the postulate can be made[8] that a portion of the water entering the crystal lattice forms a hydrate with the polymer so that the melting behavior of identical species is not being compared. The results obtained for the collagen-water and collagen-water-KCNS systems give further substance to the treatment of the phenomenon as a problem in phase equilibrium. A fundamental mechanism is outlined wherein large tensions can be developed as a result of chemical processes.

The analysis of the aforementioned systems is greatly simplified by their univariant behavior. The observed independence of the equilibrium force on the extent of the transformation implies a constancy of composition in the amorphous phase. For an open system containing a multicomponent supernatant phase, this is not to be expected generally. As the transformation progresses at constant temperature, the composition of the amorphous phase can change, caused, for example, by an unequal partitioning of monomeric components between the two phases. The equilibrium force must correspond to the composition of the mixed phase which in turn will depend on the total length of the specimen. For systems possessing more than one degree of freedom at constant pressure, the two-phase region is no longer depicted by a horizontal straight line, as in Fig. 7-3, but by a curve with positive slope and curvature. The change in force with length (in the two-phase region) reflects this compositional change and hence is affected by the corresponding change in $T_m{}^i$ and the ratio $\Delta\bar{H}/\Delta\bar{L}$. Since at constant temperature and pressure $f = f(L,n)$,

$$df = \left(\frac{\partial f}{\partial L}\right)_{T,p,n} dL + \sum_i \left(\frac{\partial f}{\partial n_i}\right)_{T,p,L,n_i} dn_i \qquad (7\text{-}54)$$

the summation extending over all components. For equilibrium between the phases,

$$\left(\frac{\partial f}{\partial L}\right)_{T,p,eq} = \left(\frac{\partial f}{\partial L}\right)_{T,p,n} + \sum_i \left(\frac{\partial f}{\partial n_i}\right)_{T,p,L,n_i} \left(\frac{\partial n_i}{\partial L}\right)_{T,p,eq} \qquad (7\text{-}55)$$

Only when the terms in the summation vanish is the idealized behavior of a pure one-component system realized.

7-4 Oriented Crystallization and Contractility in the Absence of Tension

It is widely observed for the simpler polymers, as well as the fibrous proteins, that axially oriented crystalline systems contract upon melting. For example, in Figs. 7-6 and 7-7 the change in length with temperature under zero force of fibrous natural rubber and of a collagen fiber immersed in water are illustrated. In both cases a large axial contraction is observed over a narrow temperature interval. The shrinkage is accompanied by the disappearance of properties known to be characteristic of the crystalline state, as, for example, discrete X-ray diffraction reflections and optical birefringence. Melting can therefore be deemed to have occurred. However, the original or native state, typified by axially oriented crystallinity, is not regener-

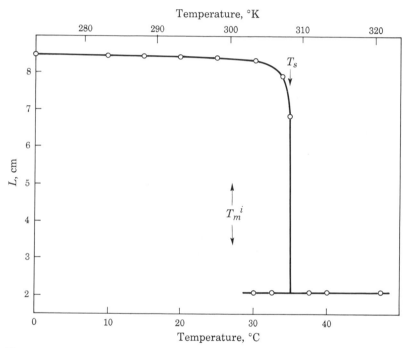

Fig. 7-6   Length under zero force, as a function of temperature, for fibrous natural rubber.   [*Oth and Flory* (10).]

ated in these examples merely by cooling in the absence of an external stress. The crystallinity that develops is typified by the random arrangement of crystallites relative to one another.

A central problem, therefore, is the development of conditions whereby the transformation between the oriented crystalline state and the liquid state can be carried out reversibly. The detailed analysis of the preceding section demonstrates that this can be accomplished by the imposition of an appropriate tensile force so that the two phases are maintained in equilibrium. Reversible systems can also be developed, however, in the absence of an applied tensile force, by taking advantage of the increase in isotropic length that ensues when axially oriented polymers are cross-linked.

According to Eq. (7-19), the isotropic length can be expressed as

$$L_i = \frac{\nu}{\sigma'} \left(\frac{\overline{r_0^2}}{3} \right)^{1/2} \langle \alpha \rangle \qquad (7\text{-}19)$$

A fundamental distinction exists in this quantity for networks formed from highly oriented molecules as contrasted with those formed from random chains. In the latter case the network is necessarily isotropic.

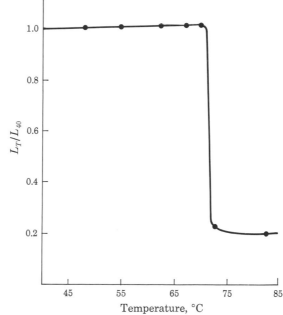

Fig. 7-7 Relative length as function of temperature for collagen from rat tail tendon. [*Flory* (20).]

Hence L_i may be identified with the length of the specimen and is independent of the number of chains ν which comprise the network. If, however, the chains are sufficiently axially oriented prior to cross-linking, the situation is quite different. As has been previously indicated, L_i is expected to increase as $\nu^{1/2}\langle \alpha \rangle$.

The predicted increase in isotropic length is substantiated by studies on networks formed by cross-linking fibrous collagen,[8,23,24] fibrous natural rubber,[25] and highly axially oriented linear polyethylene.[26] The results obtained for the latter two systems are given in Figs. 7-8 and 7-9 where the cross-links were introduced into the oriented structures by means of high-energy ionizing radiation. The ordinate

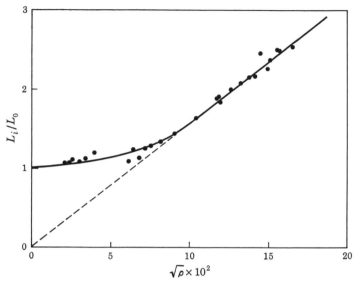

Fig. 7-8   Plot of L_i/L_0 at 25° against square root of fraction units cross-linked for fibrous natural rubber (25).

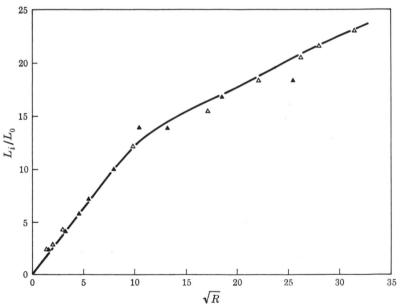

Fig. 7-9   Plot of L_i/L_0 at 140°C against square root of radiation dose for highly oriented polyethylene fibers. Solid triangles, Co^{60} gamma irradiation; open triangles, irradiation by high-energy electrons Δ (26).

in these plots represents the relative increase in length observed in the amorphous state subsequent to cross-linking the oriented chains, L_0 being the length of the specimen in the amorphous state in the absence of cross-links. The measurements were made at 25°C for natural rubber and 140°C for polyethylene in an effort to satisfy the requirement of isotropy. It is estimated that for a radiation dose of 1,000 megarep approximately 4 per cent of the chain units are cross-linked in the case of polyethylene.[26] Although exact compliance with the functional relationship of Eq. (7-19) is not found in either case, significant and substantial increases in the isotropic length are observed. The effect is particularly striking in the case of polyethylene where a 20-fold extension of length in the amorphous state is developed without the application or maintenance of an external force. When amorphous networks are mechanically deformed, the extension ratios that can be developed are severely restricted. Either crystallization intervenes to limit the amount of deformation or the rupture of the constituent polymer chains occurs. In either case, mechanical deformation does not result in extension ratios comparable to those depicted in Fig. 7-9.

The polyethylene networks described are easily crystallized by lowering the temperature. Some typical wide-angle X-ray diffraction patterns which characterize the recrystallized fibers are given in Fig. 7-10. Cross-linking the initially highly oriented fibers by ionizing radiation results in no sensible difference in the wide-angle X-ray pattern. However, after cross-linking, melting, and subsequent recrystallization, significant differences are exhibited which depend on the number of cross-links introduced. This becomes apparent if the patterns for the four different samples, representative of different irradiation levels, are examined. For the specimen into which no cross-links have been introduced, the pattern resulting after melting and recrystallization consists of a series of concentric rings. The crystalline state is thus characterized by a collection of randomly arranged crystallites. It is evident, however, from the other patterns that, as an increasing number of cross-links are introduced, a preferential orientation of the crystallites progressively develops. For example, the pattern in Fig. 7-10*d* which is observed for a fiber characterized by ρ of approximately 2.65×10^{-2} and L_i/L_0 of 18.3 indicates that the *c* axis of the crystallites is again preferentially oriented along the macroscopic fiber axis.

A collection of axially oriented crystallites is thus developed without the necessity of a tensile force being applied during the crystallization process. These observations are intimately related to the extremely large values of L_i/L_0 that are achieved in the amorphous

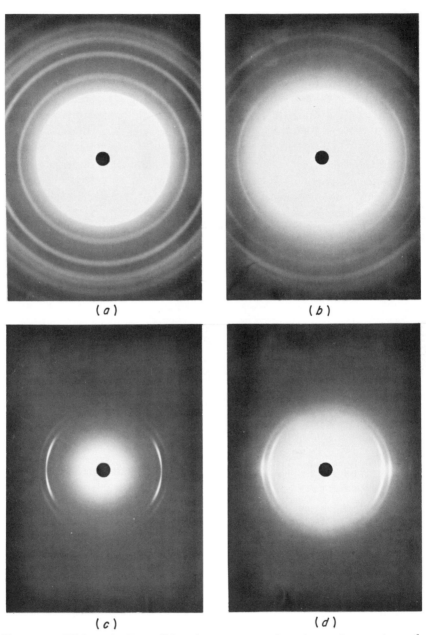

Fig. 7-10 Wide-angle X-ray diffraction patterns, taken at room temperature, of cross-linked recrystallized polyethylene fibers for various radiation doses.   (a) $R = 0, L_i/L_0 = 1$; (b) $R = 179$ megarep, $L_i/L_0 = 13.7$; (c) $R = 353$ megarep, $L_i/L_0 = 16.8$; (d) $R = 660$ megarep, $L_i/L_0 = 18.3$ (26).

state by the cross-linking process. The large extension ratios developed result in the establishment of a preferential axis for the subsequent transformation. Therefore, nuclei of the crystalline phase, which must be formed in order for the transformation to occur, are also preferentially directed, and axially oriented crystallization occurs. Evidence has also been offered for the preferential axial recrystallization of networks formed from fibrous natural rubber.[10] The preferred orientation of the crystallites in the fibers described is an inherent part

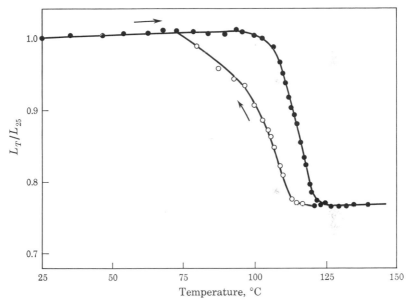

Fig. 7-11 Plot of relative length against temperature for reversibly contractile polyethylene fiber. Solid circles, heating; open circles, cooling (26).

of the system and should be present after any subsequent melting-recrystallization cycles, as long as the cross-linkages are maintained.

Appropriate dimensional changes must therefore accompany the melting and crystallization of such networks. Specifically, because of the axial orientation, contraction should occur on melting and spontaneous reelongation on crystallization from the melt. As is illustrated in Fig. 7-11, such dimensional changes are, in fact, observed. Starting in the crystalline state (obtained after melting the initially cross-linked fiber and recrystallizing), there is plotted the relative length as a function of temperature for a fiber corresponding to the one illustrated in Fig. 7-10d. A slightly positive thermal expansion coefficient, typical of the crystalline state, is observed during the initial heating. Concomitant with melting, a 25 per cent axial contraction is noted, which occurs sharply over a narrow temperature interval. The observed shrinkage is consistent with the initial axial orientation of the specimen in the crystalline state. Above the melting temperature the thermal expansion coefficient is slightly positive, as is expected in the liquid state. On cooling, crystallization of the specimen occurs, and the fiber regains its original dimensions. The heating process can then be repeated, and essentially the same melting temperature is obtained. When a slow cooling process is utilized after fusion, as is illustrated in Fig. 7-11, supercooling is observed; this is a characteristic of the crystallization of all polymeric systems. This effect, reflected in a dimensional lag in this instance, can be minimized by rapid cooling to low temperatures. Therefore, coupled with the crystal-liquid transformation, a reversible contractile system is obtained which is completely cyclic and which does not require the imposition of an external stress for its operation. The shrinkage temperature can be identified with the equilibrium melting temperature in this case.

The sharpness of the observed contraction is a consequence of the melting of a homopolymer, in harmony with the view that the process is a first-order phase transition. For a random-type copolymer, similarly constituted with respect to cross-linkages, the melting and contraction range becomes broadened. The imposition of a stress on such systems raises the melting temperature, but reversible contractility is still maintained. Consequently, fibers such as those described can serve as the working substance of an engine that converts thermal energy into mechanical work.

The generalization has already been made and demonstrated that the crystal-liquid equilibrium can be governed by chemical processes. Thus the transformation and the concomitant dimensional changes can occur isothermally. Once the principle has been established that the basic contractile process involves melting, it becomes important that a distinction be made between the contractile mechanism and that process or chemical reaction which induces or regulates the phase transition. With the acceptance of the foregoing, it is possible to investigate many reported contractile systems from a unified point of view. This is particularly true for a variety of polymers of biological interest wherein contractility is widespread and known to be induced by a diversity of chemical reagents. The principles of reversibility deduced for the polyethylene fibers can serve as a useful model in investigating these more complex systems. The fundamental basis for this mechanism does not find its origin or explanation in a detailed crystallographic analysis of the state of the fiber.

7-5 Contractility in the Fibrous Proteins

In a series of pioneering studies, Astbury and coworkers[16,27,29] have established that a wide variety of protein systems occurs naturally in the crystalline state. In addition to being crystalline, these protein systems also possess a high degree of axial orientation and are thus termed fibrous. In the category of the fibrous proteins there are the α- and β-keratins, collagen, elastoidin, and muscle fibers. The fibrous proteins as a class, therefore, possess the important initial structural requirements for contraction to accompany melting. In certain of these systems, particularly the keratins, intermolecular covalent cross-links are also present. It is presumed in these cases that the cross-links are formed subsequent to fiber formation and are thus imposed on a previously axially oriented structure. Hence reversible contractility would be expected to accompany the crystal-liquid phase transition. For the fibrous proteins that are not intermolecularly cross-linked or for those in which the cross-linkages are not maintained during the melting process, only irreversible dimensional changes would be anticipated. The fact that axial contractions can be induced in a number of different fibrous proteins by use of a variety of reagents and conditions does not obviate the premise of a basic underlying mechanism. It remains, therefore, to examine specific contractile systems in order to ascertain whether a phase transition accompanies the dimensional changes and whether reversibility is governed by the presence of appropriately introduced cross-links.

A substantial body of evidence demonstrates that the hydrothermal shrinkage of collagen (characterized by a contraction of about one-fifth the length in the native state) occurs directly as the result of melting.[7,8,30] As has been indicated previously, however, neither the oriented crystalline state nor the original dimensions are regenerated in the fiber merely by cooling the specimen below the melting temperature. The nature of the amino acid residues that are found in collagen does not indicate the presence of any intermolecular cross-links that would be expected to survive the melting process. Consequently, in harmony with the conclusions drawn from the studies of the polyethylene fibers, regeneration of the oriented crystalline state in the absence of an external tensile force would not be expected.

However, it was shown by Ewald[31] that, if collagen in the native state is cross-linked (tanned) with formaldehyde, the hydrothermal melting-crystallization process is accompanied by reversible anisotropic dimensional changes. Axially oriented crystallization develops from the molten state, as is evidenced by the wide-angle X-ray diffrac-

tion pattern and the simultaneous recovery of a significant portion of
the low-angle X-ray diffraction pattern.[32,33]   The recrystallized fiber
again contracts upon subsequent heating so that the process can be
carried out cyclically.[8,34]   An example of the latter observation is given

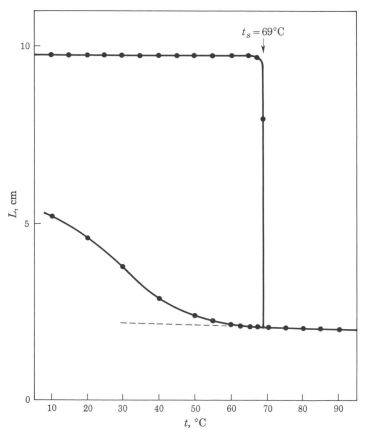

Fig. 7-12   Reversible contraction of cross-linked (tanned) collagen
fibers.   Upper curve, initial melting and shrinkage.   Lower curve,
melting after recrystallization.   [*Oth* (34).]

in Fig. 7-12.   The initial melting of the native cross-linked fiber is
extremely sharp; on cooling, a spontaneous reelongation to about half
the original dimension is observed.   On subsequent fusion the length
diminishes more gradually with increasing temperature.   The termination of the melting process is clearly defined, and a difference of only a
few degrees exists between the two melting temperatures.   The diffuse
melting and slightly lower melting temperature observed during the

fusion can be attributed to hydrolysis at the higher temperatures and to kinetic difficulties which might retard the development of the crystallinity typical of the native state.   The conclusion can be drawn, however, that reversible anisotropic dimensional changes accompany the phase transition in the absence of an external stress.

A similar example of contractility is demonstrated by the fibrous protein elastoidin.   In the native state, the crystalline structure of elastoidin is identical to that of collagen, and the amino acid composition of the two proteins is quite similar.   However, elastoidin contains about 1 to 2 per cent cystine residues, whose side groups can form stable intermolecular covalent cross-links.   Consequently, it is not unexpected that elastoidin displays reversible contraction and relaxation concomitant with melting and crystallization.[35,36]   When the native fiber is heated in water, a large axial contraction is observed at about 65°; on subsequent cooling to room temperature, about half of the initial length is regained without the application of any external force.   After the initial shrinkage, the process can be carried out cyclically with contraction occurring on heating above 65° and relaxation occurring on cooling.   Furthermore, the initial oriented collagen-type wide-angle X-ray diffraction pattern typical of elastoidin is completely converted to an amorphous pattern on shrinkage and is recovered on the subsequent relaxation.

In the foregoing examples the fibers were immersed in a liquid medium which serves to lower the melting temperature so that the process occurs without serious degradation.   Melting can also occur as a result of the interaction of groups on the polymer chain with species present in the supernatant liquid.   As an example, we can cite the effect of varying the pH of the supernatant water phase on the melting and contraction temperature of cross-linked elastoidin.[37] These results, as summarized in Fig. 7-13a, represent melting temperatures for a reversible process.   A similarly shaped curve has been obtained for the irreversible shrinkage of native collagen.[38]   In Fig. 7-13a the melting temperature remains invariant over a large pH range centered about neutrality.   It then decreases sharply at the very high and low pH regions.   In each instance contraction accompanies melting, and reversibility in both dimensions and the crystalline state are obtained on cooling.   Irrespective of the details of the chemical mechanism involved, Fig. 7-13b demonstrates the importance of the composition of the mixed phase (the amorphous polymer phase) in governing the melting temperature.   In this figure, the equilibrium swelling ratio at the transformation temperature is plotted as a function of the pH of the supernatant phase.   A striking parallelism exists between the swelling ratio and the melting temperature. When the polymer concentration in the molten phase remains invariant with pH, so does the melting temperature. When the polymer concentration decreases, the melting temperature does likewise. Hence it is clear that one of the major influences of pH on the isotropic melting

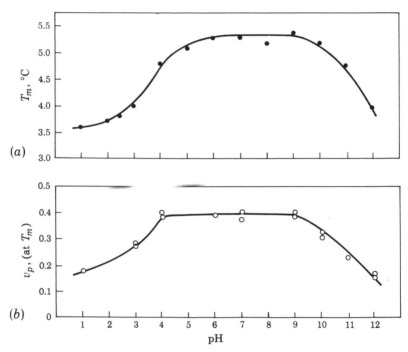

Fig. 7-13 (*a*) Plot of melting temperature T_m of elastoidin fibers as a function of the pH of the supernatant aqueous phase. (*b*) Plot of equilibrium swelling ratio of elastoidin, at its melting temperature, as a function of the pH of the supernatant aqueous phase (37).

temperature is solely a result of the changes that occur in the swelling properties of the amorphous protein.

Certain monomeric reagents, when added to the supernatant phase, are known to affect the melting (contraction) temperature of protein fibers. A typical set of examples is shown in Fig. 7-14 for the melting of elastoidin fibers immersed in such media.[39] In each instance axial contraction accompanies melting, and an X-ray diffraction analysis indicates the complete disappearance of the ordered structure. Melting and the accompanying contractility are therefore demonstrated to be produced by a diversity of reagents. The neutral

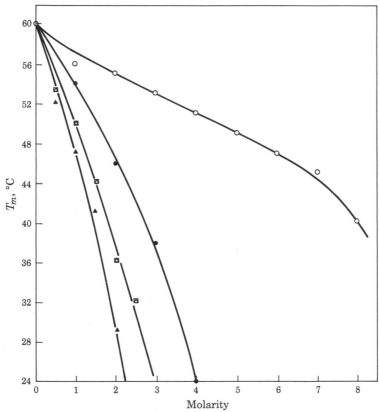

Fig. 7-14 Plot of melting temperature T_m of elastoidin fibers against concentration of monomeric reagent present in supernatant phase. Open circles, urea; squares, $CaCl_2$; solid triangles, KCNS; open triangles, KI; solid circles, LiBr (39).

salts are approximately equal in effectiveness in lowering the melting temperature and substantial decreases in this temperature can be achieved. Urea solutions, at comparable concentrations, are not nearly as effective. When the transformed fiber is cooled in the medium, two distinctly different results are obtained. For urea solutions, oriented recrystallization occurs on cooling. However, for solutions of the neutral salts, this does not occur. The fiber remains in the amorphous state after cooling. However, upon transferring the fiber to pure water, an almost instantaneous regeneration of the ordered crystalline state is observed. In contrast with the observations in urea solution and in pure water, recrystallization, in the latter cases, requires both cooling and dilution. This indicates that, besides the usual disordering of the chain structure that occurs upon melting, additional structural alterations are imparted to the chains in the molten state by the reagent, which prevents recrystallization. When the reagent is removed, crystallization and reelongation ensue.

It is well known that the α- and β-keratins exist in the oriented crystalline state, possess a high concentration of cystine residues, and undergo contraction when subjected to the action of a wide variety of reagents.[40] It was recognized by Alexander and Hudson[40] that two distinctly different types of contractile processes are observed in α-keratin fibers. One of these involves the interaction with reagents known to sever disulfide cross-links so that the dimensional changes observed are irreversible, as would be expected. Analogy can again be made to the results for cross-linked polyethylene fibers as illustrated in Fig. 7-9. In the other case, reversible anisotropic dimensional changes are observed without the breaking of intermolecular cross-links. This type of contractility is now recognized to be a consequence of melting and recrystallization.

An early example of the latter type, for both α- and β-keratins, is inherent in the observations of Whewell and Woods.[41] When the fibers are immersed in a cuprammonium solution of proper concentration, a 20 per cent decrease in length occurs at room temperature. The shrinkage is accompanied by loss of the characteristic X-ray diffraction diagram, giving clear indication that melting has occurred. In this instance isothermal melting appears to be caused by a complexing reaction between appropriate amino acid residues in the protein fiber and the cuprammonium solution. If the shrunken amorphous fibers are now immersed in dilute acid solution, the initial length and X-ray pattern are regained. The melting is reversed by the destruction of the complex.

The melting and concomitant contraction of keratin fibers can also be illustrated by their interaction with aqueous LiBr solutions. The latter reagent acts as a universal transformer of ordered polypeptide and protein structures.[42,43] When an α-keratin fiber (Lincoln wool) is immersed in a large excess of aqueous LiBr solution of fixed concentration, a sharp contraction is evidenced over a narrow temperature interval. These observations are illustrated in Fig. 7-15. The change in the wide-angle X-ray diffraction pattern again substantiates the conclusion that melting has occurred. Again, as in the case of elastoidin fibers, when LiBr is present in the supernatant phase, recrystallization does not occur merely by cooling. Dilution is again required, as is schematically illustrated by the dashed lines in Fig.

7-15. Similar behavior is observed for β-keratin (feather keratin).[43] The wide-angle X-ray patterns for feather keratin specimens are reproduced in Fig. 7-16. They represent the native axially oriented crystalline structure, the amorphous state characteristic of the molten shrunken fiber, and the recrystallized state where the native structure has been completely regenerated. All the Bragg reflections observed in the native state reappear in the recrystallized specimen. Not only

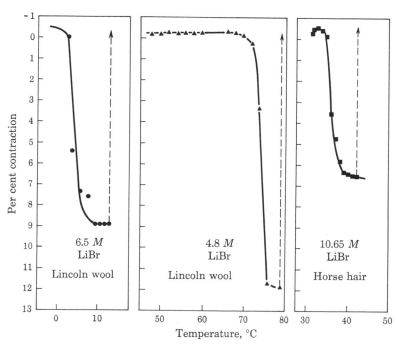

Fig. 7-15 Length-temperature relations for α-keratin fibers immersed in aqueous LiBr solutions of indicated molarity. Solid lines and points indicate heating cycle; dashed vertical line indicates regeneration of original length upon immersion in pure water (42).

has reversibility occurred in a thermodynamic sense but all the fine structural details have also been recovered.

A characteristic melting temperature exists for each concentration of LiBr and is dependent on the nature of the fiber. The relation between the melting temperature and composition of the supernatant phase for two α-keratin fibers is plotted in Fig. 7-17. The initial addition of LiBr to the supernatant phase results in a depression of T_m. A minimum in the melting temperature is reached, at about 7 M LiBr. The melting temperature then increases with a further

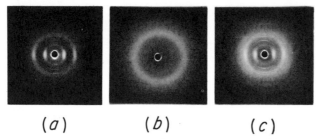

Fig. 7-16   Wide-angle X-ray diffraction patterns of feather keratin.   (*a*) Native fiber; (*b*) after contraction in 5.8 *M* LiBr solution; (*c*) after contraction in 7.7 *M* LiBr solution and immersion in pure water (43).

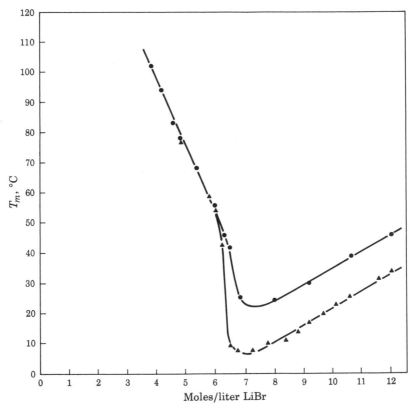

Fig. 7-17   Plot of melting temperature T_m (contraction temperature) of α-keratin fibers as a function of molarity of LiBr solution constituting the supernatant phase.   Solid triangles, Lincoln wool; solid circles, horse hair (42).

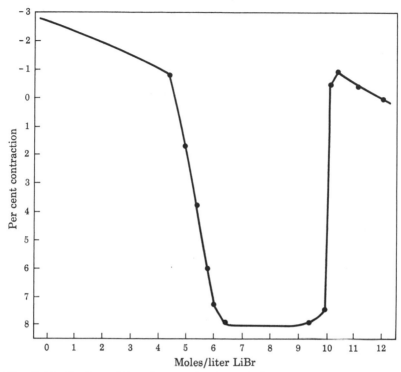

Fig. 7-18 Isothermal length-concentration relations for Lincoln wool fiber immersed in aqueous LiBr solutions at 24°. Measurements were conducted as the concentration of LiBr was decreased (42).

increase in the salt concentration. The shapes of the curves in Fig. 7-17 are strikingly reminiscent of those characteristic of the melting temperature–composition relations for random copolymers. This may be indicative of structural alterations of the polypeptide chain beyond the usual disordering associated with melting.

According to the data plotted in Fig. 7-17, it should be possible to induce melting isothermally by changing the composition of the supernatant phase. Isothermal melting for the α-keratin–LiBr–H_2O system is illustrated in Fig. 7-18. Starting with a native fiber immersed in a high concentration of LiBr at 24°, melting accompanied by contraction is observed upon dilution at the expected concentration. As the molten state is traversed, the length does not change with further dilution. However, when a concentration prescribed by the data of Fig. 7-17 is reached, recrystallization accompanied by reelongation is observed.   The demonstration that the phase transition can be conducted isothermally, by changing the concentration of the supernatant phase, portends the possibility of the utilization of fibrous macromolecules as the working substance of an engine that isothermally converts chemical energy to mechanical work.[3,25]

Muscle fibers are protein fibers that also occur naturally in the

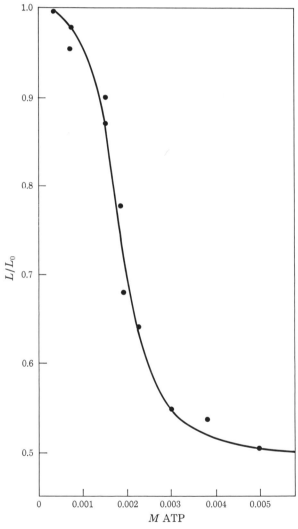

Fig. 7-19 Plot of relative change in length of glycerinated muscle fibers at 25° as a function of ATP concentration in supernatant phase (47).

axially oriented state. Restricting the discussion to the laboratory type of experiments, it can be noted that substantial shrinkages have been demonstrated by the action of such reagents as KI[44] and LiBr[45]. These are known to cause melting and contraction in other fibrous proteins. The underlying contractile mechanism can be presumed to be the same for the muscle fibers. The contraction of glycerinated muscle fibers has been studied when the specimens are immersed in aqueous solutions containing adenosine triphosphate (ATP), a reagent presumed to be involved in the physiological action of muscle.[46] The observations of the change in length of this fiber, at room temperature, caused by an increasing concentration of ATP in the supernatant phase are summarized in Fig. 7-19.[47] The curve in Fig. 7-19 gives clear indication that a cooperative phase transition is occurring. Only a slight change in the ATP concentration is needed to induce the transformation at constant temperature. A melting process is clearly indicated, and the structural changes that are expected to accompany fusion can be demonstrated. The wide-angle X-ray pattern shows that, concomitant with the completion of contraction, the native, α-keratin-type, oriented crystalline structure has disappeared.[42] This is in harmony with the observation for the other fibrous proteins. Recrystallization and reelongation do not occur in this system, either by cooling or by dilution, which can be taken to be indicative of the absence of permanent-type intermolecular cross-links in the fiber. Evidence for contraction accompanying melting has also been presented for glycerinated muscle fibers immersed in ATP–glycerol–water mixtures and ATP–ethylene glycol–water mixtures. Large, abrupt changes in length are observed with relatively small changes in solvent composition or temperature.[48]

The results cited above demonstrate that, in laboratory experiments with all the fibrous proteins, anisotropic dimensional changes can be produced as a consequence of a phase transformation between the oriented crystalline and amorphous states. This is in close analogy with the results obtained with fibrous polyethylene and other structurally simpler polymers.†

Despite the diversity of reagents that are known to induce contractility in the fibrous proteins, the same basic underlying mechanism is shown to be operative. Many important natural processes, includ-

---

† These conclusions can be further generalized to include dilute-solution transformations involving more than one molecular chain. The reversibility of the helix-coil transition of dilute solutions of DNA is greatly facilitated by the introduction of covalent cross-links in the ordered state, a process which links together complementary strands of the double helix.[49,50]

ing those of biological function, are concerned with contractility through the utilization or involvement of macromolecules. In the context of the mechanism being discussed, the macromolecules involved usually occur in the oriented crystalline state during some stage of the contractile cycle. The validity of applying the principles set forth above to actual biological processes as the mechanochemistry of muscle, cell mitosis, chromosome movement, and cell motility must await further experimentation and analyses on the actual functioning systems. The indirect evidence, cited in terms of nonphysiological experiments, lends promise to research in this direction.

It can be anticipated that in naturally functioning systems the regulating processes may be quite complex and involve a series of chemical reactions. Direct experimentation would thus be made more difficult. In principle, however, if a phase transition is involved, its major characteristics should be discernible. A particularly intriguing situation is that in which the fiber or portions of the fiber possesses enzymatic activity. The fiber, in either state, could then influence the concentration of reagents in the surrounding medium which would in turn favor either crystallization or melting. The appropriate change in dimensions, or tension if an external force is applied, should then follow.

7-6 Mechanochemistry

The characteristic high deformability coupled with the ability to regain initial dimensions allows long chain molecules to serve as converters of thermal or chemical energy into mechanical work. It is not unreasonable to assume that the deformation can be associated with alterations in the molecular configuration. There are no a priori reasons for excluding biological processes involving macroscopic dimensional changes from this generalization although the possibility must be allowed that other mechanisms may be operative in specific cases. On the other hand, one might expect that nature would take advantage of the configurational versatility of macromolecules.[51]

Distinction must be made between deformations and the associated molecular configurational changes that are restricted to the amorphous phase and those deformation processes that involve the crystal-liquid phase transition. The elastic deformation of noncrystalline networks above their glass temperature is in the former category. At a molecular level, rubber elastic deformation involves an increase in the amorphous chain length in compliance with the imposed macroscopic strain. Closely associated with this phenomenon are deformations resulting from changes in the degree of swelling of networks immersed in an excess of the supernatant phase. Swelling or deswelling of a network can be caused by changes in the intensity of polymer-solvent interactions or by various chemical reactions. For polyelectrolyte networks the degree of swelling changes with variations in the pH or ionic strength of the surrounding medium. Deformations restricted to the amorphous phase are usually isotropic unless a large stress is applied or the system is dimensionally constrained by mechanical means.[52] The anisotropic deformation and stress response involved in the crystal-liquid phase transition have already been discussed.

In considering the utilization of macromolecules for the conversion of thermal energy into mechanical work, reference can immediately be made to a Carnot cycle since there are no restrictions on the nature of the working substance. However, it is required that all processes be conducted reversibly and that all heat received or rejected by the working substance be exchanged at constant temperature. Thus, processes for which the temperature of the working substance changes are reversible adiabatics. By recalling the analogy between the intensive-extensive sets of variables, p,v and $-f,L$, a schematic diagram for a reversible Carnot thermal engine, utilizing a pure amorphous polymer as the working substance, is given in Fig. 7-20a.[22] The isothermals are represented by AD and CB, and the polymer is in contact with large heat reservoirs at temperatures T_1 and T_2, respectively. AB and CD represent the reversible adiabatics, with the system being isolated from the surroundings. A reversible thermal engine can be constructed from a deformable substance if the tension at constant length is increased by a rise in temperature and the tension-length adiabatics possess a greater slope than the corresponding isothermals. These criteria are consistent with the previously discussed thermoelastic properties of amorphous polymers. An engine of this type is exemplified in the self-energizing pendulum described by Wiegand[53] which utilizes natural rubber as a working substance. The thermodynamic efficiency of the engine illustrated in Fig. 7-20a is directly given by Carnot and depends only on the two operating temperatures. The amount of work performed per cycle is represented by the area $ABCD$.

If, instead of the deformation being rubberlike, a phase transition occurs, the isothermal processes are represented by horizontal lines (since the force is independent of the length), as in Fig. 7-20b. If each of the two cycles involves the same adiabatics, the net work done is greater for the one having the phase transition. This is analogous to

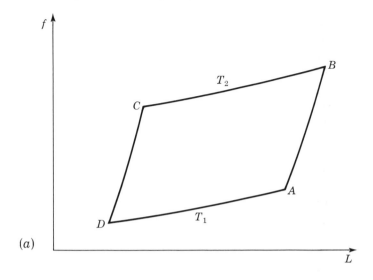

(a)

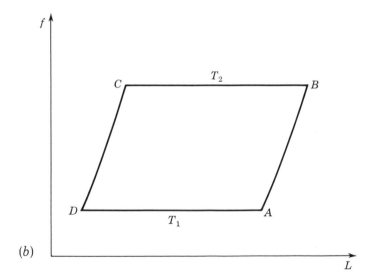

(b)

Fig. 7-20 Schematic diagram for a Carnot cycle utilizing a pure polymer as the working substance. (a) Polymer always in amorphous state; (b) intervention of an isothermal phase transition.

using a condensable vapor in the more conventional Carnot cycle. The thermodynamic efficiency remains the same since it depends only on the two temperatures at which the engine operates. The more effective deliverance of net useful work makes the intervention of a phase transition advantageous, irrespective of the molecular nature of the working substance. When fibrous macromolecules are involved, the oriented crystalline structure allows for the possibility of such a transition. A transition of this type allows for the "razor-edge" character of the contraction displayed by natural systems and permits the working substance to be a more sensitive and effective converter of thermal energy into mechanical work.

The work performed during one isothermal portion of the cycle, involving the complete melting of an oriented fiber, can be estimated. At the melting temperature T_m, under the external force f, it is required that

$$F^a - F^c = f \, \Delta L = -W \tag{7-56}$$

It is assumed that F^c does not change with deformation while F^a can be expressed as

$$F^a(T_m, f) = F^a(T_m, 0) + \Delta F_{el}{}^a(T_m, f) \tag{7-57}$$

where $\Delta F_{el}{}^a$ is the change in free energy in the amorphous state at T_m due to the elastic deformation in going from zero force to a force f. Hence

$$\Delta F_f(T_m, 0) + \Delta F_{el}(T_m, f) = f \, \Delta L = -W \tag{7-58}$$

where

$$\Delta F_f(T_m, 0) = F^a(T_m, 0) - F_c(T_m, 0) \tag{7-59}$$

Expanding $\Delta F_f(T_m, 0)$ about the isotropic melting temperature $T_m{}^\circ$

$$\Delta F_f(T_m, 0) = \Delta F_f(T_m{}^\circ, 0) + \left(\frac{\partial \, \Delta F_f}{\partial T}\right)_{T_m{}^\circ} (T_m - T_m{}^\circ) \tag{7-60}$$

$$\Delta F_f(T_m, 0) \cong -(T_m - T_m{}^\circ) \, \Delta S_f{}^\circ \tag{7-61}$$

For a system where $\Delta F_{el} = -T \, \Delta S_{el}$

$$W \cong (T_m - T_m{}^\circ) \, \Delta S_f{}^\circ + T_m \, \Delta S_{el} \tag{7-62}$$

$$W \cong -T_m{}^\circ \, \Delta S_f{}^\circ + T_m(\Delta S_{el} + \Delta S_f{}^\circ) \tag{7-63}$$

The work performed by the fiber on melting depends on two terms. One term is independent of the force, and the other depends on it through the terms T_m and ΔS_{el}. In the isotropic case, the work done must necessarily be zero, and, at $T = T_m{}^c$, $\Delta L = 0$ so that W is again zero. Hence the work done in a single cycle passes through a maximum with increasing temperature and force. The latter two quantities are related by Eq. (7-29). For small forces where T_m only slightly exceeds $T_m{}^\circ$ and ΔS_{el} is small, the work done is of the order of R cal/mole. This is comparable in magnitude to that observed in naturally occurring systems.

Of more general interest, particularly with respect to biological systems, are chemical engines that operate isothermally. For example, in a physical chemical sense, the naturally functioning muscle fiber system can be considered an engine that converts chemical energy into mechanical work. It operates by means of reversible strains induced in the working substance, which are the fibrous muscle proteins.[22] An isothermal chemical engine can be devised whose operation is similar to that of the thermal engine.[22,54] In place of the two heat reservoirs, the fiber is maintained in contact with large baths of absorbing or reacting species maintained at constant chemical potential. Processes carried out at constant chemical potential have been termed isopotentials in analogy with the isotherms of a heat engine.[54] The transfer of the fiber from one chemical potential to another occurs as an isolated system whose composition remains fixed. These processes have been termed isophores and correspond to the adiabatics of the thermal engine. In the latter case, when the entropy is held constant, the thermal potential or temperature changes. A chemical engine functions, for a fibrous working substance, when the tension at constant length increases with increased concentration of reactants and the slope of the isopotential $(\partial f/\partial L)\mu_i$ is less than the slope of the isophore $(\partial f/\partial L)_{n_i}$.

The consequences of the crystallization of the working substance in a chemical engine are the same as for a heat engine. For operation between the same level of chemical potential and for common isophores the net work delivered per cycle is greater when a phase transition occurs during the isopotential portions. An isopotential phase transition ensures that the required relations between the isophoric and isopotential force-length relations will be met. Several fibrous protein systems have already been referred to which can serve as the working substance and reactants of a chemical engine with isopotential phase transition.

For a simple engine, comprised of only a single component (besides the working substance), maintained in two reservoirs at chemical potentials μ^I and μ^{II}, respectively, the net work accomplished per cycle is given by[54]

$$W = (\mu^I - \mu^{II})\,\Delta n \tag{7-64}$$

where Δn is the quantity of reactant transferred from one reservoir to the other. The immediate source of the work obtained during the contraction can be attributed in the main to the increased entropy resulting from melting. However, for a complete cycle where the working substance returns to its original state, all the changes must be found in the surroundings. The ultimate source of the work performed comes from the free energy change involved in transferring the species from one reservoir to the other. More complex types of chemical engines, involving multicomponent systems, have been discussed in detail by Katchalsky and collaborators[54] along the principles outlined. The foregoing discussion of idealized cycles does not imply that real systems must rigidly adhere to them. It is meant only to serve as a basis for the understanding of mechanochemical processes involving macromolecules.

REFERENCES

1. Li, T. T., R. J. Volungis, and R. S. Stein: *J. Polymer Sci.*, **20**: 194 (1956); J. T. Judge and R. S. Stein: *J. Appl. Phys.*, **32**: 2357 (1961).
2. Flory, P. J.: *J. Chem. Phys.*, **15**: 397 (1947).
3. Flory, P. J.: *Science*, **124**: 53 (1956).
4. Flory, P. J.: *J. Am. Chem. Soc.*, **78**: 5222 (1956).
5. Treloar, L. R. G.: "The Physics of Rubber Elasticity," Oxford University Press, London, 1949, and P. J. Flory: *Trans. Faraday Soc.*, **57**: 829 (1961).
6. Roberts, D. E., and L. Mandelkern: *J. Res. Natl. Bur. Std.*, **54**: 167 (1955).
7. Flory, P. J., and R. R. Garrett: *J. Am. Chem. Soc.*, **80**: 4836 (1958).
8. Flory, P. J., and O. K. Spurr, Jr.: *J. Am. Chem. Soc.*, **83**: 1308 (1961).
9. Gee, G.: *Quart. Rev. (London)*, **1**: 265 (1947).
10. Oth, J. F. M., and P. J. Flory: *J. Am. Chem. Soc.*, **80**: 1297 (1958).
11. Roberts, D. E., and L. Mandelkern: *J. Am. Chem. Soc.*, **77**: 781 (1955).
12. Smith, W. H., and C. P. Saylor: *J. Res. Natl. Bur. Std.*, **21**: 257 (1938).
13. Tobolsky, A. V., and G. M. Brown: *J. Polymer Sci.*, **17**: 547 (1955).
14. Gent, A. N.: *Trans. Faraday Soc.*, **50**: 521 (1954).
15. Natta, G., and P. Corradini: *Rubber Chem. Technol.*, **33**: 703 (1960).
16. Astbury, W. T.: in A. Wasserman (ed.), "Size and Shape Changes of Contractile Polymers," p. 78, Pergamon Press, New York, 1960.
17. Bull, H. B.: *J. Am. Chem. Soc.*, **67**: 533 (1945).
18. Weber, A., and H. Weber: *Biochem. Biophys. Acta*, **7**: 214, 339 (1951).
19. Morales, M., and J. Botts: *Discussions Faraday Soc.*, **13**: 125 (1953).
20. Flory, P. J.: *J. Cellular Comp. Physiol.*, **49**: (Suppl. 1), 175 (1957).
21. Scheraga, H. A.: *J. Phys. Chem.*, **64**: 1917 (1960).
22. Pryor, M. G. M.: in J. A. V. Butler and J. T. Randal (eds.), "Progress in Biophysics," vol. I, p. 216, Butterworth-Springer, 1950.
23. Oth, J. F. M.: *Kolloid-Z.*, **162**: 124 (1959).

214   *Crystallization of Polymers*

24. Gerngross, O., and L. R. Katz: *Kolloid-Beih.*, **23**: 368 (1926).
25a. Roberts, D. E., L. Mandelkern, and P. J. Flory: *J. Am. Chem. Soc.*, **79**: 1515 (1957).
25b. Roberts, D. E., and L. Mandelkern: *J. Am. Chem. Soc.*, **80**: 1289 (1959).
26. Mandelkern, L., D. E. Roberts, A. F. Diorio, and A. S. Posner: *J. Am. Chem. Soc.*, **81**: 4148 (1959).
27. Bailey, K., W. T. Astbury, and K. M. Rudall: *Nature*, **151**: 716 (1943).
28. Astbury, W. T.: *Proc. Roy. Soc. (London), Ser. A*, **134**: 303 (1947).
29. Astbury, W. T.: *Trans. Faraday Soc.*, **34**: 378 (1948).
30. Wright, B. A., and N. M. Wiederhorn: *J. Polymer Sci.*, **7**: 105 (1951).
31. Ewald, A.: *Z. Physiol. Chem.*, **105**: 135 (1919).
32. Bear, R. S.: *Advan.* Protein *Chem.*, **7**: 69 (1952).
33. Rice, R. V.: *Proc. Natl. Acad. Sci. U.S.*, **46**: 1186 (1960).
34. Oth, J. F. M.: *Kolloid-Z.*, **162**: 124 (1959).
35. Faure-Fremet, E.: *J. Chim. Phys.*, **34**: 126 (1937).
36. Champetier, G., and E. Faure-Fremet: *J. Chim. Phys.*, **34**: 197 (1937).
37. Mandelkern, L., and W. T. Meyer: Symposium on Microstructure of Proteins, *J. Polymer Sci.*, **49**: 125 (1961).
38. Lennox, F. G.: *Biochim. Biophys. Acta*, **3**: 170 (1949).
39. Mandelkern, L., W. T. Meyer, and A. F. Diorio: *J. Phys. Chem.*, **66**: 375 (1962).
40. Alexander, P., and R. F. Hudson: "Wool, Its Chemistry and Physics," p. 55, Reinhold Publishing Corporation, New York, 1954.
41. Whewell, C. S., and H. J. Woods: "Symposium on Fibrous Proteins," p. 50, Society of Dyers and Colourists, 1946.
42. Mandelkern, L., J. C. Halpin, A. F. Diorio, and A. S. Posner: *J. Am. Chem. Soc.*, **84**: 1383 (1962).
43. Mandelkern, L., J. C. Halpin, and A. F. Diorio: *J. Polymer Sci.*, **60**: 531 (1962).
44. Bowen, W. J., and K. Laki: *Am. J. Physiol.*, **185**: 92 (1956).
45. Mandelkern, L., and J. C. Halpin: Unpublished observations.
46. Bowen, W. J.: *J. Cellular Comp. Physiol.*, **49**: (Suppl. 1), 267 (1957).
47. Mandelkern, L., A. S. Posner, A. F. Diorio, and K. Laki: *Proc. Natl. Acad. Sci. U.S.*, **45**: 814 (1959).
48. Hoeve, C. A. J., Y. A. Willis, and D. J. Martin: *Biochemistry*, **2**: 279 (1963).
49. Geiduschek, E. P.: *Proc. Natl. Acad. Sci. U.S.*, **47**: 950 (1961).
50. Marmur, J., and L. Grossman: *Proc. Natl. Acad. Sci. U.S.*, **47**: 778 (1961).
51. Flory, P. J.: *Brookhaven Symp. Biol.* No. 13, Protein Structure and Function, p. 89, 1960.
52. Flory, P. J.: "Conference on Contractility," Mellon Institute, Pittsburgh, Jan. 27–30, 1960.
53. Wiegand, W. B.: *Trans. Inst. Rubber Ind.*, **1**: 141 (1925).
54. Katchalsky, A., S. Lifson, I. Michaelis, and H. Zwick: in A. Wassermann (ed.), "Size and Shape Changes of Contractile Polymers," p. 1, Pergamon Press, New York, 1960.

CRYSTALLIZATION
KINETICS AND MECHANISMS

8-1 Introduction

In discussing the crystalline state of polymers we have heretofore been concerned primarily with equilibrium situations that have been deduced theoretically and observed experimentally. Although it has been firmly established that the fusion of polymers is a problem in phase equilibria, rather stringent experimental procedures must be employed to demonstrate this. From equilibrium theory it can be concluded that for polymers of high molecular weight and regular structure very high levels of crystallinity should be attained. However, this deduction is contrary to usual experience. Since the crystalline phase develops at a finite rate only at temperatures well below the melting temperature, the state observed in most real systems represents one formed under conditions far removed from equilibrium. The constitution and properties of the state that is achieved are the resultants of the competition between the kinetic factors involved in the transformation and the requirements of thermodynamic equilibrium. This generalization is not unique to polymeric systems but

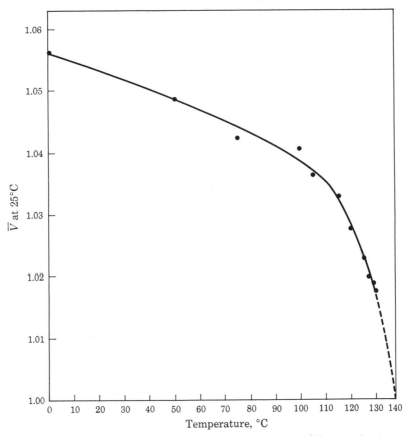

Fig. 8-1   Plot of specific volumes at 25° for unfractionated linear polyethylene (Marlex-50) against temperature of crystallization.   Time of crystallization is adjusted so that crystallization is essentially complete at the specified temperature (1).

holds for a vast majority of substances that undergo a liquid-to-crystal transformation.

As an example of the foregoing, we can examine how a very simple property, the specific volume or density, depends on the crystallization conditions.[1]   In Fig. 8-1 the specific volume at 25° for unfractionated linear polyethylene (Marlex-50) is plotted against the crystallization temperature.   The crystallization was conducted isothermally from the molten state, and the times of crystallization were adjusted so that no significant crystallization occurred subsequent to the density determination.   For the crystallizations conducted at relatively low temperatures, the specific volumes varied from 1.06 to 1.04. This is in the range of values usually reported for this polymer. However, as the crystallization temperature is increased, there is a rather sharp decrease in the specific volume. This quantity is now very sensitive to small changes in crystallization temperature. The lower specific volumes are indicative of the higher levels of crystallinity that are achieved as the crystallization is conducted at temperatures closer to the melting temperature. The extrapolation of the specific volume–crystallization–temperature plot, as indicated by the dashed curve in Fig. 8-1, portends the distinct possibility that at still higher crystallization temperatures even higher densities would be observed. For crystallization conducted at the melting temperature, a specific volume of about 1.00 is predicted. This corresponds to the density of the completely crystalline polymer as deduced by Bunn from the X-ray determination of the crystal structure of polyethylene[2] and implies the formation of a nearly perfect macroscopic single crystal. Experimental confirmation of the extrapolated curve would involve crystallization for such intolerably long periods of time as to be impractical to carry out.

It can thus be demonstrated that a wide range of densities can be obtained at 25° for the same crystalline homopolymer. In the experiments cited, the values depended directly on the crystallization temperature. Other thermodynamic, physical, and mechanical properties are also very sensitive to the manner in which the transformation is conducted. The morphology or crystalline texture of polymers can also be expected to be governed by the crystallization conditions. A complete understanding of the properties and behavior of crystalline polymeric systems thus requires knowledge and information with respect to the mechanism involved in the transformation in addition to the equilibrium characterization. In principle, this information can be deduced from studies of the kinetics of the process.

Experimental observations of the development of crystallinity in polymers have consisted, in the main, of two general kinds. One has been concerned with assessing the isothermal rate at which the total amount of crystallinity develops from the supercooled liquid. In carrying out these experiments, it is necessary to follow the changes of a property that is very sensitive to the presence of crystallinity. Measurements of the changing density of the sample are usually both a very sensitive and convenient method. In some favorable cases the change in an infrared absorption band can be used, and the measurement of the depolarization of transmitted light has found some applicability. The other type of observation that has been widely employed consists of the direct determination, by means of light microscopy, of the isothermal rate of spherulite formation and subsequent growth. It is from these kinds of experimental information that deductions must be made in regard to the crystallization mechanism. A serious limitation on the data available is the lack of direct information on the formation and growth of individual crystallites in bulk systems.

8-2   General Experimental Observation
for the Crystallization of Pure Homopolymers

The isothermal rate at which the total amount of crystallinity develops in a pure homopolymer follows an almost universal pattern first observed by Bekkedahl[3] in his study of natural rubber. Some typical

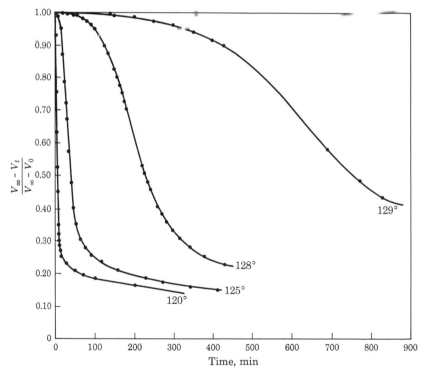

Fig. 8-2   Plot of quantity $(V_\infty - V_t)/(V_\infty - V_0)$ against the time for the crystallization from the melt of a linear polyethylene. Temperature of crystallization is indicated for each isotherm. [*Reprinted with permission from R. H. Doremus, B. W. Roberts, and D. Turnbull (eds.), "Growth and Perfection of Crystals," John Wiley & Sons, Inc., New York, 1958.*]

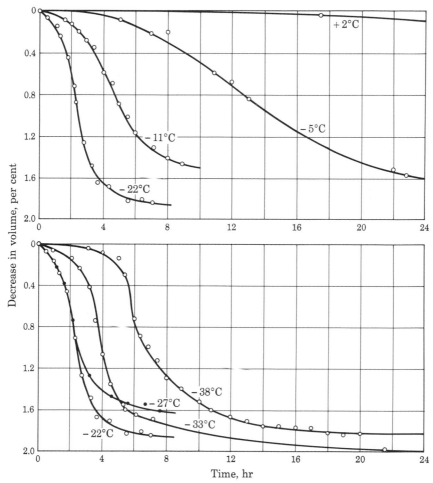

Fig. 8-3 Crystallization of natural rubber at various temperatures as measured by the decrease in specific volume. Temperature of crystallization is indicated for each isotherm. [*From Wood and Bekkedahl* (5).]

isotherms for the crystallization from the melt of a linear polyethylene[4] and of natural rubber[5] are illustrated in Figs. 8-2 and 8-3. Changes in the specific volume were utilized to follow the crystallization process in both of these cases. For polyethylene the relative extent of the transformation is plotted against the time; for natural rubber the percentage decrease in volume is given. In such experiments, when the polymer sample is quickly transferred from a temperature above the melting temperature to the predetermined crystallization temperature, there is a well-defined time interval during which no crystallinity is observed. This time interval obviously must depend on the sensitivity of the crystallinity detector. After the onset of observable crystallization, the process proceeds at an accelerating rate, which is almost autocatalytic in character. Finally a pseudo-equilibrium level of crystallinity is approached. However, the development of a small but definite amount of crystallinity at very slow rates persists for many decades of time. The crystallization process is continuous, with no sudden changes or discernible discontinuities observed in the isotherms. The sigmoidal-shaped isotherms illustrated in Figs. 8-2 and 8-3 are characteristic of the crystallization of all homopolymers that have been studied.

When kinetic experiments are conducted in such a manner that prior to crystallization the sample is completely molten and degradative processes are avoided, the resulting isotherms are extremely reproducible and independent of the initial temperature of the melt at which the sample is held,[6] This is true even if the initial temperature is only slightly greater than the melting temperature. It appears to be important that complete melting be ensured. The question whether this reproducibility would still be maintained at very high initial melt temperatures remains to be answered. There are many reports, however, that the above indicated reproducibility was not readily observed. The aforementioned conditions may not be operative or the rate of cooling of the specimen may be such that isothermal crystallization cannot occur at the anticipated temperature.

Another major characteristic of the crystallization process is the very strong dependence of the rate on the crystallization temperature. The change in the rate with temperature over the complete range for which crystallization is possible, i.e., between the melting temperature and the glass transformation temperature, is exemplified for natural rubber[5] in Fig. 8-4. The time taken for half the crystallization to develop is plotted as a function of the crystallization temperature. Similar behavior has been observed for a variety of other homopolymers as, for example, polyethylene terephthalate,[7] polyethylene adipate,[8] and polyethylene succinate.[9] At temperatures in the vicinity of T_m° the crystallization rate is very slow, and for any reasonable time of measurement the appearance of crystallinity will not be detected. As the temperature is lowered, the rate progressively increases and eventually passes through a maximum. At crystallization temperatures below the maximum, the over-all rate of crystallization becomes small again. This tempertaure interval invariably coincides with the temperature range of glass formation for the supercooled polymeric liquid. For many polymers, however, the rate becomes so rapid at temperatures below $T_m°$ that it is extremely difficult to study isothermal crystallization experimentally and to detect the temperature at which the rate is a maximum.

The extreme sensitivity of the crystallization rate to temperature in the vicinity of $T_m°$ is easily discerned from the data plotted in Fig. 8-2. At 129° the appearance of crystallinity is not detected for 400 min. However, when the crystallization temperature is lowered merely 4°, crystallinity is observed in 6 min with the same sensitivity of detection. A 60-fold change in rate occurs over a 4° temperature interval. This is truly a remarkable temperature coefficient for a rate process.

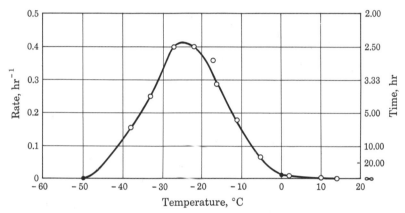

Fig. 8-4 Plot of the rate of crystallization of natural rubber over an extended temperature range. The rate plotted is the reciprocal of the time required for one-half the total volume change. [*From Wood and Bekkedahl* (5).]

In Fig. 8-5 the ratio of $(V_\infty - V_t)/(V_\infty - V_0)$ is plotted against the logarithm of time for each crystallization temperature, utilizing the data of Fig. 8-2. The major characteristics of the isotherms are still maintained in this plot. In addition, the observation can now be made that the individual isotherms can be brought into coincidence merely by shifting each of the curves an appropriate distance along the horizontal axis.[4,6] This is a characteristic property of the isotherms of all homopolymers studied, when this classification is invoked in its strictest sense. Detailed studies have shown that the superposition of isotherms is not restricted to temperatures in the vicinity of $T_m°$ but also occurs when the experiments are conducted over the complete temperature range of crystallization.[8,10]† A consequence of

† The superposition of the isotherms for homopolymers holds for at least 80 per cent of the process. There is some uncertainty as to whether superposition exists in the final or "taillike" portions of the isotherms.

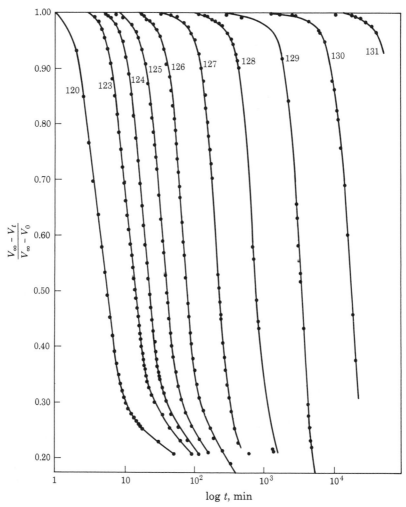

Fig. 8-5 Plot of quantity $(V_\infty - V_t)/(V_\infty - V_0)$ against the logarithm of time for the crystallization of a linear polyethylene. Temperature of crystallization is indicated for each isotherm. [*Reprinted with permission from R. H. Doremus, B. W. Roberts, and D. Turnbull (eds.), "Growth and Perfection of Crystals," John Wiley & Sons, Inc., New York,* 1958.]

these observations is that the temperature coefficient is invariant throughout the major portion of the process. Consequently, from a purely experimental point of view, a single isotherm based on a reduced variable involving time and temperature can be constructed that is representative of the crystallization of a given homopolymer.

With respect to microscopic observations, carefully conducted experiments have shown that in thin polymer films it is possible for spherulites to develop sporadically in both time and space.[8,11,12] Repetitive experiments have indicated that spherulites do not necessarily form at identical positions after complete melting of the samples. However, for polydecamethylene terephthalate, Sharples[13] has observed that, although spherulites are formed sporadically with time, they appear in identical positions in the sample. In this system the experimental evidence indicates that the spherulitic centers are initiated from a fixed number of heterogeneities. The usual experience, however, is a strong tendency for spherulites to appear in the same position in the field of view after successive crystallizations.[14-18] For branched polyethylene, Richards and Hawkins[12] have shown that this observation is solely a result of incomplete melting. This may also be true for the other cases cited or could be attributed to the presence of a finite number of nucleation catalysts discretely located within the polymer melt.

In the vicinity of the melting temperature the rate at which spherulites are generated depends very strongly on the crystallization temperature and increases very rapidly as the temperature is lowered. For example, for polydecamethylene adipate the rate at which spherulitic centers are generated decreases by a factor of 10^5 as the crystallization temperature is raised from 67 to 72°.[11]

An impressive body of experimental evidence, for a variety of polymers, demonstrates that at fixed temperature the radius of a growing spherulite increases linearly with time over a wide range of crystallization temperatures. These observations are consistent with the autocatalytic nature of the isotherms illustrated in Figs. 8-2 and 8-3. The linear growth rate is also very sensitive to temperature.[8,11,18] For example, studies by Takayanagi[8a] on polyethylene adipate show that as the crystallization temperature is lowered the growth rate increases until a maximum is observed. With a further decrease in the temperature, the rate of growth diminishes. Figure 8-6 illustrates a typical set of results for this system. The linear rate of growth is clearly defined, and the changes that occur in the slopes of the straight lines as the crystallization temperature is varied are readily discernible. The temperature variation of the spherulitic growth rate is thus qualitatively similar to the temperature coefficient of the over-all rate of development of crystallinity previously described. The temperature at which the maximum in the rate occurs for polyethylene adipate is almost identical for both types of experiments. Problems of resolution caused by the overlapping of spherulites make difficult the counting and measuring of spherulite sizes as the level of crystallinity

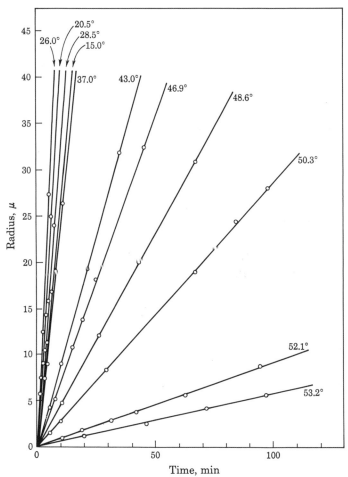

Fig. 8-6 Plot of growth rate of spherulites against the time at
various crystallization temperatures for polyethylene adipate of
molecular weight 9,900. [*From Takayanagi (8a).*]

becomes appreciable.   Consequently this technique, as a quantitative
tool, is restricted to the observation of small amounts of crystallinity.

8-3   Mathematical Formulation of the Kinetics of Phase Changes

The development of a new phase within a mother phase, as a crystal
within a liquid, involves the birth of the phase and its subsequent
development.   The former process is termed nucleation and the latter
growth.   For most cases of interest, isothermal crystallization can be

described in terms of the nucleation frequency N and the growth rates G_i of each of the crystallographic planes. The amount of material transformed as a function of the time can be calculated subject to any restrictive assumptions that are imposed on the kinetic process. We discuss first the crystallization process for monomeric substances, and let $\dot{N}'$ be the steady-state nucleation frequency per unit of untransformed mass. The number of nuclei generated in a time interval $d\tau$ is

$$dn = \dot{N}(\tau)[1 - X(\tau)] \, d\tau \qquad (8\text{-}1)$$

Here $X(\tau)$ is the fraction of material transformed at time τ. If $w(t,\tau)$ is the mass of a given center at time t, which was initiated at time τ ($\tau \leq t$) and which grew without restriction, then

$$X(t) = \int_0^t w(t,\tau) \, dn = \int_0^t w(t,\tau)\dot{N}'(\tau)[1 - X(\tau)] \, d\tau \qquad (8\text{-}2)$$

Alternatively, Eq. (8-2) can be expressed as

$$X(t) = \frac{\rho_c}{\rho_l} \int_0^t v(t,\tau)\dot{N}(\tau)[1 - X(\tau)] \, d\tau \qquad (8\text{-}3)$$

where $\dot{N}(\tau)$ is now the nucleation frequency per unit of untransformed volume, $v(t,\tau)$ is the corresponding volume of the growing center, and ρ_c and ρ_l are the densities of the crystalline and liquid phases, respectively.

Equation (8-2), derived by Von Goler and Sachs,[19] is termed the free growth approximation. The evolution of an individual growing center is assumed to be completely independent of the mass already transformed as well as the growth of other centers. In particular, the effect of the impingement of growing centers upon one another is neglected.

In order to solve Eq. (8-3) it is necessary that $v(t,\tau)$ and $\dot{N}(\tau)$ be specified. The simplifying assumption is usually made that $\dot{N}(\tau)$ is constant, independent of the amount of material transformed. It is frequently found, particularly for one-component systems, that the growth process is linear. If G_x, G_y, G_z are the linear growth vectors for the x, y, z directions, then, with the neglect of impingement,

$$v(t,\tau) = fG_xG_yG_z(t - \tau)^3 \qquad (8\text{-}4)$$

The growth vectors are assumed to be independent of time, and the shape factor f is characteristic of the geometry of the growing center. The assumption of a linear rate of growth implies that the rate of volume change of a growing center is proportional to its surface area. Growth is therefore governed by processes that occur at the crystal-

liquid interface. If, on the other hand, the diffusion of the crystallizing entities to the interface is rate-controlling, a linear dimension of
the growing center will increase in proportion with the square root of
the time. In this case, $v(t,\tau)$ varies with $(t - \tau)^{3/2}$. For a linear growth
which is restricted to two dimensions,

$$v(t,\tau) = fG_x G_y \gamma (t - \tau)^2 \tag{8-5}$$

where γ represents the dimensions held fixed. Similarly, for growth in
one dimension,

$$v(t,\tau) = fG_x \gamma_1 \gamma_2 (t - \tau) \tag{8-6}$$

We take, as an illustrative example, a spherically symmetrical
center growing linearly. Hence $f = 4\pi/3$ and $G_x = G_y = G_z = G$.
Equation (8-3) can then be written

$$X = \frac{4\pi}{3} G^3 \dot{N} \frac{\rho_c}{\rho_l} \int_0^t (t - \tau)^3 (1 - X) \, d\tau \tag{8-7}$$

For the initial portion of the transformation, this can be approximated by

$$X \cong \frac{\pi}{3} \frac{\rho_c}{\rho_l} G^3 \dot{N} t^4 \tag{8-8}$$

Equation (8-8) is termed the free growth approximation. As would be
expected from the assumptions employed, the complete solution of
Eq. (8-3) leads to unrealistic results.

A more exact description of the kinetics of phase transformations
must take into account the mutual impingement of growing centers
upon one another. This problem was treated by Johnson and Mehl,[20]
Avrami,[21] and Evans,[22] utilizing very similar methods.[23] The assumption is made that, upon impingement, the growth of the centers
involved ceases. A hypothetical analog is assumed in this analysis,
wherein nuclei are allowed to form throughout the entire system, i.e.,
fictitious nuclei are permitted to develop in the mass already transformed. The total number of nuclei, real and fictitious, that are
generated in the time interval $d\tau$ is given by

$$dn' = \dot{N}'(1 - X) \, d\tau + \dot{N}'X \, d\tau = \dot{N}' \, d\tau \tag{8-9}$$

Here $\dot{N}'X \, d\tau$ represents the number of nuclei that would have origi-
nated in the mass fraction X if it had not become transformed. It is
convenient to calculate the fraction transformed without concern for
impingement but allowing the fictitious nuclei to form and grow. This

quantity can be expressed as

$$X' = \int_0^t w(t,\tau) \, dn' = \int_0^t w(t,\tau) \dot{N}'(\tau) \, d\tau \tag{8-10}$$

The actual fraction transformed is related to X' by

$$\frac{dX}{dX'} = 1 - X \tag{8-11}$$

A rigorous mathematical derivation of (8-11) has been given by Avrami.[21] The physical basis for this result is seen from the following argument. The growth of a real center is retarded as it encounters regions already transformed because of impingement. Thus, the actual mass fraction transformed in a time interval dt will be less than dX'. Since nuclei, both real and hypothetical, have been formed at random throughout the entire mass, the shells of transformed material are in random regions. In the vicinity of growing centers the fraction of the mass that is available for transformation is thus the same as the over-all total fraction available. The expected incremental increase in the actual mass transformed is then given by Eq. (8-11).

The integration of Eq. (8-11) yields

$$X = 1 - \exp(-X') \tag{8-12}$$

When X' from Eq. (8-10) is substituted in Eq. (8-12),

$$X = 1 - \exp\left[-\int_0^t w(t,\tau) \dot{N}'(\tau) \, d\tau \right] \tag{8-13}$$

or, alternatively,

$$X = 1 - \exp\left[-\frac{\rho_c}{\rho_l} \int_0^t v(t,\tau) \dot{N}(\tau) \, d\tau \right] \tag{8-14}$$

are obtained as the expressions for the basic laws governing the kinetics of phase transformations for one-component monomeric substances.

The integrals appearing in Eqs. (8-13) and (8-14) can be evaluated by specifying the nucleation and growth laws that are operative. A quantitative description of the fraction transformed as a function of time is thus obtained. If the steady-state rate of nucleation is reached at time $t = 0$ and is invariant with respect to the fraction of material transformed, $\dot{N}(\tau)$ can be treated as a constant. With this simplifying assumption, analytical solutions are obtained from these expressions for different growth processes. For three-dimensional linear growth

$$\ln \frac{1}{1-X} = \frac{\pi}{3} \frac{\rho_c}{\rho_l} \dot{N} G^3 t^4 \equiv k_s t^4 \tag{8-15}$$

The exponent of t in this equation, a quantity which we shall designate as n, is indicative of the fact that we have treated a homogeneous nucleation process with growth occurring in three directions. For a disk of fixed thickness l_c developing radially according to a linear growth law,

$$\ln \frac{1}{1 - X} = \frac{\pi}{3} l_c \frac{\rho_c}{\rho_l} \dot{N}G^2 t^3 \equiv k_d t^3 \qquad (8\text{-}16)$$

Similarly, for a one-dimensional growing system, $n = 2$. The values of n appropriate to homogeneous nucleating systems, whose nucleation rates are invariant with time and whose growth is linear, are summarized in Table 8-1.

TABLE 8-1
Values of exponent n for various types of nucleation and growth acts

Growth habit	Homogeneous nucleation		Heterogeneous nucleation†
	Linear growth	Diffusion controlled growth	Linear growth
Three-dimensional	4	$\frac{5}{2}$	$3 \leq n \leq 4$
Two-dimensional	3	2	$2 \leq n \leq 3$
One-dimensional	2	$\frac{3}{2}$	$1 \leq n \leq 2$

† For type specified by Eq. (8-19).

When the growth of a developing center is controlled by diffusional processes occurring in the untransformed regions, a linear dimension increases in proportion to $t^{1/2}$. If the same restrictions are applied to the nucleation act, equations very similar to those given above are obtained. However, as is indicated in Table 8-1, the value of the exponent n is different for the same growth geometry.

When the arbitrary restrictions of a homogeneous and constant nucleation rate are relaxed, a variety of other possibilities exist. A similar statement can also be made if the growth-rate constants are not held invariant. We focus attention on the consequences of removing certain of the restrictive conditions on the nucleation rate. If, for example, we allow the rate of nucleus formation to follow a first-order rate law with the specific rate constant ν or if there is initially present a fixed number $\bar{N}$ of potential nuclei or heterogeneities with specific probability ν of developing, then the number of such sites remaining after time τ, where $\tau = \nu t$, is given by[21]

$$N' = \bar{N} \exp\,(-\tau) \tag{8-17}$$

The corresponding nucleation rate is therefore

$$\dot{N}' = \bar{N} \exp\,(-\tau) \tag{8-18}$$

For three-dimensional linear growth, Eq. (8-14) yields

$$\ln \frac{1}{1-X} = \frac{8\pi G^3 \bar{N}}{\nu^3}\frac{\rho_c}{\rho_l}\left[\exp\,(-\nu t) - 1 + \nu t - \frac{(\nu t)^2}{2!} + \left(\frac{\nu t^3}{3!}\right)\right] \tag{8-19}$$

When the quantity νt is large, which corresponds to a high probability for the initial growth of all potential or preferred nuclei sites that are present, Eq. (8-19) reduces to

$$\ln \frac{1}{1-X} = \frac{4\pi}{3}\frac{\rho_c}{\rho_l} G^3 \bar{N} t^3 \tag{8-20}$$

This equation is of the same form as that obtained for a homogeneously nucleated system growing linearly in two dimensions. In the other extreme, if νt is small, Eq. (8-19) reduces to

$$\ln \frac{1}{1-X} = \frac{\pi}{3}\frac{\rho_c}{\rho_l} G \bar{N} \nu t^4 \tag{8-21}$$

which corresponds in form to Eq. (8-15). In the latter approximation not all the growing centers are initiated at $t = 0$. Instead, nuclei are activated at a constant rate throughout the course of the transformation. For situations between these two extremes, nuclei become depleted at some intermediate state of the transformation. The value of n is then in the range 3 to 4. It can be easily verified that, when the nucleation rate follows Eq. (8-18), an equation of the form

$$\ln \frac{1}{1-X} = kt^n \tag{8-22}$$

is obtained in the two extreme cases for the diverse types of possible growth geometries. As is indicated in the last column of Table 8-1 for two-dimensional growth, $2 \leq n \leq 3$, while for one-dimensional growth, $1 \leq n \leq 2$. It is apparent that, even with these relatively mild restrictions on the nucleation and growth processes, details of the growth geometry and type of nucleation cannot be elucidated from the kinetic isotherms solely by specifying the value of the exponent n.

For isotherms that adhere to Eq. (8-22) the temperature-dependent terms are all embodied in the parameter k which is independent of *t*.   A characteristic time scale involving the temperature and the real time can then be defined.   In terms of this variable, the kinetics of the phase change will remain unaltered.   Hence when a function of $1 - X$ is plotted against log *t*, superposable isotherms should result from experiments conducted at different temperatures.   However, when the complete Eq. (8-19) is followed, the isotherms are superposable only if the ratio G/ν is independent of temperature.

With this background, the formal theory for the crystallization kinetics of polymeric systems can be developed.   The superposability of the isotherms and the accompanying invariance of the temperature coefficient of the crystallization rate that have been observed lend support to the concurrence of the nucleation and growth processes. The widespread observations that the radius of a growing spherulite increases linearly with time lead to the assumption that growth is controlled by processes occurring at the spherulite-melt interface.   These assumptions are consistent with the Johnson-Mehl[20] and Avrami[21] treatments of the problem so that similar results are anticipated.

Inherent in the theory for monomeric systems, however, is the assumption that the phase transformation goes to completion.   In polymers complete crystallinity is rarely, if ever, attained.   The impediments to the development of crystallinity must be specified and introduced into the theory.   In many respects this complicates the treatment of impingement since not all the untransformed mass at a time *t* is available for crystallization.   For polymeric systems the analog of Eq. (8-11) can be expressed as[6,24]

$$\frac{dX}{dX'} = 1 - U(t) \tag{8-23}$$

where $U(t)$ is the "effective fraction" of the mass transformed at time *t*.   It is defined as that fraction of the total mass into which further crystal growth cannot occur.   This quantity includes the actual mass transformed as well as the amorphous chain segments which are in a noncrystallizable situation at time *t*.   The assumption is made[25] that the "effective fraction" transformed is proportional to the actual mass fraction transformed, the proportionality factor being $1/1 - \lambda(\infty)$. The weight fraction of polymer that is crystalline at the termination of the process is $1 - \lambda(\infty)$.   The proportionality factor has been arbitrarily assumed to be independent of time.   For small values of the amount transformed, $dX \cong dX'$, and this difficulty is alleviated. When

$$U(t) = \frac{X}{1 - \lambda(\infty)} \tag{8-24}$$

the integration of Eq. (8-23) yields

$$\ln \frac{1}{1 - X/[1 - \lambda(\infty)]} = \frac{1}{1 - \lambda(\infty)} X'(t) \qquad (8\text{-}25)$$

Since $X'(t)$ is the same as for monomeric substances, we obtain by use of (8-10)

$$\ln \frac{1}{1 - X/[1 - \lambda(\infty)]} = \frac{1}{1 - \lambda(\infty)} \frac{\rho_c}{\rho_l} \int_0^t v(t,\tau)\dot{N}(\tau) \, d\tau \qquad (8\text{-}26)$$

In order to express the dependence of X on the time, the details of the nucleation and growth processes must again be specified. If the integration of Eq. (8-26) is carried out under the same set of assumptions utilized for monomers, an equation of the general form

$$\ln \frac{1}{1 - X/[1 - \lambda(\infty)]} = \frac{1}{1 - \lambda(\infty)} kt^n \qquad (8\text{-}27)$$

results. The interpretation of the exponent n, as given, for example, in Table 8-1, is still valid. The results, as embodied in Eqs. (8-16) and (8-27), are highly restrictive in the sense that the growth rate coefficients G have been assumed constant and only one of many possible variations of the nucleation rate with time has been discussed. These limitations must be borne in mind when experimental results are compared with theory.

The theoretical isotherms are expressed directly in terms of the mass transformed, notwithstanding the fact that this quantity is seldom directly observed. In order to compare theory with experiment, the equations must be recast in terms of directly measured quantities. For example, if the specific volume is being measured, Eq. (8-27) can be rewritten as

✗
$$\ln \frac{V_\infty - V_t}{V_\infty - V_0} = - \frac{1}{1 - \lambda(\infty)} kt^n \qquad (8\text{-}28)$$

where V_0 is the initial volume (the volume of the melt at $t = 0$), V_∞ is the final volume, and V_t the volume at time t. Other properties that change with the amount of the transformation can be treated in a similar manner. If expressed in terms of the relative volume shrinkage $a(t) = (V_0 - V_t)/V_0$, Eq. (8-28) becomes

$$\ln \left[1 - \frac{a(t)}{a(\infty)} \right] = - \frac{1}{1 - \lambda(\infty)} kt^n \qquad (8\text{-}29)$$

If the degree of crystallinity $1 - \lambda(t)$ is defined as $(V_c - V_t)/$

$(V_l - V_c)$,† then

$$1 - \lambda(t) = [1 - \lambda(\infty)] \left\{ 1 - \exp\left[-\frac{1}{1 - \lambda(\infty)} kt^n \right] \right\} \quad (8\text{-}30)$$

For small amounts of crystallinity, Eq. (8-30) reduces to $1 - \lambda(t) \cong kt^n$ which corresponds to the case of free growth.

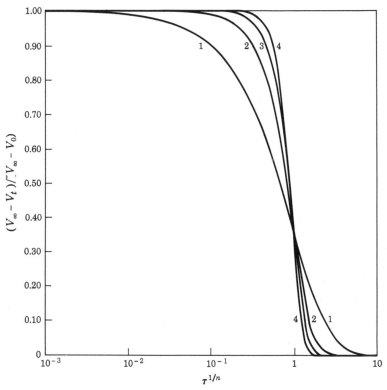

Fig. 8-7 Plot of theoretical isotherms according to Eq. (8-28) for $n = 1$, 2, 3, and 4.

In Fig. 8-7 theoretical isotherms are plotted in accordance with Eq. (8-28) for values of $n = 1$, 2, 3, and 4. By defining $1/[1 - \lambda(\infty)]kt^n$ as τ, the abscissa, plotted as $\tau^{1/n}$, is directly proportional to the time. The curves in Fig. 8-7 have several important features in common. The general shapes of the isotherms are in qualitative accord with the experimental results described in the preceding section. Differences

† This definition is predicated on the assumption that the specific volumes of the crystalline and amorphous phases are additive in a polymer that is only partly crystalline.

between the theoretical curves exist which are, in principle, distinguishable from one another. As n increases from 1 to 4, the time until the onset of crystallinity is detected becomes greater. Once the transformation develops perceptibly, however, the crystallization rate becomes greater, the higher the value of the exponent n. All the curves have a common point of intersection at $\tau^{1/n} = 1$; beyond this point, termination of the transformation is more rapid, the larger the value of n. The similarity of the theoretical curves indicates that in the analysis of experimental data (even for systems that adhere to the assumptions involved) it is a difficult matter to decide whether $n = 3$ or 4 or possibly even 2. This is particularly true for the early stages of the transformation. This is the region, however, where the most reliable experimental data are obtained.

8-4 Analysis of the Bulk Isothermal Crystallization of Homopolymers

The experimental results can now be quantitatively analyzed in terms of Eq. (8-27) or (8-28) of the preceding section. According to these equations, the isotherms are simply and completely described by specifying the rate constant k and the time exponent n. For a given set of superposable isotherms the relative rates of crystallization can also be depicted by the time necessary for the argument of the logarithmic term in Eq. (8-28) to reach a preassigned value. It is often convenient to examine the quantity $t_{1/2}$, which is defined as the time necessary for this term to equal 0.5. A set of experimental data can also be analyzed by plotting $\ln \ln [(V_\infty - V_t)/(V_\infty - V_0)]$ against $\ln t$. If the simplified theory that has been developed is obeyed, a straight line should result from which the parameters n and k can be obtained. Because of the lack of sensitivity inherent in using a double logarithm, this method bars from analysis the rather important time interval where only a small amount of crystallinity is detected. A more direct and perhaps illuminating method of comparing theory with experiment is to construct plots of $(V_\infty - V_t)/(V_\infty - V_0)$ against the $\log \tau^{1/n}$, for different values of the parameter n. A plot of the experimental data is then made on the same scale, with $\log t$ as the abscissa. If the two graphs are superimposed and shifted horizontally until the best fit is obtained, the agreement between theory and experiment can be critically examined and the appropriate values of n and k determined.

The data of Takayanagi[8a] for the over-all crystallization kinetics of polyethylene adipate are plotted in Fig. 8-8, using the double-logarithmic method. A set of parallel straight lines is obtained for

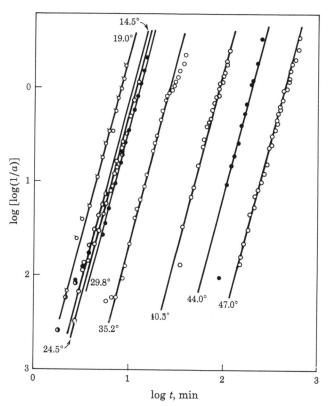

Fig. 8-8 Plot of log [log (1/a)] against log t for fractionated polyethylene adipate. M = 9,900. [*From Takayanagi (8a).*]

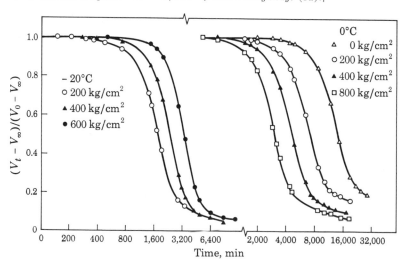

Fig. 8-9 Plot of quantity $(V_\infty - V_t)/(V_\infty - V_0)$ against log t for natural rubber at indicated temperatures and pressures (25).

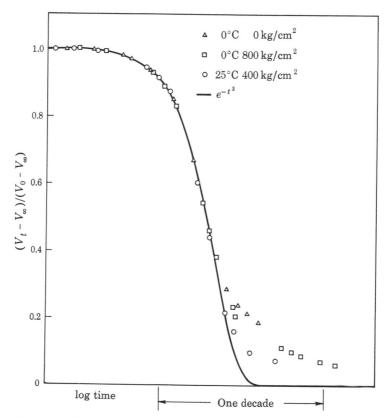

Fig. 8-10 Demonstration of superposability of isotherms for natural rubber. Solid line plotted according to Eq. (8-28) with $n = 3$ (25).

each crystallization temperature. The slope of the lines, in each case, is 4. Close adherence to Eq. (8-28) is thus indicated. A literal interpretation of the value of the slope would imply, according to Table 8-1, a constant rate of sporadic nucleation with concurrent three-dimensional linear growth.

The isotherms for natural rubber have very similar shapes irrespective of the temperature and pressure of crystallization.[25] Some typical results are illustrated in Fig. 8-9. The superposability of these isotherms is demonstrated in Fig. 8-10. The experimental points represent the isotherms obtained at the indicated temperatures and pressures. They are plotted on an arbitrary time scale so as best to bring them into coincidence. The solid line, drawn in accordance with Eq. (8-28), demonstrates that the data adhere to the theory for the

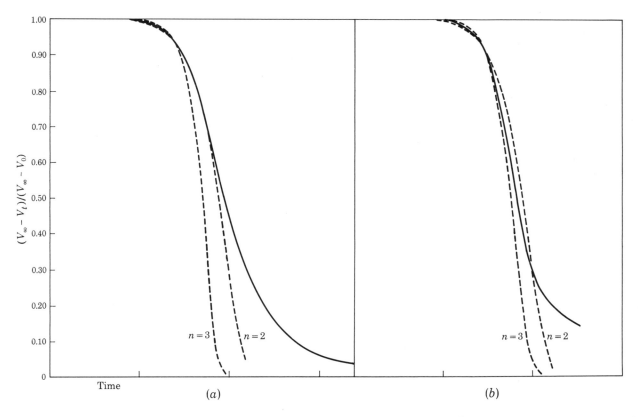

Fig. 8-11 Typical isotherms for molecular weight fractions of linear polyethylene. (*a*) Plot of $(V_\infty - V_t)/(V_\infty - V_0)$ against log t for $M = 24,000$. Dashed line represents best fit that can be obtained from Eq. (8-28) with $n = 3$; (*b*) similar plot for $M = 360,000$ (31).

major portion of the transformation. For this case, the appropriate value of n is 3. The deviations from theory begin to develop toward the termination of the transformation, with the crystallization proceeding at a more protracted rate than is predicted. This disparity manifests itself at a level of crystallinity of about 25 per cent. The analysis of kinetic studies for a diversity of homopolymers shows a similar adherence to Eq. (8-28).[4,6,7,8,9,10,14,15,26,27,28,29,30] The results illustrated can thus be construed to represent typical homopolymer crystallization.

A more careful comparison between theory and experiment can be accomplished by analyzing data for two molecular weight fractions of linear polyethylene. The isotherms for each of the fractions are again superposable (though not with each other). Typical isotherms for $M = 24,000$ and $M = 360,000$ are given in Fig. 8-11a and b, along with curves that give the best fit when calculated according to Eq. (8-28) for $n = 2$ and $n = 3$.[31] For the 24,000 molecular weight fraction the curve for $n = 3$ appears to be most suitable for about one-third of the total transformation on the normalized plot. Beyond this point, which corresponds to about 25 per cent of the actual material transformed, crystallization proceeds at a much slower rate than predicted. For the 360,000 molecular weight fraction there appears to be essentially equal choice between the theoretical curves for $n = 2$ and $n = 3$. The same sort of deviations from theory are observed, which again set in at levels of crystallinity of about 20 to 25 per cent. Very similar observations have been reported by Gordon and coworkers[31a] on fractions of linear polyethylene encompassing the same molecular weight range.

It is apparent that the shapes of the isotherms for the two molecular weight fractions must be different. This is illustrated in Fig. 8-12 for the two fractions discussed and a low molecular weight fraction of $M = 5,300$. Typical isotherms for each fraction were shifted along the horizontal axis so as to bring them into the best coincidence. Polymers containing a small number of chain atoms possess certain unique features which will be discussed separately in a subsequent section. Present attention is focused on the two higher molecular weight fractions. Although the differences in isotherm shape are small, they are experimentally discernible and cannot be ignored in any complete theoretical analysis. The crystallization of the higher molecular weight fraction is definitely more retarded.[32] As has been reported by many investigators, a lower level of crystallinity is eventually attained for the higher molecular weight fractions.[33,34,35] It can be parenthetically noted that the isotherm for the very low molecular weight fraction is of quite different shape and is the most retarded of

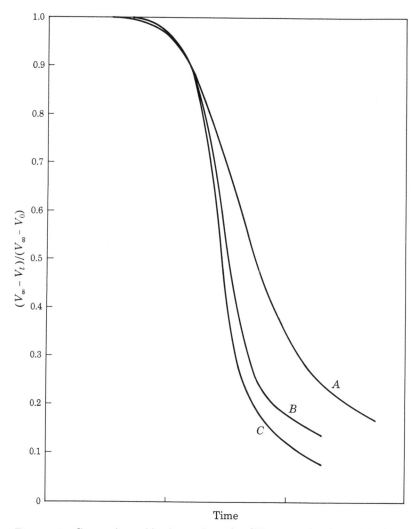

Fig. 8-12 Comparison of isotherm shape for different molecular weight fractions of linear polyethylene. Plot of quantity $(V_\infty - V_t)/(V_\infty - V_0)$ against $\log t$. Curve A: $M = 5,300$; curve B: $M = 364,000$; curve C: $M = 24,000$ (31).

the three. To be explicable, within the framework of the general theory that has been propounded, the differences attributable to molecular weight must reside in either or both the nucleation and growth processes.

Although strong emphasis has been given to the differences between theory and experiment, the widespread agreement observed for the initial portions of the transformation cannot be ignored. This is particularly significant when cognizance is taken of the drastic simplifying assumptions that were invoked in deriving Eq. (8-28). The universally observed superposition of the isotherms of homopolymers has a natural explanation from this development, and the general features of isotherm shape are adequately described. The conclusion can therefore be reached that, in close harmony with the behavior of monomeric substances, nucleation and growth processes are the basic mechanisms involved in the development of crystallinity in polymers. The crystallization kinetics of polymers adheres to the very general mathematical formulation of the kinetics of phase changes.[20,21] Hence a change in phase occurs in accordance with and support of the same conclusion deduced from the study of the fusion process. It is also apparent that in polymers the transformation from the liquid to crystal phase is rarely, if ever, complete. This, however, in no way vitiates the treatment of the phenomenon as a problem in phase equilibrium.[36]

The differences observed between theory and experiment warrant further inquiry. The general conclusion can be reached that, as the transformation progresses, the rate at which crystallinity develops is less than that predicted. For those systems analyzed in detail, it appears that the retardation in rate initially manifests itself when about 25 to 30 per cent of the substance has become crystalline. Moreover, the shape of the isotherm depends on molecular weight (for fractions); the higher the molecular weight, the more protracted the crystallization. Consequently the simplifying assumptions introduced in the derivation of Eq. (8-28) are in need of reexamination. Since the absolute amount of crystallization appears significant in delineating the deviations, attention should be focused on the possibility that the nucleation and growth rates depend on the extent of the transformation.

An essential feature of the mathematical treatment was the tacit assumption that N and G are independent of the extent of the transformation. These assumptions are introduced primarily to simplify the mathematical analyses. They are also consistent with the fact that for homopolymers of sufficiently high molecular weight the composition of the melt is invariant with the extent of the transformation. However, the constitution of the melt need not be constant. As crystallization progresses, amorphous sequences of finite length become isolated between two successive crystalline sequences. Some of these isolated sequences are not able to participate in the nucleation act (see following discussion) because of their restricted length. As a result, the effective concentration of units available for crystallization is continuously diminished as the transformation progresses. Hence the proportionality factor introduced into Eq. (8-24) need not be a constant. More properly, it should be a function of the extent of the crystallization so that $U(t)$ becomes proportionally greater than X with time. When introduced into the theory, this concept should result in better agreement with experiment. An analysis of the sequence isolation problem for a single polymer chain, although not directly applicable to the three-dimensional problem, indicates that approximately 25 per cent of the chain units are not available for crystallization as a result of their location in amorphous sequences of limited size.[37]

In addition to this property, which is unique to the crystallization of long chain molecules, other factors must also be taken into account. The assumption of a linear growth rate, though in accordance with the direct observations of spherulitic development at low levels of crystallinity, may need revision as the amount transformed becomes appreciable. As the concentration of the available amorphous material is depleted, the diffusion of polymer segments to the interface between the crystal and melt can become rate-determining. If this is the case, the radius of a growing center becomes proportional to the square root of the time, and the crystallization process is retarded accordingly. The molecular chain length would then be expected to influence both the crystallization rate and isotherm shape.

Moreover, if nucleation is catalyzed by a finite number of heterogeneities, which are sporadically activated with time, the consumption of these heterogeneities prior to the completion of the process will yield theoretical isotherms described by Eq. (8-19). With an appropriate rate of depletion, isotherms similar to those observed experimentally can be calculated.

Various reasons can be suggested, therefore, based on physical realities, for deviations from the simple postulates proposed in the initial theoretical development. Serious discrepancies can be expected as the amount of crystallinity developed becomes appreciable. It is this region of the transformation that is obviously in need of theoretical improvement.

If the assumption is made that one primary nucleus gives rise to one spherulite, then by the direct measure of both the rate of formation and growth of spherulites the crystallization rate constant k_s can be calculated from Eq. (8-15). A comparison can then be made between this quantity and the corresponding value determined from measurements of the over-all rate of the development of crystallinity. Good agreement in rate constants for several systems has been obtained by this procedure.[11,38]   Table 8-2 gives the results obtained for poly-(decamethylene sebacate).   We can conclude from the above data that in homopolymers the process of spherulite formation and growth is closely related to the total development of crystallinity.

TABLE 8-2
Crystallization rate constants k for poly(decamethylene sebacate)

T, °C	k_s (dilatometric)	T, °C	k_s (microscopic)
72.6	5.51×10^{-15}	72	2.03×10^{-18}
71.6	4.30×10^{-16}	71.1	6.84×10^{-15}
70.7	4.32×10^{-13}	70.1	1.56×10^{-12}
69.7	1.00×10^{-10}	69.1	5.00×10^{-10}
68.6	2.38×10^{-8}	68.1	7.85×10^{-8}
67.7	1.28×10^{-5}	67.1	2.02×10^{-5}
66.7	1.50×10^{-4}		

SOURCE: Ref. 11a.

8-5   Temperature Coefficient of Homopolymer Crystallization

Since isothermal crystallization is adequately described by the assumption of nucleation and growth mechanisms, the unique temperature coefficient observed should be explained naturally in terms of the temperature coefficients of these two processes.   We therefore examine, in turn, the temperature coefficients of each.

If two phases of a single component are in equilibrium at T_m and if phase B has the lower free energy at temperatures below T_m, it does not necessarily follow that phase B will spontaneously form when the temperature is lowered.   For the macroscopic phase to form, it must first pass through a stage where it consists of relatively small particles. It is therefore possible for small structural entities of phase B to be in equilibrium with phase A at temperatures less than T_m, since the decrease in Gibbs free energy that would normally characterize the development of a large phase can be offset by contributions from the surfaces of the small particles.   Hence the relative contribution of the surface area and the volume of the particle determines the conditions for stability.   Nucleation may be termed the process by which a new phase is initiated within a parent phase, a nucleus being a small structural entity of the new phase.   Nuclei can be formed homogeneously by means of statistical fluctuations in the parent phase; this process can be catalyzed by the presence of appropriate heterogeneities.

Before discussing the problem of nucleation in polymeric systems, it is instructive to investigate formal nucleation theory as it has been developed for monomeric substances. The free energy of homogeneously forming a spherical nucleus of radius r, from a monomeric melt, can be expressed as

$$\Delta F = -\tfrac{4}{3}\pi r^3\,\Delta f_v + 4\pi r^2\gamma \qquad (8\text{-}31)$$

where Δf_v is the bulk free energy change per unit volume and γ is the surface free energy per unit area. This function is illustrated in Fig.

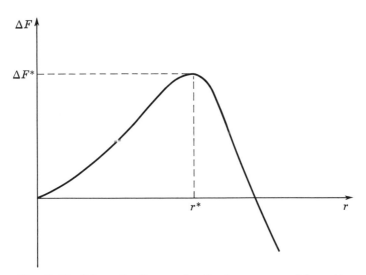

Fig. 8-13 Schematic diagram for the free energy of formation of spherically shaped nuclei.

8-13. As the radius increases, ΔF initially increases until a maximum is reached at $r = r^*$. The free energy then decreases precipitously and becomes negative. At the maximum,

$$r = r^* = \frac{2\sigma}{\Delta f_v} \qquad (8\text{-}32)$$

and

$$\Delta F = \Delta F^* = \frac{16\pi}{3}\frac{\sigma^3}{(\Delta f_v)^2} \qquad (8\text{-}33)$$

If the usual approximation that $\Delta f_v = \Delta H_v (T_m - T)/T_m$ is invoked, these equations can be expressed as

$$r^* = \frac{2\sigma T_m}{\Delta H_v\,\Delta T} \qquad (8\text{-}34)$$

and

$$\Delta F^* = \frac{16\pi}{3}\frac{\sigma^3}{(\Delta H_v)^2}\frac{T_m^2}{(\Delta T)^2} \qquad (8\text{-}35)$$

Here, $T_m - T$ is identified with ΔT and is termed the undercooling. The minimum thermodynamic conditions for stability are attained when $\Delta F = 0$ so that

$$r_s = \frac{3\sigma}{\Delta f_v} \qquad (8\text{-}36)$$

Nuclei smaller than r^* are inherently unstable and disappear from the system since ΔF increases with increasing size. However, those nuclei which exceed this critical dimension can easily grow to sizes exceeding that of minimum stability since ΔF now decreases with increasing size. ΔF^* thus represents the free energy barrier that must be surmounted for a stable new phase to be developed. The essence of classical nucleation theory, as embodied in Eq. (8-31), is to consider the free energy contribution of a structurally perfect phase of finite size and to add to it the excess surface free energy due to the presence of a surface.† This classical concept, attributable to Gibbs,[39] implies that the nucleus is sufficiently large so that its interior is homogeneous and its exterior surface is well defined. When ΔT becomes very large, the size of the nuclei approaches atomic dimensions. The above conditions no longer hold, and more sophisticated theories are required.[40,41] Despite these complications, the classical theory of nucleation has been shown to have widespread applicability.

The simplicity of the foregoing analysis is a consequence, to a large extent, of introducing spherical symmetry into the problem. More appropriate to problems involving polymer molecules is the formation of asymmetric nuclei. It is appropriate, therefore, to examine the problem of the formation of cylindrically shaped nuclei of monomeric substances. Other geometries can be treated equally well by the methods given. The results for the various geometries differ only in the values of certain constant factors. The free energy of forming a cylindrical nucleus that contains ρ molecules in cross section and ζ molecules in length is

$$\Delta F = 2\zeta \sqrt{\pi\rho}\, \sigma_u + 2\rho\sigma_e - \zeta\rho\, \Delta f_u \qquad (8\text{-}37)$$

where Δf_u is the free energy of fusion per molecule, σ_u the lateral interfacial free energy per molecule, and σ_e the interfacial free energy per molecule at the cylinder end. The contributions of strain and edge

---

† In the sense employed here, a perfect phase is one possessing the lowest free energy corresponding to the constraints imposed on the system. Hence the presence of equilibrium-type defects, as, for example, lattice vacancies, is automatically included. The possibility that non-equilibrium-type defects may exist in the macroscopic crystal or crystallite that eventually develops is not pertinent to the problem of nucleus formation.

free energies are neglected.[42]   The free energy surface represented by
Eq. (8-37) contains a saddle point.   The coordinates of the saddle
point are obtained by setting $(\partial \Delta F / \partial \zeta)_\rho$ and $(\partial \Delta F / \partial \rho)_\zeta$ equal to zero.
It is then found that

$$\rho^* = \frac{4\pi\sigma_u{}^2}{\Delta f_u{}^2} \tag{8-38}$$

$$\zeta^* = \frac{4\sigma_e}{\Delta f_u} \tag{8-39}$$

which represent the dimensions of a critical-size nucleus.   At the
saddle point,

$$\Delta F = \Delta F^* = \frac{8\pi\sigma_u{}^2\sigma_e}{\Delta f_u{}^2} \tag{8-40}$$

It is convenient to define a set of reduced variables

$$\bar{\rho} = \frac{\rho}{\rho^*}$$

$$\bar{\zeta}' = \frac{\zeta}{\zeta^*} \tag{8-41}$$

$$\Delta \bar{F} = \frac{\Delta F}{\Delta F^*}$$

Equation (8-37) can then be rewritten as

$$\Delta F = 2\bar{\zeta}\bar{\rho}^{1/2} + \bar{\rho} - 2\bar{\zeta}\bar{\rho} \tag{8-42}$$

A graphical representation of Eq. (8-42) is given in Fig. 8-14 as a
contour map for constant values of $\Delta\bar{F}$.   The free energy barrier that
must be overcome is $\Delta\bar{F} = 1$ which is found at the saddle point
$\bar{\zeta} = \bar{\rho} = 1$.   A stable nucleus is achieved when the contour line
$\Delta\bar{F} = 0$ is crossed.   The attainment of stability thus involves an
increase in dimensions over that characterizing a critical-size nucleus.
A large number of different paths originate at the saddle point, which
allows for stability to be achieved.   However, the pursuit of certain
paths is futile.   From Fig. 8-14, it is seen that $\bar{\rho}$ must exceed unity,
irrespective of the value of $\bar{\zeta}$, in order for $\Delta\bar{F}$ to become negative.
On the other hand, $\bar{\zeta}$ can remain fixed at unity and stability will still
be achieved if $\bar{\rho}$ exceeds 4.   Hence growth need not occur beyond the
critical size in the ζ direction.   A firm requirement of Eq. (8-42) is that
$\bar{\zeta}$ must exceed $\frac{1}{2}$ for a stable nucleus to be formed even if unrestricted
lateral growth is allowed.   Although forbidden paths can be deline-
ated, it is not a priori possible, for asymmetric nuclei, to prescribe a
unique path for the growth of a critical-size nucleus to a crystallite of
thermodynamic stability.

The foregoing has been restricted to homogeneous nucleation, wherein nuclei are developed solely by means of statistical fluctuations in the melt. It is well known, however, that extraneous solids, grain boundaries and cavities, can catalyze the nucleation process.[43,44,45] It has also been shown that embryonic nuclei can be retained even in cavities above the melting temperature.[46] When such inclusions are

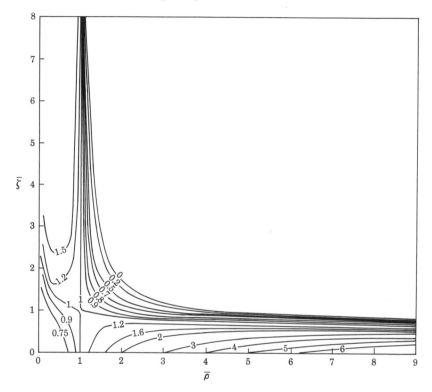

Fig. 8-14 Contour diagram for constant values of $\Delta \bar{F} = \Delta F / \Delta F^*$, according to Eq. (8-42).

present, the nucleation frequency is dependent on the thermal history of the sample until a temperature is reached where all the embryos are destroyed. Nuclei can still be formed in the cavities on cooling below the melting temperature or formed on the surfaces of foreign bodies already present. ΔF_h^*, the expression for the free energy of heterogeneously forming a nucleus in the absence of retained embryos, is qualitatively similar to that for the homogeneous case. For the examples treated, it is found that $\Delta F_h^* = f(\theta) \, \Delta F^*$, with $f(\theta)$ assuming values between zero and unity. The temperature dependence of the free energy of nucleus formation is identical in both cases but less free energy is expended in forming a nucleus heterogeneously.

Another type of nucleus of interest is that formed on an already developed crystal face, thus involving the unimolecular deposition of a collection of molecules. The free energy of forming such a nucleus, ρ units in breadth and ζ units in length, is given by

$$\Delta F = 2\sigma_e \rho + 2\zeta \sigma_u - \rho \zeta \, \Delta f_u \qquad (8\text{-}43)$$

For this two-dimensional nucleus, this critical condition is specified by

$$\rho_2^* = \frac{2\sigma_u}{\Delta f_u} \qquad (8\text{-}44)$$

$$\zeta_2^* = \frac{2\sigma_e}{\Delta f_u} \qquad (8\text{-}45)$$

$$\Delta F_2^* = \frac{4\sigma_e \sigma_u}{\Delta f_u} \qquad (8\text{-}46)$$

We note that ζ_2^* corresponds to the minimum size required for the thermodynamic stability of a crystal even if the lateral dimensions are unrestricted. Hence, if this kind of surface nucleation is involved in any real crystallization process, the longitudinal dimensions (ζ) must increase beyond critical size for a stable crystallite to form. This is in contrast to the situation for a three-dimensional nucleus where stability is achieved without the need for increasing ζ^*.

Utilizing transition-state theory, Turnbull and Fisher[47] have developed an expression for the rate of nucleation in condensed systems. The steady-state nucleation rate per unit volume and time is given, to a satisfactory approximation, by

$$\dot{N} = N_0 \exp\left(-\frac{E_D + \Delta F^*}{RT}\right) \qquad (8\text{-}47)$$

where E_D is the free energy of activation for transport across the liquid-nucleus interface and $N_0 = n_1 kT/h$; n_1 is the number of molecules per unit volume in the liquid. This rate function has certain unique properties that distinguish it from the usual expression for activated chemical processes. Recalling that ΔF^* is inversely proportional to $1/(T_m - T)^2$, it can be seen that the nucleation rate has the property of being zero at absolute zero and at T_m and attains a maximum value at some intermediate temperature. At temperatures just below T_m, the nucleation rate has a very large negative temperature coefficient, primarily as a result of the variation of the term $\exp(-\Delta F^*/RT)$. As the temperature is decreased further, the nucleation rate increases at a much slower rate, reaches a maximum value, and then decreases.

At temperatures below the maximum, the positive temperature coefficient is a result of the dominance of the transport term in Eq. (8-47). If the nucleation process is assisted by the presence of foreign bodies or by surface heterogeneities, its temperature dependence is the same as in the homogeneous case although the numerical factors differ.

The extreme sensitivity of the nucleation rate to undercooling, or to supersaturation in multicomponent systems, is well established by studies of monomeric systems.   For example, Turnbull has observed[48] that a mercury sample can be held for 1 hr at an undercooling of 43° without any detectable change in phase but it completely solidifies within a minute when the temperature is lowered 3°.   Similar effects of the relation between time and temperature have already been noted for crystallization in polymeric systems.   It is thus strongly suggestive that nucleation theory might be utilized to explain the temperature coefficients of the crystallization rate that are observed in polymers.

In developing a nucleation theory appropriate to chain molecules, the same formal procedures that have been utilized for monomeric substances have been followed.   For a given geometry the free energy contribution of the interfaces present are added to the bulk free energy required to form an equilibrium crystalline phase of finite dimensions. Not only must an over-all geometry be assumed but, for polymers of finite molecular weight, it is also necessary to specify the chain disposition within the crystallite.   Hence a model must be invoked.

It has been shown that a crystallite model wherein different crystalline sequences from the same chain are assigned to different crystallites, multiple participation by a chain in a crystallite being excluded, is unrealistic for most cases of interest.[49]   This is a consequence of the spatial requirements imposed by crystallites of large lateral dimensions.†   However, these restrictions do not apply to an array of a small number of crystalline chains; hence the model is an acceptable one for nucleus formation.   The free energy of forming a nucleus from a bundle of N polymer chains each x units long can be expressed as[24,50]

$$\Delta F = 2\zeta\sigma_u(\pi\rho)^{1/2} - \frac{\zeta\rho}{xN}\Delta f_u$$
$$+ RT\left[\frac{1}{x}\ln\left(1 - \frac{\zeta\rho}{xN}\right) + \frac{\rho}{xN}\left(\ln D + \ln\frac{x - \zeta + 1}{x}\right)\right] \quad (8\text{-}48)$$

In this expression ζ is redefined as the number of repeating units along the length of the cylindrically shaped nucleus and ρ is the number of

† This important conclusion is developed and discussed in much greater detail in Chap. 9.

units in a cross section.   The quantity D has been previously defined
[Eq. (2-2)] and σ_e represents the excess interfacial free energy per
repeating unit as it emerges from the crystal face normal to the chain
direction.   Equation (8-48) is very unwieldy for simple analytical purposes.   However, for large molecular weights, in the approximation
that $x \to \infty$ and $\zeta \ll x$, it reduces to

$$\Delta F = 2\zeta\sigma_u(\pi\rho)^{\frac{1}{2}} + 2\rho\sigma_e - \zeta\rho\,\Delta f_u \qquad (8\text{-}49)$$

which is identical in form to Eq. (8-37).   For this model, therefore,
the expression for the free energy of forming a nucleus from polymers
of infinite molecular weight is the same as for an equivalent number of
monomeric units similarly arranged.   The free energy surfaces are
identical for the two cases so that ρ^*, ζ^*, and ΔF^* are given by Eqs.
(8-38), (8-39), and (8-40).   The contribution of the chainlike character
of the molecules to the free energy of nucleus formation vanishes in
this approximation since problems concerned with the disposition of
molecular ends are neglected.

Another model for the nucleus has been proposed; it is based on
the observations that platelike single crystals are formed from dilute
solution and that bulk crystallized homopolymers possess lamellar
structure.   It has been postulated, therefore, that the nucleus is composed of perfectly and regularly folded polymer chains.[51]   No restrictions or stipulations are made as to the disposition of the chain ends.
From the previous discussion, it is immediately apparent that this
model corresponds exactly to that of a collection of monomeric units
asymmetrically arranged.   It is not surprising, therefore, that the free
energy of nucleus formation is given by Eq. (8-37) and the critical conditions by (8-38), (8-39), and (8-40).   The fold period (in the nucleus)
can be identified with ζ, while ρ is the number of crystalline sequences
in a cross section.

The theories that have been developed for the primary nucleation
act in polymers are, strictly speaking, applicable only to polymers of
infinite molecular weight.   Consequently they are formally identical
with each other and with the classical theory of monomer nucleation.
The only differences that exist are in the values to be assigned to the
interfacial free energies for the different cases.   These quantities have
evaded any fundamental theoretical calculation.   Since the free energy
surface depicted in Fig. 8-14 still applies, the restrictions on the development of stable crystallites from critical-size nuclei are also valid for
polymers.

A characteristic of all the nucleation theories is the strong dependence of the critical dimensions on the undercooling.   Equations (8-39)

and (8-40) can be expressed as

$$\zeta^* = \frac{4\sigma_e T_m}{\Delta H_u \, \Delta T} \tag{8-50}$$

$$\rho^* = \frac{4\pi\sigma_u{}^2 T_m{}^2}{(\Delta H_u)^2(\Delta T)^2} \tag{8-51}$$

and are graphically represented in Figs. 8-15 and 8-16 for different

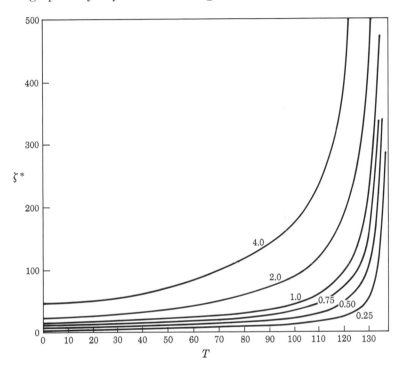

Fig. 8-15 Plot of ζ^* against T according to Eq. (8-50). Values of ratio $\sigma_e/\Delta H_u$ are indicated, and T_m was taken to be 137.5°.

values of the parameters $\sigma_e/\Delta H_u$ and $\sigma_u/\Delta H_u$. For the illustrative example, T_m was taken to be 137.5°. Although ζ^* and ρ^* depend on the ratio of the appropriate interfacial free energy to the heat of fusion, the qualitative nature of the temperature dependence is not very sensitive to the values of these quantities. At T_m the critical dimensions are infinite and decrease sharply but continuously with a lowering of the temperature. For crystallization temperatures well removed from T_m (ΔT of the order of 40 to 50° in this example), the critical dimensions become exceedingly small and are essentially insensitive to temperature variation.   It can be seriously questioned whether the classical nucleation concepts are valid for the small nuclei dimensions developed at very large undercoolings.   From Eqs. (8-41) it is evident that ΔF^* is also a strongly dependent continuous function of temperature.

The subsequent discussion will emphasize the importance of nucleation processes in the development of the crystalline phase in

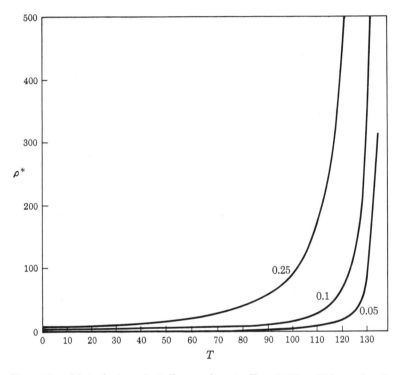

Fig. 8-16   Plot of ρ^* against T according to Eq. (8-51).   Values of ratio $\sigma_u/\Delta H_u$ are indicated, and T_m was taken to be 137.5°C.

polymers.   Its understanding, however, does not resolve or explain all the problems that are posed.   It should be realized that there is no a priori requirement that a critical nucleus, be it of a polymeric or monomeric substance, must reflect in its structure any of the features of the mature crystallite that eventually evolves.

The major conclusions of nucleation theory have received experimental verification for monomeric substances from studies of the crystallization of metals,[52,53] simple molecular liquids,[54,55] and the low molecular weight n-alkanes.[56]   The observed dependence of the nucleation rate on the undercooling is in very good agreement with the predictions of Eq. (8-47) and substantiates the applicability of classical nucleation theory to the liquid-crystal transformation.

For polymeric systems, the validity of applying nucleation theory to the crystallization process is deduced primarily from an analysis of the temperature coefficients of the rate of formation and growth of spherulitic centers as well as from the over-all rate of crystallization. Equation (8-47) can be used with n_1 being identified with the concentration of polymer segments per unit volume. From Eqs. (8-41) and (8-47) the steady rate of homogeneous nucleation becomes

$$\dot{N} = N_0 \exp\left[-\frac{E_D}{RT} - \frac{8\pi\sigma_e\sigma_u{}^2 T_m{}^2}{RT\,\Delta H_u{}^2(\Delta T)^2} \right] \qquad (8\text{-}52)$$

which can be conveniently written as

$$\dot{N} = N_0 \exp\left[-\frac{E_D}{RT} - \frac{\kappa T_m{}^2}{T(\Delta T)^2} \right] \qquad (8\text{-}53)$$

Here the polymer segments play a role analogous to that of molecules in the formation of molecular crystals of low molecular weight substances.

The results of Flory and McIntyre[11a] for the rate of formation of spherulitic centers in molten poly(decamethylene adipate) can be utilized to examine the validity of Eq. (8-52). At small values of ΔT the second term dominates the equation. In this temperature interval a plot of log $\dot{N}$ against the variable $(T_m{}^2/T)(1/\Delta T)^2$ should yield a straight line. If the measured rate is identified with $\dot{N}$, the straight line in the plot of Fig. 8-17 results. In these experiments the undercooling ranges from 11 to 16° and the nucleation rate changes by a factor of 10^4. Hence the large negative temperature coefficient observed in the vicinity of T_m has a natural explanation in terms of nucleation theory. In Fig. 8-17 the same data are also plotted against the temperature variable $(T_m/T)(1/\Delta T)$, and a straight line is again obtained. Within the uncertainty with which the equilibrium melting temperature can be specified, either functional relation is satisfied by experiment. This conclusion is true for most of if not all the different kinds of experimental data that describe the temperature coefficient of the crystallization process in polymers. The simple three-dimensional nucleus described by Eqs. (8-41) leads to the $(T_m{}^2/T)(1/\Delta T)^2$ law. The dependence on $1/\Delta T$ is theoretically possible and can result either from the formation of a monolayer nucleus [Eq. (8-46)] or from a three-dimensional nucleus with an extraordinarily large contribution from an edge or line free energy.[42,51] The initiation of spherulite formation by a monolayer nucleus would require the presence of a very

$$(T_m/T)(1/\Delta T) \times 10^2$$

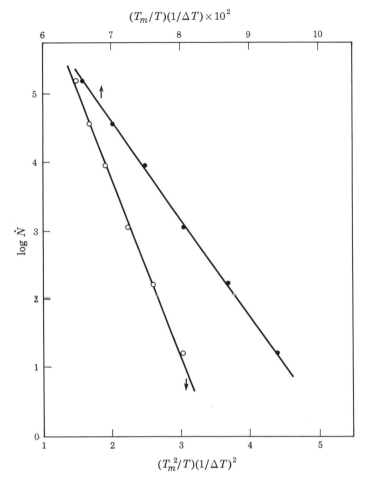

Fig. 8-17   Plot of log $\dot{N}$ against $(T_m{}^2/T)(1/\Delta T)^2$ (open circles) and against $(T_m/T)(1/\Delta T)$ (solid circles) for poly(decamethylene sebacate). [*Reprinted with permission from R. H. Doremus, B. W. Roberts, and D. Turnbull (eds.), "Growth and Perfection of Crystals," John Wiley & Sons, Inc., New York, 1958. Data from Flory and McIntyre (11a).*]

unique type of heterogeneity.   Hence it can be concluded that the primary nucleation act involves the formation of an unrestricted three-dimensional nucleus.   Moreover, unless the various excess free energies are assigned unusual values, the logarithm of the nucleation rate varies as $(1/\Delta T)^2$.

The negative temperature coefficient characteristic of the linear growth rate of spherulites in the vicinity of T_m has already been indicated. Despite the diversity of polymer types studied, essentially the same experimental results have been obtained. For polymers that can be studied over an extended temperature range, a maximum in the rate is observed similar to that occurring in the over-all rate of crystallization. From the data previously cited, the conclusion must be reached that the growth of spherulites is controlled by a secondary nucleation process. Distinction must therefore be made between the growth of a crystallite generated by a primary nucleation act and the evolution of a spherulite as new crystallites are formed.

In principle, at least, an analysis of the temperature coefficient of the rate of spherulitic growth should yield information in regard to the secondary nucleation act, thus aiding in elucidating details of the growth mechanism. For homopolymers the linear growth rates G of spherulites in the vicinity of T_m adhere to a relation of the form

$$\log G = \text{const} - \frac{C_1 T_m{}^m}{RT(T_m - T)^m} \tag{8-54}$$

where $m = 1$ or 2, and C_1 contains the interfacial and heat of fusion terms. Unfortunately, critical analysis of experimental data does not allow for discrimination between the two cases. A typical example of this dilemma is given in Fig. 8-18 for poly(decamethylene sebacate). It is evident that very good straight lines are obtained for either type of temperature dependence. This is essentially a universal result for all systems studied.[4] More precise rate measurements and an unequivocal assignment of $T_m{}^\circ$ are clearly needed in order to resolve this important question.

Since the growth of spherulites involves the formation of crystallites in the neighborhood of existing ones, it is tempting to speculate that the new crystallites are nucleated on the faces of existing ones.[18,57] This assumption leads to a growth rate that depends exponentially on $(T_m/T)(1/\Delta T)$ and presumes that nucleation involves the deposition of a unimolecular layer of polymer segments. When this nucleation process is invoked, it is mandatory that provision be made for subsequent growth in the chain direction. Otherwise, as has been previously noted, the size of the resulting crystallite will be such that it is inherently unstable. However, the possibility also exists for three-dimensional-growth nucleation. The presence of a parent crystallite could influence the orientation and organization of the adjacent amorphous regions and thus promote nucleation in its vicinity. The critical free energy necessary to promote secondary nucleation would be less than that for the homogeneous formation of primary nuclei. This postulate is in accord with the data presented in Figs. 8-17 and 8-18.

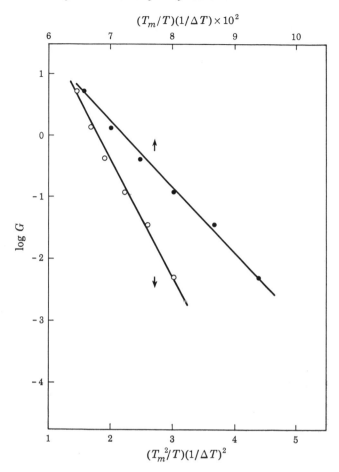

Fig. 8-18   Plot of log G against $(T_m{}^2/T)(1/\Delta T)^2$ (open circles) and against $(T_m/T)(1/\Delta T)$ (solid circles) for poly (decamethylene sebacate). [*Reprinted with permission from R. H. Doremus, B. W. Roberts, and D. Turnbull (eds.), "Growth and Perfection of Crystals," John Wiley & Sons, Inc., New York, 1958. Data from Flory and McIntyre (11a).*]

The slope of the curve representing the three-dimensional nucleation process in Fig. 8-18 is about half the value of the corresponding curve in Fig. 8-17 for the initiation process. Consideration of these typical data makes clear that nucleation is the rate-determining process in spherulitic growth. However, from present kinetic studies, no definite conclusions can be reached in regard to the detailed kind of nucleus that is involved.

The formulation of an expression for the temperature coefficient of the over-all rate of crystallization of bulk polymers requires specifying the temperature dependence of the primary and secondary nucleation processes. Primary nucleation can be represented by an equation of the form of Eq. (8-53), whereas the type of secondary nucleation (involved in spherulite growth) cannot be unequivocally specified. Hence a choice exists in the manner in which the complete expression is formulated. As an example, we shall assume that secondary nucleation is three-dimensional in character; i.e., it does not involve the deposition of polymer chains in monolayers on the surface of an existing crystallite. It will be seen that these assumptions are formally consistent with experimental results. Furthermore, we make the postulate that the critical free energy required to form a secondary nucleus is less by a factor $\bar{a}$ than that for primary nucleation.[11] Consequently

$$\ln k_s = \ln k_0 - \frac{nE_D}{RT} \frac{[1 + (n-1)\bar{a}]\kappa T_m{}^2}{T(\Delta T)^2} \qquad (8\text{-}55)$$

If the rate constant is expressed in terms of the half-time ($\tau_{1/2}$) of the process, then the expression

$$\ln \frac{1}{\tau_{1/2}} = \frac{1}{n(\ln k_0 + \ln \ln 2)} - \frac{E_D}{RT} - \frac{[1 + (n-1)\bar{a}]\kappa T_m{}^2}{n} \qquad (8\text{-}56)$$

can be alternatively employed in lieu of Eq. (8-55).† The last terms of Eq. (8-55) or (8-56) dominate at the lower undercoolings. Hence in this temperature interval a plot of $\ln k_s$ or $\ln (1/\tau_{1/2})$ against the temperature variable $T_m{}^2/T(\Delta T)^2$ should be linear.

An analysis of some typical kinetic data according to the above equations is illustrated in Fig. 8-19. If T_m is taken to be 80° for this polymer, poly(decamethylene sebacate), the plot is definitely curved. However, a good straight line results if T_m is 83°. This temperature has been shown to be a reasonable estimate of the true equilibrium melting temperature for this polymer. Hence, within the uncertainty with which the equilibrium melting temperature can be measured and assigned, adherence to Eq. (8-55) is observed. Although the absolute uncertainty in T_m is small, it is of significant concern since it is the undercooling and not the absolute temperature that is important in the present analysis.

† If a two-dimensional nucleation process is involved in secondary nucleation, a similar kind of expression is obtained with, however, a more complex temperature coefficient.[51]

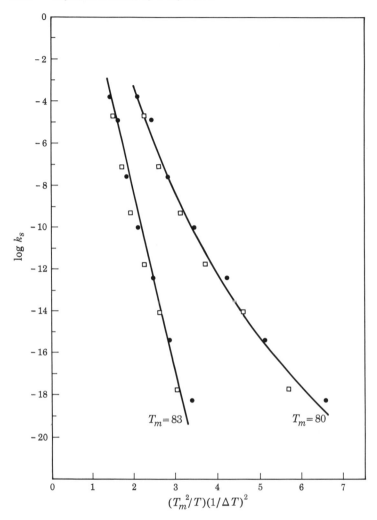

Fig. 8-19   Plot of log k_s against $(T_m{}^2/T)(1/\Delta T)^2$ for poly (decamethylene sebacate).   Circles indicate dilatometric data; squares indicate
microscopic data. [*Reprinted with permission from R. H. Doremus,
B. W. Roberts, and D. Turnbull (eds.), "Growth and Perfection of
Crystals," John Wiley & Sons, Inc., New York, 1958.   Data from Flory
and McIntyre (11a).*]

A similar analysis of the over-all rate of crystallization can be
made for unfractionated linear polyethylene (Marlex-50).[4]   As is indicated in Fig. 8-20, a straight line results when the directly observed
melting temperature of this polymer, 137.5°, is utilized in the calculation.   As indicated by the other two straight lines in the plot, the

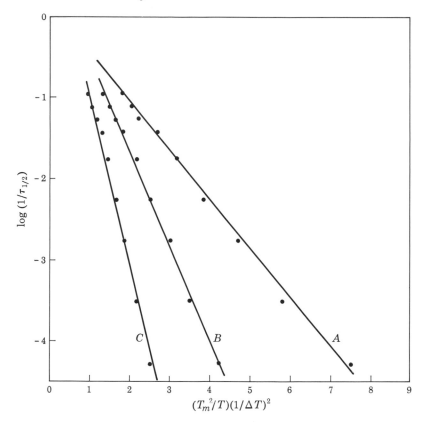

Fig. 8-20 Plot of log $(1/\tau_{1/2})$ against $(T_m{}^2 T/)(1/\Delta T)^2$ for unfractionated linear polyethylene (Marlex-50). Straight lines represent three different values assigned to $T_m{}^\circ$. Curve A: $T_m{}^\circ = 137.5^\circ$; curve B: $T_m{}^\circ = 140^\circ$; curve C: $T_m{}^\circ = 143^\circ$. [*Data from* (4).]

linear relation would still be maintained even if the true equilibrium melting temperature were several degrees higher. On the other hand, the lack of sensitivity in discriminating between the different temperature coefficients is demonstrated in Fig. 8-21. It is clear that the data can also be represented by a linear function of the temperature variable $T_m/T \, \Delta T$. Although some deviations from linearity are noted at the lower temperatures in this plot, the half-times are quite small. Hence, in terms of the experimental error involved, these deviations cannot be considered very significant.

In Fig. 8-22 the logarithm of $\tau_{1/2}$ is plotted against the crystallization temperature for three molecular weight fractions of linear poly-

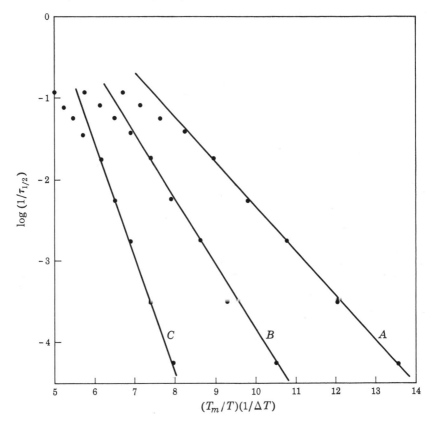

Fig. 8-21 Plot of log $(1/\tau_{1/2})$ against $(T_m/T)(1/\Delta T)$ for unfractionated linear polyethylene (Marlex-50). The same data are utilized as in Fig. 8.20, and there is the same representation for the three straight lines. [*Data from* (4).]

ethylene and a sample of the unfractionated polymer.[4,31] The curves for the two lower molecular weights are similar in shape but displaced from one another about 5° along the temperature axis. A portion of this difference can be attributed to the lower melting temperature of the smallest molecular weight fraction so that, for the same absolute temperature, it is crystallized at a lower undercooling. However, the shape of the curve for the highest molecular weight fraction is different. At the higher temperatures the larger molecular weight actually crystallizes at a slightly faster rate than the $M = 24,000$ fraction. However, at lower temperatures an inversion of this effect is observed, with the lower molecular weight sample crystallizing faster. The data for the unfractionated parent polymer (Marlex-50, $M_n = 10,000$,

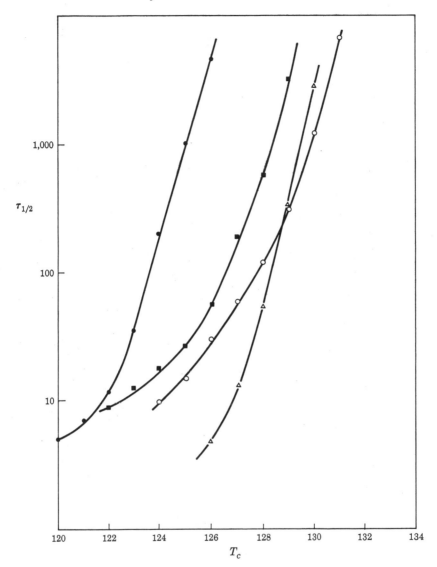

Fig. 8-22 Plot of log $(1/\tau_{1/2})$ against crystallization temperature T for fractionated and unfractionated polyethylene. Solid circles, $M = 5,300$; triangles, $M = 24,000$; open circles, $M = 364,000$; squares, unfractionated Marlex-50 (31).

$M_w = 130,000$) display its own unique characteristics. Similar experimental observations have been reported by Buckser and Tung.[26] It is clear that the influence of molecular weight and molecular weight distribution on the crystallization rate, even in the vicinity of T_m, is more complicated than would be anticipated solely from the considerations of the thermodynamic barrier in the simple nucleation theories developed.

Since ΔH_u can be determined independently of any kinetic experiments, in principle it is possible to deduce values for the quantity $\sigma_u{}^2\sigma_e$ from data of the kind illustrated in Figs. 8-17 to 8-22. The variety of simplifying assumptions inherent in Eqs. (8-55) and (8-56) has already been detailed; these hold not only for the particular example chosen but for other combinations of nucleation as well. Hence, an absolute value of the product of the interfacial energies should not be expected from an analysis of the temperature coefficient of bulk crystallization. A minimum requirement necessary to achieve this goal is the unequivocal resolution of the temperature coefficient of the secondary nucleation process. Despite these reservations, it is informative and useful to define a quantity $\bar{\sigma} = (\sigma_u{}^2\sigma_e)^{1/3}$. This quantity represents a mean interfacial free energy which is deduced by utilizing either Eq. (8-55) or (8-56) and assuming only a primary, homogeneous nucleation process, that is, $\bar{a} = 1$. This defined interfacial energy is equal to or less than the true mean value since nucleation catalysis by heterogeneities and the possibility of a decreased secondary nucleation rate have been ignored. Some representative values of $\bar{\sigma}$ are given in Table 8-3; they range from about 3 to 6 ergs/cm². Although these are slightly smaller than the corresponding quantities deduced from nucleation studies in metals and low molecular weight liquids, they do not appear unreasonable by themselves. However, this is based on the premise of an isotropy in interfacial free energies. The distinct possibility exists that, for long chain molecules, σ_e could be appreciably greater than σ_u. The former is representative of an interface wherein chains are emerging from a crystallite face. On the other hand, surfaces parallel to the chain axis should be of the more conventional type, characterized by interfacial energies similar to those for monomeric systems. An analysis of the fusion of copolymers[58] has already indicated that σ_e characteristic of a mature crystallite is about 170 ergs/cm². When utilized in conjunction with the values of $\bar{\sigma}$ that have been deduced from kinetic studies, a ridiculously low value of σ_u results.

In monomeric systems, the parameters governing nucleation have been deduced from studies of the crystallization of small isolated droplets.[45] The probability for the occurrence of an accidental heterogeneity in a liquid sample decreases directly with the sample volume or area. It is possible, therefore, to subdivide a liquid into such small droplets that most are free of heterogeneities. The heterogeneities are isolated in a relatively few droplets, so that they are ineffective in catalyzing nucleation. It follows, therefore, that the undercooling required to initiate crystallization will increase markedly as the sample size is decreased, if the promotion of nucleation by heterogeneities is an important factor.

It has been observed experimentally that small droplets can be undercooled an extraordinary amount relative to bulk liquids.[45,48,52,56]

TABLE 8-3
Representative values of $\bar{\sigma}$ as determined from Eqs. (8-55) and (8-56)
for $n = 3$ and $a = 1$

Polymer	Method[†]	T_m	Slope[‡]	$\sigma_u{}^2\sigma_e,$ ergs^3/cm^6	$\bar{\sigma}$	Ref.
Polyethylene (unfractionated)	$t_{1/2}$	137.5	−0.6	58	3.9	(4)
		140	−1.2	99	4.7	
		143	−2.0	195	5.8	
Polyethylene (fraction)						
$M = 24,000$	$t_{1/2}$	138.5	−0.86	84	4.4	(31)
		137.5	−0.69	68	4.1	
$M = 364,000$	$t_{1/2}$	138.5	−0.50	49	3.7	(31)
		139.5	−0.69	68	4.1	(31)
Natural rubber	k_s	30	−12.0	27	3	(25)
Polyethylene oxide	k_s	66	−4.4	76	4.3	(6)
Polydecamethylene adipate	k_s	79.5	−3.40	33	3.2	(6)
Polydecamethylene sebacate	k_s	83	−9.35	90	4.5	(11)
Poly(N,N'-sebacoyl piperazine)	k_s	183	−6.16	24	3.9	(6)

† Designates whether data were analyzed by means of half-time ($t_{1/2}$) or by direct determinations of k_s.

‡ Determined from plot of either log ($1/t_{1/2}$) or log k_s against $T_m/T(\Delta T)^2$.

For example, in droplet form, metals such as mercury and tin have been undercooled in amounts ranging from 40 to 120°. However, dispersions of droplets formed from n-alkanes, such as $C_{17}H_{36}$ and $C_{24}H_{50}$, have been undercooled only about 12 to 14°C.[56] By the application of classical nucleation theory of condensed systems to such data, values of $\bar{\sigma}$ appropriate to homogeneous nucleation can be deduced. For the n-alkanes this is approximately 10 ergs/cm^2.

Cormia, Price, and Turnbull[59] have prepared small droplets, 3 to 9 μ in diameter, of linear polyethylene which they dispersed in various liquid media. No appreciable crystallization was observed above 122 to 123°, and only about 5 per cent of the droplets solidified above 100°. (For bulk linear polyethylene, crystallization is extremely rapid below

120°.)   About 50 per cent of the droplets solidified in the range 85 to 87°, and solidification was complete at 84°C.   This corresponds to an undercooling of about 55°C which is substantially greater than that observed for the bulk polymers and the small droplets of the n-alkanes.[†] Again, utilizing classical theory for the rate of nucleus formation and Eq. (8-40) for the free energy of forming a nucleus, a value of $\bar{\sigma} = 56$ is obtained.   If the interfacial free energy for the n-alkanes can be identified with σ_u for polyethylene, it is concluded that, for the polymer, $\sigma_e \cong 170$ ergs/cm².   This value is in agreement with that previously deduced from copolymer studies.

The large supercoolings that can be demonstrated for the dispersed material indicate that the apparent low value of $\bar{\sigma}$ obtained in bulk systems results from the presence of nucleation catalysts.   However, the shape of the isotherms and the manner in which spherulites form in many cases require that these heterogeneities be of the kind that allow nucleation to occur sporadically in time and space.   Even in the absence of the droplet-type crystallization experiment, high values of σ_e are demanded by copolymer melting and the interpretation of low-angle X-ray diffraction (see Chap. 9).   The most important conclusion from these studies, which is consistent with a variety of observations, is that σ_e is abnormally high for polymers when compared with the interfacial free energies for other substances.   This implies the presence of a unique interface which can be expected to play an important role in influencing the morphology and crystalline texture that evolve.

Attention has been directed, heretofore, to crystallization in the vicinity of the melting temperature, where the large temperature coefficients of the rate offer advantages in theoretical analyses.   For temperatures of crystallization well removed from T_m, the second terms in Eqs. (8-55) and (8-56) no longer dominate and the complete equations must be considered.   If the simplifying assumptions are made that k_0, E_D, and K are independent of temperature, then the maximum in the crystallization rate occurs at a temperature T_1 specified by

$$E_D = \frac{R}{n}[1 + (n-1)\bar{a}]\kappa T_m{}^2 \frac{3T_1 - T_m}{(T_m - T_1)^3} \qquad (8\text{-}57)$$

[†] The tacit assumption has been made in the analysis of these experiments[59] that the droplets are composed of pure polyethylene.   Unfortunately, some of the dispersing media chosen were such that liquid-liquid phase separation, involving the polymeric species, occurs in the temperature range of interest.   Thus if any semblance to equilibrium prevailed prior to crystallization, an unknown but finite amount of nonpolymeric liquid would be present in the droplets.   Consequently, the crystallization process would not be that characteristic of pure polymer.

The maximum rate is given by

$$\ln k_s = \ln k_0 - [1 + (n-1)\bar{a}]\kappa \frac{T_m{}^2}{T} \left[\frac{3T_1 - T_m}{(T_m - T_1)^3} + \frac{1}{(T_m - T)^2} \right]$$

$$(8\text{-}58)$$

Equation (8-58) adequately describes the results for the crystallization of natural rubber over an extended temperature range. This is illustrated in Fig. 8-23 for crystallization conducted at both atmospheric

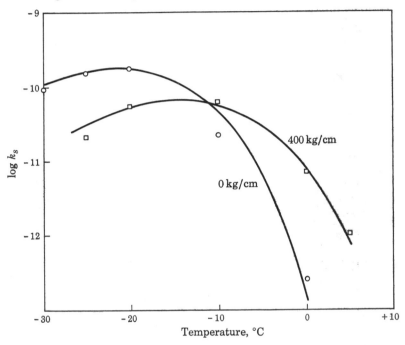

Fig. 8-23 Plot of log k_s against the temperature for natural rubber at the two indicated hydrostatic pressures. Solid lines drawn according to Eq. (8-58) (25).

pressure and at a pressure of 400 kg/cm². The adequacy of such a simple expression is surprising in terms of what is known about the relaxation and transport properties of polymer segments in bulk amorphous systems, particularly in the vicinity of the glass temperature. The crystallization temperatures range from 40 to 70° above the glass temperature; in this region a strong increase in E_D with temperature is expected and is actually observed in completely amorphous systems.[60] It is possible that, in the temperature range encompassed by the crystallization experiments, there might exist compensatory contribution from other terms that would make the constancy of E_D more apparent than real.

Of perhaps greater significance is the fact that the ratio of T_1/T_m for natural rubber is 0.83 at 1 atm and decreases only slightly as the pressure is increased. This value for the ratio appears to be typical of a variety of polymers, as is indicated in Table 8-4. If Eq. (8-57) is utilized as a guide, the implications of the results in Table 8-4 is that the quantity E_D/κ is similar for all polymers.

TABLE 8-4
Relation between temperature of maximum crystallization and melting temperature for various polymers

Polymer	T_m, °K	T_1, °K	T_1/T_m	Ref.
Natural rubber	303	249	0.83	(5), (10), (25)
Polyethylene terephthalate	537	453	0.84	(7)
Polyethylene adipate	332	271	0.815	(8)
Polyethylene succinate	379.5	303	0.78	(9)
Polypropylene	~453	348	~0.77	(29)
Polyhexamethylene adipamide	537	~423	~0.79	(29)

Although the ratios of T_1/T_m are similar for a variety of polymers, the actual rate constants and consequently the time scale of crystallization at the maximum vary by several orders of magnitude. This is illustrated in Table 8-5 for several different homopolymers.

TABLE 8-5
Half-time of crystallization at temperature of maximum crystallization rate

Polymer	T_m, °K	$\tau_{1/2}$ at T_1	Ref.
Natural rubber	303	2.5 hr	(5)
Polyethylene adipate	332	3 min	(8)
Polyethylene succinate	379.5	4 min	(9)
Polyhexamethylene adipamide	537	5 sec	(29)
Polyethylene terephthalate	537	40 sec	(7)

There is a trend in the data to indicate that the time scale of crystallization depends on the melting temperature. The higher the melting temperature of a polymer, the more rapid the crystallization at a comparable temperature. Recalling the earlier conclusion, in respect to the relation that exists between the configuration of the individual chain and the melting temperature, it would appear that a similar relation also holds for the crystallization time scale. Chains in more extended configuration, though crystallizing by the same mechanism, transform more rapidly. For the higher melting polymers, the rapid rates of crystallization could be a result of the similarity of chain configuration in the two states.

8-6 Crystallization of Chains Containing Structural Irregularities

The studies of the fusion of polymers have shown that there is a significant difference in the melting process for pure homopolymers when compared with chains containing structural irregularities such as copolymerized units, branch points, cross-links, and end groups. These units play a role analogous to that of foreign ingredients or second noncrystallizing components in influencing the melting of low molecular weight substances. The melting points are depressed and the melting range broadened. For simple liquids, it is well known that the introduction of a second component can significantly alter the nucleation rate and consequently the over-all rate and mode of crystallization from the melt.[61,62] The phase diagrams for these two-component systems govern to a large extent the character of the crystallization process in so far as it is sensitive to compositional variations of the two phases. For polymers the addition of a true second component has a similar effect. Moreover, the noncrystallizing species can also be present within the chain itself. Hence, for copolymers a change in the nature of the crystallization process is expected.

Kinetic studies of copolymers support this conclusion. For example, in Fig. 8-24 a set of kinetic isotherms for an emulsion polymerized polybutadiene is plotted. This polymer contains 80 per cent of crystallizable 1,4 trans units and its melting point is 37 ± 1. It is quite evident that in this case the character of the isotherms is markedly different from that expected for a pure homopolymer. The isotherms are no longer superposable; their shapes depend on the crystallization temperature. For crystallizations conducted at the larger undercoolings, however, the shape of the isotherms begins to resemble that for bulk polymers. This is illustrated by the dashed curve in Fig. 8-24, which is calculated from Eq. (8-28) with $n = 3$. However, as the crystallization temperature is raised, the transformation proceeds more slowly and the isotherms spread out in fanlike fashion along the time axis. Similar isotherms have been observed in kinetic studies of branched polyethylene,[63,64] cross-linked polymers,[65] and polypropylene samples of limited stereoregularity.[66] It appears to be the representa-

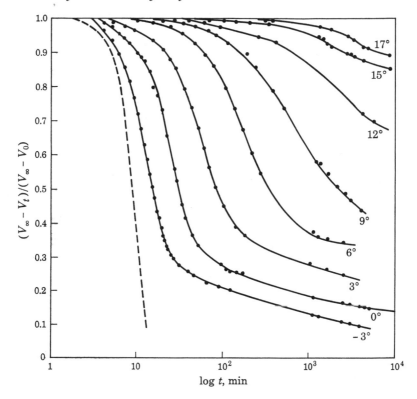

Fig. 8-24 Plot of quantity $(V_\infty - V_t)/(V_\infty - V_0)$ against log t for the crystallization of a polybutadiene containing 80 per cent 1,4 trans units. Temperature of crystallization is indicated for each isotherm. [*Reprinted with permission from R. H. Doremus, B. W. Roberts, and D. Turnbull (eds.), "Growth and Perfection of Crystals," John Wiley & Sons, Inc., New York, 1958.*]

tive crystallization pattern for polymer chains containing structural irregularities. The results obtained for branched polyethylene are plotted in Fig. 8-25. The strong similarity between these data and those of Fig. 8-24 is quite apparent.

A quantitative explanation of these results can be developed if it is assumed that, during the transformation, the structurally irregular units are rejected by the crystalline phase. This postulate is in complete harmony with the analysis of the fusion curves of many copolymers.† Hence as crystallization progresses the molten phase becomes

† It has already been indicated that there are situations in which the second component is capable of entering the crystal lattice of the major component or even to form a new crystal structure with it. These special cases are not treated in the following development.

enriched in the noncrystallizing component, and the melting temperature is continuously lowered. During an isothermal transformation
the crystallization temperature is fixed so that the actual undercooling
decreases and depends on the extent of the transformation. An
attenuation in the primary and secondary nucleation rates with crystallization can thus be anticipated. Equation (8-28), which describes
the kinetics for bulk homopolymers, was derived on the premise that
the nucleation rates are invariant with the extent of the transformation. Further generalization and revision are required, therefore, to

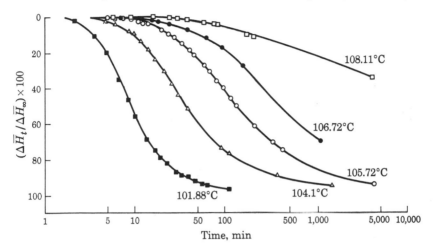

Fig. 8-25 Plot of quantity $(V_\infty - V_t)/(V_\infty - V_0)$ against log t for the crystallization of a branched polyethylene. Temperature of crystallization is indicated for
each isotherm. [*From Buchdahl, Miller, and Newman* (64).]

account for the changing composition and constitution of the melt as
the amount of crystallinity increases.

As a first step in the effort to generalize the kinetic equations, we
examine the crystallization of a copolymer composed of A and B units.
These are arranged in random sequence distribution and only the A
units are allowed to enter the crystal lattice.[67]   It is convenient to
characterize the extent of the transformation at time t by a parameter
$\theta = [1 - \lambda(t)]/[1 - \lambda(\infty)]$, where $\lambda(\infty)$ is the fraction of amorphous
material at the completion of the transformation and $\lambda(t)$ is the corresponding quantity at time t. With these conventions, the nucleation
rate at the conversion θ can be expressed as

$$\dot{N}(\theta) = N_0 X_A{}^\theta \exp\left(-\frac{E_D}{RT} - \frac{\Delta F^*_\theta}{RT}\right) \qquad (8\text{-}59)$$

where $X_A{}^\theta$ is the mole fraction of A units in the melt and ΔF^* is the free energy of forming a nucleus of critical size at θ. In terms of the composition of the completely molten phase,

$$\dot{N}(\theta) = \dot{N}(0) \frac{X_A{}^\theta}{X_A{}^\circ} \exp\left(-\frac{\Delta F^* - \Delta F_0^*}{RT}\right) \tag{8-60}$$

$\dot{N}(0)$ is the steady-state nucleation rate at $t = 0$ which corresponds to the composition $X_A{}^\circ$. For a cylindrically shaped nucleus

$$\Delta F_\theta^* = \frac{8\pi\sigma_u{}^2\sigma_e}{\Delta f(\theta)^2} \tag{8-61}$$

where $\Delta f(\theta) \cong \Delta H_u[(T_0 - T)/T_\theta]$, T_θ being defined as the equilibrium melting point of the system at conversion θ. From the expression for the melting point depression of random copolymers,

$$\frac{1}{T_\theta} - \frac{1}{T_m} = -\frac{R}{\Delta H_u} \ln \frac{X_A{}^\theta}{X_A{}^\circ} \tag{8-62}†$$

Since the ratio of $X_A{}^\theta/X_A{}^\circ$ can be expressed as

$$\frac{X_A{}^\theta}{X_A{}^\circ} = \frac{1 + (W_B/W_A)(M_A/M_B)}{1 + (W_B/W_A)(M_A/M_B)\{1 - \theta[1 - \lambda(\infty)]/W_A\}} \tag{8-63}$$

the attenuation in the primary nucleation rate is given by

$$\frac{\dot{N}(\theta)}{\dot{N}(0)} = \left(\frac{X_A{}^\theta}{X_A{}^\circ}\right) \exp\left\{+\frac{\kappa}{T}\left[\left(\frac{T_m}{T_m - T}\right)^2 - \left(\frac{T_\theta}{T_\theta - T}\right)^2\right]\right\} \tag{8-64}$$

The reduction in the nucleation rate can be readily calculated, provided κ and ΔH_u are known for the parent homopolymer. The results of such a model calculation for a random ethylene copolymer are given in Fig. 8-26, taking $M_A/M_B = 0.44$ and $1 - \lambda(\infty) = 0.75$. When small amounts of coingredient are added, a slight but perceptible attenuation of the nucleation rate is predicted at large undercoolings. This manifests itself primarily at the latter portions of the transformation. However, if the undercooling is decreased or if the concentration of B units is slightly increased, the attenuation in the nucleation rate becomes quite marked and significant. These changes

---

† The use of Eq. (8-62) involves the assumption that T_θ depends solely on the ratio of $X_A{}^\theta/X_A{}^\circ$, that is, on the chemical composition of the melt. However, it is known from theory and experiment that, for copolymers at finite levels of crystallinity, a further reduction in T_θ will result from the sequence distribution of the crystallizable units. In the present context, therefore, the value of T_θ for random copolymers is underestimated.

are now predicted to occur for even very small amounts of crystallization. These effects result from the decrease in the true undercooling $(T_\theta - T)$ with the extent of the transformation. For large nominal undercoolings, the relative change with the transformation is small, so that the nucleation rate is only slightly reduced. However, at small nominal undercoolings, the change in T_θ with conversion is such that

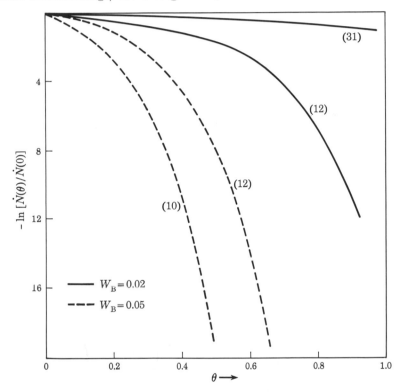

Fig. 8-26 Theoretical plot of $-\ln[\dot{N}(\theta)/\dot{N}(0)]$ against θ for two random copolymers of indicated composition. The initial undercoolings are indicated by numbers in parentheses (67).

an appreciable reduction in the nucleation rate is predicted. This effect becomes more significant as the initial concentration of the B units is increased.

It is now necessary to develop the general mathematical formulation for the kinetics of phase changes allowing for the exclusion of noncrystallizing units from the lattice. In essence, this involves accounting for the changes, with crystallization, of the primary nucleation rate and of the growth rate when evaluating the integral appearing in Eq. (8-14). To accomplish this, we express the primary nucleation rate as

$$\frac{\dot{N}(\tau)}{\dot{N}(0)} = h(\tau) \tag{8-65}$$

The linear growth rate $G(z)$ is written as $G(0)g(z)$, where $G(0)$ is the initial rate at $t = 0$. Then

$$v(t,\tau') = KG(0)^{n-1}[\phi(t,\tau')]^{n-1} \tag{8-66}$$

where

$$\phi(t,\tau) = \int_{\tau'}^{t} g(z)\,dz \tag{8-67}$$

The more general expression for the kinetics of phase changes then becomes[67]

$$\frac{1 - \lambda(t)}{1 - \lambda(\infty)} = 1 - \exp\left\{\frac{nk}{1 - \lambda(\infty)} \int_0^t h(\tau)[\phi(t,\tau)]^{n-1}\,d\tau\right\} \tag{8-68}$$

where $k = (1/n)(\rho_c/\rho_l)K\dot{N}(0)G(0)^{n-1}$. Since the growth rate is expected to be nucleation-controlled, both $h(\tau)$ and $g(\tau)$ are, in general, functions of $1 - \lambda(t)$. When $g(\tau)$ and $h(\tau)$ are equal to unity, Eq. (8-14) is regenerated.

Equation (8-68) is not susceptible to any simple analytical solution and must be evaluated by numerical methods. For purposes of calculation, it has been assumed that growth proceeds by means of a three-dimensional nucleation process. The attenuation of the nucleation rate previously described has been utilized. The results are summarized in Fig. 8-27 where $1 - \theta$ is plotted against the reduced time rate variable $(t/\tau_{1/2}^*)$, $\tau_{1/2}^*$ being the hypothetical half-time that would be observed if Eq. (8-28) were obeyed.

It is evident from Fig. 8-27 that noncrystallizing units incorporated into the chain can be expected to cause significant changes in the isotherm shape as compared with those for homopolymers. Deviations from superposable behavior are predicted; they become more pronounced with increasing concentration of the noncrystallizable coingredient and decreasing undercooling. However, at rather large values of the undercooling, isotherm shapes resembling those typical of homopolymers are approached. The dashed curves in Fig. 8-27 represent isotherms calculated from Eq. (8-28) for invariant nucleation and growth rates with $n = 4$. When compared with this simple case, the isotherms under discussion indicate a retardation of the crystallization process. A characteristic fanning out along the time axis is invariably observed. However, all the isotherms tend toward superposability in the limit of low levels of crystallinity. The changes in isotherm shape occur despite the fact that the kind of nucleation and the growth habit have not been changed as compared with the homopolymer. The differences result solely from the changing composition of the melt caused by the rejection of the chain irregularities by the crystalline phase as the transformation proceeds. The extreme sensitivity of the crystallization isotherms to small amounts of irregular structure is demonstrated in Fig. 8-27 for the case of $W_B = 0.01$. Although deviations from Eq. (8-28) are not observed until $1 - \theta = 0.6$, a small but significant departure from the homopolymer theory develops as the level of crystallinity increases further. Crystallization kinetics thus presents a method by which small amounts of noncrystallizing chain units can be detected.

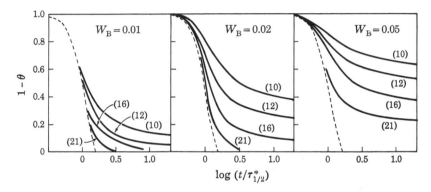

Fig. 8-27 Theoretical plot of $1 - \theta$ against $\log (t/\tau_{1/2}^*)$ for three different copolymers. Undercoolings are indicated in the parentheses. Dotted curve calculated from Eq. (8-28) with $n = 4$ (67).

The theoretical isotherms of Fig. 8-27 strongly resemble those that have been experimentally observed for polybutadiene and branched polyethylene (Figs. 8-24 and 8-25). The characteristic isotherms of the latter systems can therefore be attributed to their copolymeric character, with the attendant compositional and constitutional changes occurring in the molten phase as crystallization progresses. This explanation is consistent with the fusion properties of such systems and can be taken as further evidence for the coexistence of crystalline and amorphous regions in copolymers. The isotherms can be fitted to the simplified version of the kinetics equation (8-28) only when the value of the exponent n is assumed to vary with the amount of crystallization as dictated by the individual experimental results. This leads, however, to an erroneous interpretation of the mechanism, since it would then be concluded that the nucleation and growth processes change with increasing amounts of crystallinity. However, as has been noted, the results are naturally explicable, without invoking any changing nucleation and growth acts, when it is realized that the composition of the melt is continuously changing. Other factors that cause a change in ΔF^* as crystallization progresses could, in principle, be analyzed in a similar manner. It is not difficult to envisage that, even for pure homopolymers, the constitution of the melt will change as the level of crystallinity increases. The shape of the isotherm will be altered because of the concomitant change in ΔF^*. If the results were interpreted in terms of an invariant nucleation rate (characteristic of the initial portions of the transformation), one would inevitably conclude that the kind of nucleation or growth was changing. This of course need not be the case.

The demonstration that random copolymers and cross-linked polymers crystallize, and do so relatively easily, indicates that a nucleus comprised of regularly folded chains is not required for the initiation of crystallization of chain molecules. Such an arrangement of chain units cannot be formed from such systems. We also note that ΔF^* represents the critical free energy required to form a nucleus of A units from a melt of a given composition. If B units indiscriminately entered the crystal lattice as nonequilibrium defects, as has been postulated,[68,69] then ΔF^* would not change very much with θ. Hence the type of isotherms that are experimentally observed would not be expected.

The melting temperatures of polymers of low molecular weight depend on the chain length because of the significant concentration of chain ends that are present. In the appropriate molecular weight range, as crystallization progresses isothermally, the concentration of chain ends in the melt increases and the apparent melting temperature is lowered. The crystallization process envisaged for polymers of low molecular weight is distinctly different from that involved when molecular crystals are formed from chain molecules. In the latter case, the chain ends from the different molecules define one of the major crystallographic planes. Hence no compositional changes occur in the melt with the extent of the transformation. Isotherms should result which would adhere to the predictions of an invariant nucleation and growth rate. However, the isotherms for the low molecular weight polymer would be expected to be different. This expectation is borne out by experimental studies of low molecular weight samples of polyethylene oxide[70] and a fraction of linear polyethylene of molecular weight 5,300.[31] The isotherms possess characteristics distinctly different from those for higher molecular weight fractions, as was illustrated in Fig. 8-12. The isotherms are not as steep and do not display the characteristic acceleration in crystallization rate. Although a definite fanning out of the isotherms is observed, it is not as pronounced as in random copolymers. The isotherms maintain their property of super-posability over an appreciable portion of the transformation.

8-7 Crystallization of Polymer-diluent Mixtures

The quantitative kinetic studies of polymer-diluent mixtures have been concerned mainly with the over-all rate of development of crystallinity at temperatures in the vicinity of the melting temperature. A direct

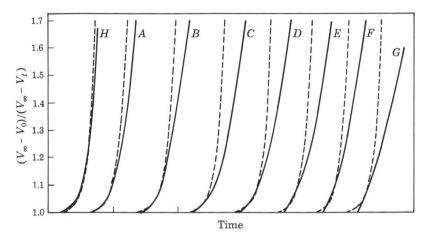

Fig. 8-28 Crystallization isotherms for polymer-diluent mixtures. Plot of $(V_\infty - V_0)/(V_\infty - V_t)$ against $\log t$ for mixtures of polyethylene oxide with diphenyl ether. Solid lines represent the composite isotherm for each mixture. Curve A, $v_1 = 0.094$; curve B, $v_1 = 0.182$; curve C, $v_1 = 0.295$; curve D, $v_1 = 0.398$; curve E, $v_1 = 0.494$; curve F, $v_1 = 0.601$; curve G, $v_1 = 0.689$; curve H, $v_1 = 0.000$. The dashed lines represent the theoretical isotherm for $n = 4$, calculated according to Eq. (8-28). The position of each isotherm relative to the abscissa is arbitrary; short vertical lines along the abscissa indicate the length of one decade (24).

microscopic study of crystal growth from very dilute polyethylene solutions has also been reported.[71] When compared with pure systems, dilution of the melt should influence the free energy of nucleus formation as well as the transport processes involved in both nucleus formation and crystallite growth.

Concentrated and moderately concentrated solutions, i.e., mixture containing up to 70 per cent diluent, display a characteristic behavior. The crystallization process is again typified by large negative tempera-

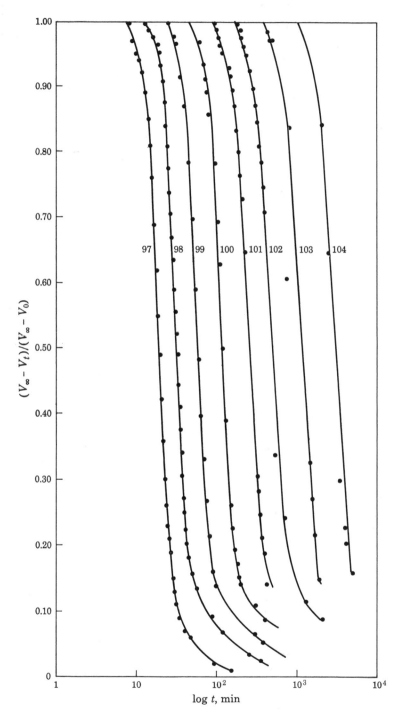

Fig. 8-29 For descriptive legend see opposite page.

274

ture coefficients. For a given composition, the shapes of the isotherms obtained at different temperatures are very similar to one another and are approximately superposable. As the polymer concentration is decreased, however, the shapes and character of the isotherms change. The crystallization process becomes more protracted with dilution. This typical behavior is illustrated in Fig. 8-28 for a series of polyethylene oxide–diphenyl ether mixtures. The solid curves represent a composite isotherm obtained from the approximate superposability of the real isotherms. Each curve is representative of a different composition. The dashed lines, inserted to serve as a comparative guide, are calculated from Eq. (8-28) with $n = 4$.

For mixtures containing small amounts of diluent, the experimental curves compare favorably with the theoretical homopolymer curve. However, as the diluent concentration is increased, serious discrepancies develop. Agreement is not obtained even at the early stages of the process so that there is no longer even superficial resemblance between the simplified homopolymer isotherm and that observed experimentally for the diluent mixtures. In order to explain the data in a formal manner, one could assign an arbitrarily decreasing value to the parameter n which would depend on the amount of the transformation and the composition. If this procedure were adopted, it would be implied that the nucleation and growth processes were changing. This has been shown to be an incorrect and misleading premise for copolymer crystallization. For polymer-diluent mixtures, as the transformation proceeds, compositional changes also occur in the melt. Hence there is a concomitant decrease in the thermodynamic driving force favoring crystallization. Moreover, the diffusion of polymer segments to the crystallite-liquid interface should begin to assume a more important role in the growth process as the system is diluted. A retardation in the rate of growth from this cause can also be expected.

Isotherms for mixtures of linear polyethylene and α-chloronaphthalene are similar to those illustrated in Fig. 8-28 over a comparable concentration range.[4,31] However, as the polymer concentration is further reduced, a significant change in isotherm shape is noted. They resemble once again the isotherms characteristic of pure homopoly-

Fig. 8-29 Plot of quantity $(V_\infty - V_t)/(V_\infty - V_0)$ against log t for the dilute-solution crystallization of linear polyethylene from α-chloronaphthalene. Weight per cent of polymer in initial mixture was 0.25 per cent. Temperatures of crystallization are indicated. [*Reprinted with permission from R. H. Doremus, B. W. Roberts, and D. Turnbull (eds.), "Growth and Perfection of Crystals," John Wiley & Sons, Inc., New York, 1958.*]

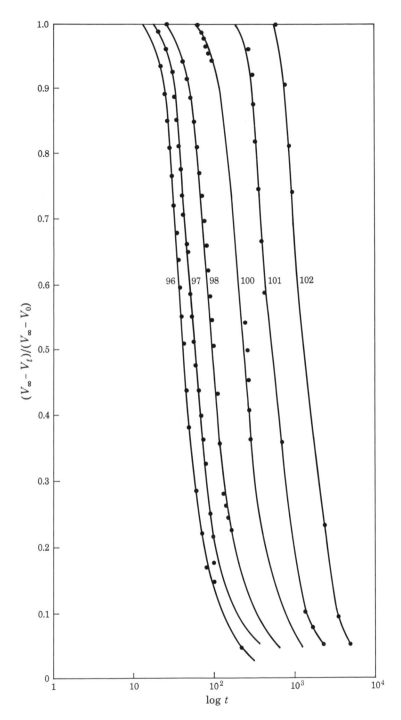

Fig. 8-30 For descriptive legend see opposite page.

276

mers. The results for very dilute solutions are shown in Figs. 8-29 and 8-30, and the similarity to homopolymer kinetics is evident. It is in this dilute concentration range that the "single crystals" of plate-like or dendritic habit are precipitated.

In summary, the isotherm shapes and consequently the kinetic processes that determine them are very dependent on concentration. Subsequent to the initial dilution, the characteristic homopolymer-type isotherm is distorted and destroyed but is regained again in very dilute systems. It would be premature, however, to conclude that the crystallization mechanisms are the same in the very concentrated and in the very dilute regions but are different in the intermediate region. A more detailed analysis is necessary before a mechanistic interpretation can be given to the data.

From the previous analysis of copolymer crystallization, it would appear pertinent to examine the effect of compositional changes on the free energy required for nucleus formation. The free energy of form-ing a nucleus from a polymer-diluent mixture can be expressed as[24]

$$\Delta F(v_2) = \zeta\rho\,\Delta f_u' - 2\rho\sigma_e - 2\zeta\sigma_u(\pi\rho)^{1/2} + RT\ln v_2{}^\rho \qquad (8\text{-}69)$$

The last term in Eq. (8-69) is an entropic contribution to the free energy which results from the probability of selecting the ρ crystalline polymer sequences from the two-component mixture. The other terms are similar to those for homopolymer nucleation, and $\Delta f_u'$ is the bulk free energy of fusion at the specified composition. For concentrated and moderately concentrated solutions, where the polymer segment concentration is uniform throughout the solution, v_2 can be identified with the actual volume fraction of polymer that is present. However, in the dilute range the solution can be thought of as consisting of two distinguishable regions, one devoid of polymer segments and the other containing a low concentration of segments. The concentration within the domain of the molecule, which is the one that must be used with Eq. (8-69), cannot be identified with the composition of the solution as a whole.

The analysis of the above free energy surface yields for the coordi-

Fig. 8-30 Plot of quantity $(V_\infty - V_t)/(V_\infty - V_0)$ against log t for the dilute-solution crystallization of linear polyethylene from α-chloro-naphthalene. Weight per cent of polymer in initial mixture was 0.05 per cent. Temperatures of crystallization are indicated. [*Reprinted with permission from R. H. Doremus, B. W. Roberts, and D. Turnbull (eds.), "Growth and Perfection of Crystals," John Wiley & Sons, Inc., New York,* 1958.]

nates of the saddle point

$$\zeta^* = \frac{4\sigma_e - 2RT \ln v_2}{\Delta f_u'(v_2)} \qquad (8\text{-}70)$$

and

$$\rho^* = \frac{4\pi\sigma_u{}^2}{[\Delta f_u'(v_2)]^2} \qquad (8\text{-}71)$$

The free energy required to form a nucleus of minimum stability is then given by

$$\Delta F^*(v_2) = \frac{8\pi\sigma_u{}^2\sigma_e - 4\pi RT\sigma_u{}^2 \ln v_2}{[\Delta f_u'(v_2)]^2} \qquad (8\text{-}72)$$

$\Delta f_u'$ represents the free energy of fusion plus that of dilution per polymer unit. It can be approximated by[24] $\Delta f_u' \cong \Delta H_u(T_m - T)/T_m$, where T_m is the melting point of the polymer-diluent mixture of the given composition. Accordingly,

$$\Delta F^*(v_2) = \frac{8\pi\sigma_u{}^2\sigma_e - 4\pi RT\sigma_u{}^2 \ln v_2}{(\Delta H_u \, \Delta T)^2} \, T_m{}^2 \qquad (8\text{-}73)$$

and the steady-state nucleation rate can be expressed as

$$\dot{N}(v_2) = N_0 v_2 \exp\left[-\frac{E_D(v_2) - \Delta F^*(v_2)}{RT}\right] \qquad (8\text{-}74)$$

Since decreasing the polymer concentration influences the preexponential factor, the activation energy for transport and ΔF^*, the steady-state nucleation rate, should be significantly altered by dilution. Of particular interest are the changes that occur in ΔF^*. When the effective polymer concentration is of the order of a few per cent (which is typical of a nominally dilute solution), then ΔF^* becomes excessively high as a consequence of the $\ln v_2$ term in Eq. (8-72). Nucleation therefore does not proceed at a measurable rate at an undercooling comparable to more concentrated systems. It then becomes necessary to increase severely the undercooling in order to decrease the number of sequences involved in the nucleation act. This is true even if the nucleation process involves only a single molecule, since the polymer segments have to be selected from within the domain of an effective average concentration v_2 and transferred to the pure crystalline phase.

Dilution of the melt is accomplished either by the direct addition of a second monomeric component or as crystallization of the polymeric species proceeds from the mixture. For concentrated systems, as crystallization progresses, the temperature of equilibrium between the crystalline and liquid phases decreases according to the relation previously cited [Eq. (3-9)]. The undercooling is lowered, and an attenuation in the nucleation rate occurs. Hence a retardation in the over-all rate of crystallization results. These conclusions are in qualitative accord with the isotherms depicted in Fig. 8-28. A detailed quantitative comparison must await the calculation of theoretical isotherms for polymer-diluent mixtures with an appropriately varying nucleation rate.

At higher dilutions, when v_2 is of the order of 0.10 or less, the change in undercooling with crystallization at fixed temperature is usually very small. Since the melting point is not very sensitive to polymer concentration in this range, the depression is of the order of 1° or less. This constancy of undercooling is consistent with the isotherm shape observed in this concentration range. The isotherms approach those calculated for a system that possesses an invariant nucleation and growth rate. It is implied, however, that the logarithm term in Eq. (8-72) does not vary significantly with concentration. If actual concentrations were employed, this would, of course, not be true for dilute solutions. The results thus emphasize the importance of utilizing effective polymer concentration in dilute solutions.

The similarity between the isotherms for a bulk homopolymer and those for a very dilute solution ($v_2 \leq 0.01$) deserves closer scrutiny. The theoretical explanation of the former is predicated on the assumption that the impingement of growing centers results in the cessation of growth. This leads to the observation of sigmoidal-shaped isotherms. In very dilute solutions, the impingement of growing centers obviously cannot be of serious consequence. It is thus apparent that similarly shaped isotherms can be obtained from two different sets of premises. In dilute solutions it can be assumed that growth proceeds from isolated, widely spaced centers that do not impinge upon one another. The cessation of growth then results from the depletion of the crystallizing component in the supernatant fluid. These postulates are similar to those that have been invoked to explain the precipitation kinetics of monomeric substances from supersaturated dilute solutions.[45]

For a dilute system of particles, growth is governed either by processes which occur at the particle-solution interface or by the diffusion of the solute component in the supernatant phase. The diffusional flux is greatest when the particles are smallest. Under these circumstances, the growth rate should be controlled by interfacial processes. As the particle size increases, the attendant decrease in the flux of material at the surface tends to increase the influence of diffusional processes. A detailed review of the mathematical analysis of the kinetics of precipitation has been given by Turnbull.[45] Although the concurrent processes of interface and diffusion control can be given a mathematical treatment, it suffices for present purposes to consider the two as independent events.

Besides the concern with the growth mechanism, it is also necessary to specify the nature of the initiation or nucleation act. Either new particles can form sporadically in time, or they can all develop simultaneously at the start of the precipitation. When it is assumed that nuclei are formed sporadically in time, the integral equation that results cannot be solved analytically. If, however, it is assumed that a fixed number n of negligibly small particles are initiated at time $t = 0$ and this number remains invariant with time, it is readily shown that† for diffusion-controlled growth[45]

$$\frac{1}{2} \ln \left[\frac{X^{2/3} + X^{1/3} + 1}{(X^{1/3} - 1)^2} \right] + \sqrt{3} \tan^{-1} \frac{-X^{1/3} \sqrt{3}}{2 + X^{1/3}} = k_d n^{2/3} Dt = K_d \tau$$

$$(8\text{-}75)$$

Here X is the fraction transformed, D is the diffusion coefficient, and k_d is a constant. For interface control[45]

$$\frac{1}{2} \ln \left[\frac{X^{2/3} + X^{1/3} + 1}{(X^{1/2} - 1)^2} \right] + \sqrt{3} \tan^{-1} \frac{X^{1/3} \sqrt{3}}{2 + X^{1/3}} = k_i n^{1/3} ut = \kappa_i t \quad (8\text{-}76)$$

where k_i is another constant and u is the reaction rate constant for the interfacial process.

The dependence of the fraction untransformed $1 - X$ on the reduced time variable κt is plotted in Fig. 8-31 in accordance with Eqs. (8-75) and (8-76). The isotherms for diffusion and interface control are quite similar, and their sigmoidal nature is apparent. They resemble the isotherms for a pure bulk polymer. This is indicated by the dashed line in Fig. 8-31 which is calculated from Eq. (8-28) for $n = 3$. The dotted line represents a typical experimental isotherm for crystallization from a very dilute solution. With the exception of the very initial and final portions of the isotherms, exceptionally good agreement is obtained between experiment and the curve calculated from Eq. (8-76) for interface-controlled growth. The discrepancies can be attributed to an oversimplification of the analysis. It would appear that a fixed number of particles are not formed at $t = 0$. Moreover, toward the completion of the process, when the

---

† This assumption, as opposed to the sporadic formation with time of new centers, is made because of mathematical simplification. The similar problem encountered in the crystallization of undiluted polymers is circumvented by the introduction of phantom nuclei to account for the impingement of growing centers.

particles become larger, diffusional processes become more important. This is manifested by the experimentally observed retardation in rate. It can thus be concluded, without needing to concern oneself with the morphology or crystal habit that is produced, that the crystallization of polymers from dilute solutions obeys the same kinetic laws as monomeric substances under comparable conditions.

For small values of X, Eqs. (8-75) and (8-76) reduce to

$$1 - X = \exp{(-bt^n)} \qquad (8\text{-}77)$$

with $n = \frac{3}{2}$ for diffusion control and $n = 3$ for interface control.

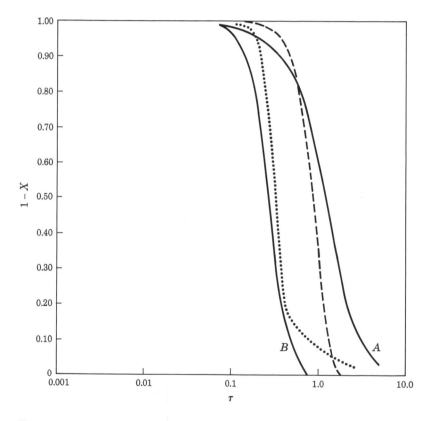

Fig. 8-31 Plot of fraction untransformed $1 - X$ against log of reduced time variable for dilute-solution crystallization. Curves A and B, theoretical isotherms for diffusion and interface control as calculated from Eqs. (8-75) and (8-76), respectively. Dashed curve, theoretical isotherm for pure homopolymer crystallization as calculated from Eq. (8-28) for $n = 3$. Dotted curve, typical experimental isotherm for crystallization from dilute solution.

This is of the same form as Eq. (8-16) derived for the crystallizate kinetics of pure bulk homopolymers.

The magnitude of the rate constant for crystallization and its temperature coefficient show an interesting behavior as the polymer composition is varied. It is convenient to define the rate by the time $\tau_{0.9}$ at which 10 per cent of the relative amount of the transformation occurs. This allows for a rational comparison of different compositions and avoids the complication of a changing undercooling as the crystallization progresses isothermally. Irrespective of the nominal concentration, the initial portions of the isotherms adhere to the simplified mathematical formulation for the kinetics of phase changes as embodied in Eq. (8-28). Hence, in analyzing the data, we utilize the conventional formulation of the rate constant k as a guide. Thus

$$k_s(v_2) = k_0(v_2) \exp\left[-\frac{nE_D(v_2)}{RT} - \frac{1 + (n-1)\bar{a}}{RT} \Delta F^*(v_2) \right] \quad (8\text{-}78)$$

so that

$$\log \frac{1}{\tau_{0.9}} = \frac{1}{n} \left[\log k_0(v_2) + \log \log \frac{1}{0.9} \right]$$
$$- \frac{E_D(v_2)}{RT} - \frac{[1 + (n-1)\bar{a}] \Delta F^*(v_2)}{2.3RT} \quad (8\text{-}79)$$

with $\Delta F^*(v_2)$ being given by Eq. (8-73). It should be recalled that v_2 does not necessarily represent the nominal concentration but rather the polymer concentration within the swollen coil. In concentrated systems the two quantities tend to be identical.

Equation (8-79) suggests that at low undercoolings a plot of $\log (1/\tau_{0.9})$ against the temperature variable $T_m^2/T(\Delta T)^2$ should be linear when the equilibrium melting temperature is employed. For dilute systems this requires that the melting or solubility temperature (at the appropriate concentration) be determined for a bulk crystallized and well-annealed sample.[72] Rate data encompassing a wide range of polymer concentrations are plotted in Fig. 8-32 according to this suggestion. There results a family of straight lines whose slopes gradually increase with decreasing polymer concentration until a polymer concentration of 1 per cent is reached. With a further reduction in polymer concentration, the slope remains constant despite the hundredfold additional decrease in polymer concentration. From these data the conclusion can be drawn that the crystallization process is still nucleation-controlled even in the very dilute range. This conclusion is in accord with the microscopic observation of crystal growth in this concentration range.[70]

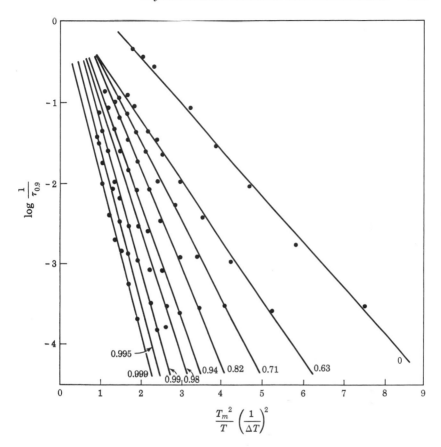

Fig. 8-32 Plot of log $(1/\tau_{0.9})$ against the temperature variable $T_m{}^2/T(\Delta T)^2$ for unfractionated linear polyethylene–α-chloronaphthalene mixtures. Initial volume fraction of polymer in melt v_1 is indicated (31).

According to Eq. (8-79), the slopes of the straight lines can be expressed as

$$S = \frac{1 + (n-1)\bar{a}}{n}\, \frac{8\pi\sigma_u{}^2\sigma_e}{2.3R\,\Delta H_u{}^2} - \frac{4\pi\sigma_u{}^2 T \log v_2}{\Delta H_u{}^2} \qquad (8\text{-}80)$$

For polyethylene, in the temperature interval of interest, the ratio of the slope at a concentration v_2 to that of pure polymer $(v_2 = 1)$ is given by

$$\frac{\text{slope }(v_2)}{\text{slope }(v_2 = 1)} = K = 1 - \frac{2.3RT \log v_2}{2\Delta H_u(\sigma_e/\Delta H_u)} \cong 1 - \frac{0.9 \log v_2}{\sigma_e/\Delta H_u} \qquad (8\text{-}81)$$

Plots of the slope S and relative slope K obtained from the straight lines of Fig. 8-32 are plotted as a function of $-\log v_2$ in Fig. 8-33. Linear relations are obtained in both plots for solutions as dilute as $v_2 = 0.03$. With further dilution, the linearity is lost and higher effective concentrations are required in order to maintain the straight-line relations. However, the formulation of (8-81) would still be valid if

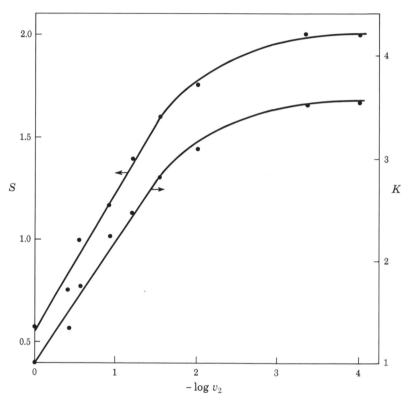

Fig. 8-33   Plot of slope S and relative slope K from straight lines of Fig. 8-32, against $-\log v_2$.

the effective polymer concentration were of the order of $v_2 = 0.02$ to 0.03, although the actual concentration is many times less. This volume fraction is a reasonable value for the concentration of polymer segments within the domain of a swollen polymer coil in a dilute solution. The constancy in slope in going from a 1 per cent to a 0.01 per cent solution lends credence to this conclusion.

From the linear portion of Fig. 8-33 estimates can be made of the quantities $\sigma_u/\Delta H_u$ and $\sigma_e/\Delta H_u$. Depending on the values assigned to

n and $\bar{a}$, $\sigma_u/\Delta H_u$ ranges from 1 to 2×10^{-2} and $\sigma_e/\Delta H_u = 0.75$. When considered by themselves, these values of the interfacial energy are quite low. However, the low values of σ_e and σ_u that are deduced solely from an analysis of the effect of dilution are no different from those from an analysis of the temperature coefficient of the crystallization of the undiluted bulk polymer. In fact, the product $\sigma_e\sigma_u{}^2$ deduced from Fig. 8-33 is in good quantitative agreement with that obtained from the slope of curve A in Fig. 8-32. For the purpose of treating the effect of dilution, where the question of the absolute values of the interfacial energies does not enter, the formulation of Eq. (8-78) is adequate. From pure polymer to about a 3 per cent solution, the change in the temperature coefficient (the slopes of the lines in Fig. 8-32) can be attributed to the $\ln v_2$ term in ΔF^*, with v_2 being identified with the nominal concentration. At higher dilutions, an effective polymer concentration of about 3 per cent needs to be employed.

The effect of total composition on the time scale of the crystallization process can also be discerned from Fig. 8-32. For the same value of the temperature variable $(T_m{}^2/T)(1/\Delta T)^2$ the rate constants decrease with dilution. Significantly greater undercoolings are required for the crystallization to proceed at a measurable rate in the more dilute systems. In fact, the data indicate that crystallization at low undercoolings is not practicable for dilute systems. The undercooling must be continuously increased with dilution in order to achieve a constant rate. This is true even for very dilute solutions. These observations are not consistent with the concept that, in dilute solution, nucleation occurs intramolecularly among single isolated molecules. However, for a sufficiently dilute solution, the point must eventually be reached where intramolecular nucleation must by necessity occur.

Although a consistent analysis can be obtained of the influence of diluent on the kinetics, in the range of low undercoolings, only the role of nucleation has been considered. The effect of dilution on the transport and relaxation processes has been ignored. Changes in these mechanisms cannot be completely disregarded in a more complete analysis.

Another kinetic process that occurs in very dilute solution involves the regeneration of the ordered helical structure from the random coil form of polypeptides and nucleic acids. The transformation of the coil to the helix (or the reverse process) may be presumed to proceed by a succession of steps, each of which involves the conversion of one unit at the junction between helical and random coil sequences. Steps in the opposite direction compete. Hence the over-all process is similar to a one-dimensional diffusion or a one-dimensional biased random

walk, the bias depending on the relative probability of each of the
competing steps.   Besides propagating the helical form as described
above, the initiation of a helical sequence is also required.   This may
occur at an end of an initially completely randomly coiled chain or,
with greater difficulty, start at a point in the propagating chain that is
not yet transformed.

The conversion of a single isolated chain from coil to helix may be
schematically represented as[73]

$$C_n \underset{k_b}{\overset{k_i}{\rightleftharpoons}} C_{n-1}H_1 \underset{k_b}{\overset{k_f}{\rightleftharpoons}} C_{n-2}H_2 \underset{k_b}{\overset{k_f}{\rightleftharpoons}} \cdot \cdot \cdot C_1H_{n-1} \underset{k_b}{\overset{k_f}{\rightleftharpoons}} H_n$$

where $C_{n-i}H_i$ denotes a species comprised of a sequence of $n - i$ coiled
units adjoining a sequence of i helical units.   The rate constant for
initiation is k_i; that for propagation of the helix is k_f, and the rate
constant for the reverse step is k_b.   The rate of the reversion can be
equated to the rate of initiation multiplied by the expectation that the
incipient sequence generated will ultimately encompass the whole
molecule.

By utilizing either steady-state kinetics[74] or the gambler's ruin
problem of probability theory[73] the rate of helix formation is given by

$$\frac{dC_H}{dt} = k_i C_c \left(1 - \frac{k_b}{k_f} \right) \tag{8-82}$$

where C_H and C_c are the concentration of units that are helical and
coiled, respectively.   The ratio k_b/k_f can be equaled to K^{-n}, where
K is the equilibrium constant for a helix $\rightleftharpoons$ random coil.   In the
vicinity of the melting or transition temperature for this process,

$$\frac{dc_H}{dt} = k_i C_c \frac{\Delta H_u}{RT^2} (-\Delta T) \tag{8-83}$$

when ΔH_u is the enthalpy change per unit in going from helix to coil
and ΔT is the supercooling at which the process is conducted.

If we assume that the random coil is the stable form at high temperatures, then as the temperature is decreased below T_m the quantity
$(\Delta H_u/RT^2)(-\Delta T)$ must increase.   However, if k_i is assumed to be
analogous to the rate constant for a chemical reaction, it will decrease
with a decrease in temperature.   The former quantity will dominate
at small degrees of supercooling, so that in the vicinity of the transition temperature the temperature coefficient of the rate of helix formation should be negative.   For greater degrees of supercooling the
exponential dependence of k_i on temperature should dominate and the

temperature coefficient should become positive. The rate should therefore pass through a maximum as the temperature is lowered. A similarity can be immediately noted between the temperature dependence for the unidimensional development of a helix and that for the three-dimensional crystallization of polymers. The resemblance is qualitative, however, as a comparison of the appropriate equations will indicate.

The theory for a single-stranded helix can be extended to problems involving helix formation from two or more chain molecules. The kinetic order of the process will be altered as we can expect the initiation rate to depend on the number of molecules that are involved. Flory and Weaver[75] have studied the rate of reversion of transformed collagen. They observed a marked negative temperature coefficient which, however, depended more strongly on temperature than the predictions of Eq. (8-83). The process was found to be first-order, contrary to expectations based on the three-chain compound helix model for collagen. In order to circumvent this difficulty, it was necessary to postulate that the rate-determining step involved the formation of an unstable intermediate which could be a single-strand helix.

Ross and Sturtevant[76] have studied the rate at which polyriboadenylic acid (poly A) and polyribouridylic acid (poly U) combined to form an ordered 1:1 complex poly(A + U). X-ray diffraction analysis has shown that fibers of this complex possess a two-stranded helical structure similar to that of naturally occurring deoxyribonucleic acid (DNA). The kinetics observed is complex. Initially, second-order kinetics is observed which deviates to first-order behavior as the transformation proceeds. This is consistent with the view that the initiation of the poly(A + U) complex involves the formation of a few hydrogen bonded base pairs followed by the growth of ordered helical regions. When equimolar solutions of the individual polymers are combined, the initial rate is directly proportional to the square of the monomer concentration.

The rate of formation of the poly(A + U) complex, as measured by the apparent second-order rate constant, is illustrated in Fig. 8-34 as a function of the temperature at which the reactants were mixed. As the temperature is lowered below the transition temperature, the rate increases, passes through a well-defined maximum, and then decreases as the temperature is decreased further. The temperature at which the rate is a maximum depends on the transition temperature, increasing with an increase in the transition temperature. The existence of a maximum in the rate-temperature plot is in accord with the theory outlined.

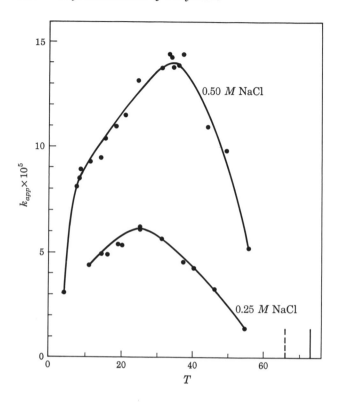

Fig. 8-34   Plot of the apparent second-order rate constant, k_{app}, as a function of temperature for the formation of the poly(A + U) complex.   The two vertical lines rising from the abscissa denote the transition temperatures for the two salt concentrations indicated.   Polymer phosphate concentration 3.6×10^{-5} M.   [*Ross and Sturtevant* (76).]

REFERENCES

1. Mandelkern, L., A. S. Posner, A. F. Diori, and D. E. Roberts: *J. Appl. Phys.*, **32**: 1509 (1961).
2. Bunn, C. W.: *Trans. Faraday Soc.*, **35**: 483 (1939).
3. Bekkedahl, N.: *J. Res. Natl. Bur. Std.*, **13**: 411 (1934).
4. Mandelkern, L.: in R. H. Doremus, B. W. Roberts, and D. Turnbull (eds.), "Growth and Perfection of Crystals," John Wiley & Sons, Inc., New York, 1958.
5. Wood, L. A., and N. Bekkedahl: *J. Appl. Phys.*, **17**: 362 (1946).
6. Mandelkern, L., F. A. Quinn, Jr., and P. J. Flory: *J. Appl. Phys.*, **25**: 830 (1954).
7. Cobbs, W. H., Jr., and R. L. Burton: *J. Polymer Sci.*, **10**: 275 (1953).
8*a*. Takayanagi, M.: *Mem. Fac. Eng.*, *Kyushu Univ.*, **16**(3): 111 (1957).
8*b*. Takayanagi, M., and T. Yamashito: *J. Polymer Sci.*, **22**: 552 (1956).

9. Ueberreiter, K., G. Kanig, and A. S. Brenner: *J. Polymer Sci.*, **16**: 53 (1955).
10. Gent, A. N.: *J. Polymer Sci.*, **18**: 321 (1955).
11a. Flory, P. J., and A. D. McIntyre: *J. Polymer Sci.*, **18**: 592 (1955).
11b. McIntyre, A. D.: Ph.D. Thesis, Cornell University, Ithaca, N.Y., 1956.
12. Richards, R. B., and S. W. Hawkins: *J. Polymer Sci.*, **4**: 515 (1949).
13. Sharples, A.: *Polymer*, **3**: 250 (1962).
14. Allen, P. W.: *Trans. Faraday Soc.*, **48**: 1 (1952).
15. Morgan, L. B.: *Phil. Trans. Roy. Soc. London, Ser. A*, **247**: 13, 23 (1954).
16. Morgan, L. B., F. D. Hartley, and F. W. Lord: *Ric. Sci. Suppl. A*, **25**: 577 (1955).
17. Price, F. P.: *J. Am. Chem. Soc.*, **74**: 311 (1952).
18. Burnet, B. B., and W. F. McDevit: *J. Appl. Phys.*, **28**: 1101 (1957).
19. Von Goler, F., and G. Sachs: *Z. Physik*, **77**: 281 (1932).
20. Johnson, W. A., and R. F. Mehl: *Trans. Am. Inst. Mining Met. Engrs.*, **135**: 416 (1939).
21. Avrami, M.: *J. Chem. Phys.*, **7**: 1103 (1939); **8**: 212 (1940); **9**: 177 (1941).
22. Evans, R. U.: *Trans. Faraday Soc.*, **41**: 365 (1945).
23. Burke, J. E., and D. Turnbull: "Progress in Metal Physics," vol. 3, p. 220, Interscience Publishers, Inc., New York, 1952.
24. Mandelkern, L.: *J. Appl. Phys.*, **26**: 443 (1955).
25. Martin, G. M., and L. Mandelkern: *J. Appl. Phys.*, **34**: 2312 (1963).
26. Buckser, S., and L. H. Tung: *J. Phys. Chem.*, **63**: 763 (1958).
27. Griffith, J. H., and B. G. Ranby: *J. Polymer Sci.*, **38**: 107 (1959).
28. Kahle, B.: *Z. Elektrochem.*, **61**: 1318 (1957).
29. Magill, J. H.: *Polymer*, **2**: 221 (1961); **3**: 35 (1962).
30. Hoffman, J. D., J. J. Weeks, and W. M. Murphey: *J. Res. Natl. Bur. Std., A*, **63**: 67 (1959).
31. Mandelkern, L., and F. A. Quinn, Jr.: Abstracts, 134th Meeting of the American Chemical Society, Chicago, Ill., September, 1958; unpublished results, 1962.
31a. Banks, W., M. Gordon, R. J. Roe, and A. Sharples: *Polymer*, **4**: 61 (1963).
32. Matsuoka, S., and C. J. Aloisio: *Bull. Am. Phys. Soc., Ser.* II, **8**(3) (1963).
33. Chiang, R., and P. J. Flory: *J. Am. Chem. Soc.*, **83**: 2857 (1961).
34. Tung, L. H., and S. Buckser: *J. Phys. Chem.*, **62**: 1530 (1958).
35. Kojima, H., and K. Yamaguchi: *Chem. High Polymers (Tokyo)*, **19**: 715 (1962).
36. Flory, P. J.: *Nature*, **124**: 53 (1956).
37. Gornick, F., and J. L. Jackson: *J. Chem. Phys.*, **38**: 1150 (1963).
38. Falkai, B. V., and H. A. Stuart: *Kolloid-Z.*, **162**: 138 (1959).
39. Gibbs, J. W.: "Collected Works," vol. 1, pp. 55–372, Longmans, Green & Co., Inc., New York, 1931.
40. Tolman, R. C.: *J. Chem. Phys.*, **16**: 758 (1948); **17**: 118, 333 (1949).
41. Buff, F. P., and J. G. Kirkwood: *J. Chem. Phys.*, **18**: 991 (1950).
42. Bradley, R. S.: *Quart. Rev. (London)*, **5**: 315 (1951).
43. Turnbull, D.: *J. Chem. Phys.*, **18**: 198 (1950).
44. Hollomon, J. H.: "Thermodynamics in Metallurgy," pp. 161–177, American Society for Metals, Cleveland, 1950.

45. Turnbull, D.: "Solid State Physics," vol. 3, Academic Press Inc., New York, 1956.
46. Turnbull, D.: *J. Chem. Phys.*, **20**: 411 (1952).
47. Turnbull, D., and J. C. Fisher: *J. Chem. Phys.*, **17**: 71 (1949).
48. Turnbull, D.: Principles of Solidification, in "Thermodynamics in Physical Metallurgy," American Society for Metals, Cleveland, 1949.
49. Flory, P. J.: *J. Am. Chem. Soc.*, **84**: 2857 (1962).
50. Flory, P. J.: *J. Chem. Phys.*, **17**: 223 (1949).
51. Hoffman, J. D., and J. I. Lauritzen: *J. Res. Natl. Bur. Std.*, *A*, **64**: 73 (1960); **65**: 297 (1961).
52. Turnbull, D.: *J. Appl. Phys.*, **20**: 817 (1949); **21**: 1022 (1950).
53. Turnbull, D., and R. E. Cech: *J. Appl. Phys.*, **21**: 804 (1950).
54. Thomas, D. G., and L. A. K. Stavely: *J. Chem. Soc.*, p. 4569, 1952.
55. De Nordwall, H. S., and L. A. K. Stavely: *J. Chem. Soc.*, p. 224 1954.
56. Turnbull, D., and R. L. Cormia: *J. Chem. Phys.*, **34**: 820 (1961).
57. Price, F. P.: *Ann. N.Y. Acad. Sci.*, **83**: 20 (1959).
58. Richardson, M. J., P. J. Flory, and J. B. Jackson: *Polymer*, **4**: 221 (1963).
59. Cormia, R. L., F. P. Price, and D. Turnbull: *J. Chem. Phys.*, **37**: 1333 (1962).
60. Williams, M. L., R. F. Landel, and J. D. Ferry: *J. Am. Chem. Soc.*, **77**: 3701 (1955).
61. Holloman, J. H., and D. Turnbull: "Progress in Metal Physics," vol. 4, p. 333, Pergamon Press, Ltd., London, 1953.
62. Chalmers, B.: "Physical Metallurgy," p. 249, John Wiley & Sons, Inc., New York, 1959.
63. Kovacs, A.: *Ric. Sci.*, *Suppl. A*, **25**: 668 (1955).
64. Buchdahl, R., R. L. Miller, and S. Newman: *J. Polymer Sci.*, **36**: 215 (1959).
65. Halpin, J. C., and L. Mandelkern: Unpublished results.
66. Stein, R. S., and S. Newman: Private communication.
67. Gornick, F., and L. Mandelkern: *J. Appl. Phys.*, **33**: 907 (1962).
68. Wunderlich, B.: Abstract of Paper, Division of Polymer Chemistry, American Chemical Society Meeting, Atlantic City, N.J., September, 1962, p. 63.
69. Eby, R. K.: Abstract of Paper, Division of Polymer Chemistry, American Chemical Society Meeting, Atlantic City, N.J., September, 1962, p. 74.
70. Barnes, W. B., W. G. Luetzel, and F. P. Price: *J. Phys. Chem.*, **65**: 1742 (1961).
71. Holland, V., and P. Lindenmeyer: *J. Polymer Sci.*, **57**: 589 (1962).
72. Jackson, J. B., P. J. Flory, and R. Chiang: *Trans. Faraday Soc.*, **59**: 1906 (1963).
73. Flory, P. J.: *J. Polymer Sci.*, **49**: 105 (1961).
74. Saunders, M., and P. D. Ross: *Biochem. Biophys. Res. Commun.*, **3**: 314 (1960).
75. Flory, P. J., and E. S. Weaver: *J. Am. Chem. Soc.*, **82**: 4518 (1960).
76. Ross, P. D., and J. M. Sturtevant: *J. Am. Chem. Soc.*, **84**: 4503 (1962).

MORPHOLOGY

chapter 9

9-1 Polymers Crystallized from the Melt

It has been briefly indicated, in the introductory chapter, that crystalline polymers possess characteristic morphological features at all levels that are susceptible to investigation. For studies at dimensions exceeding those of the unit cell, techniques of electron microscopy, scattering by electromagnetic radiation, and direct observation with the light microscope have been used in an effort to elucidate the crystalline texture. Most polymers diffusely scatter X rays at low angles but in many systems relatively sharp diffraction maxima are also observed. Typically, diffraction maxima of many orders are found in the naturally occurring fibrous proteins such as the keratins,[1] collagen,[2] and muscle fibers.[4,5] Predominantly meridional reflections are observed in certain axially oriented synthetic fibers[6–11] and in polymer "single crystals" grown from dilute solution.[12,13] Many nonoriented polymers, crystallized from the melt, also display discrete low-angle diffraction maxima.[14,15,16] In the latter case the X-ray

291

reflections are not restricted to the meridian, but the pattern exhibits a circular-shaped maximum.

A molecular interpretation of these results is important in the understanding of the nature of individual crystallites and their organization relative to one another. A consistency must be sought and maintained between the thermodynamic nature of the crystalline state as deduced from phase equilibrium studies, the basic kinetic mechanisms that govern the crystallization, and the morphological observations. It is from this point of view that we examine the problem of the origin of the low-angle X-ray scatter and the influence of crystallization conditions on the diffraction maxima.

Hermanns and Weidinger[17] have studied the absolute intensity of scatter at low angles for a variety of unoriented and oriented crystalline polymers. Except for cellulose fibers, where the scattering is determined mainly by the microvoids present,[18] the absolute scattering can be quantitatively explained by the fluctuations in electron density related to the crystalline-amorphous content. The polymers studied include polyethylene, polyethylene terephthalate, polycaproamide, and polyoxymethylene. This conclusion is consistent with the earlier postulates of Hess and Kiessig[19] as to the origin of the diffraction maximum in oriented fibers. It was suggested then that the discrete meridional diffraction maxima observed at low angles in oriented synthetic macromolecules find their origin in the crystalline and amorphous structure of polymeric systems. The periodicity is presumed to arise from the alternation of the ordered crystalline regions and disordered amorphous regions. The periodic change in electron density is attributed to the actual density difference of the two states. The coexistence of crystalline and amorphous regions has been demonstrated by phase equilibria studies and by the analysis of crystallization kinetics. Hence, the postulated origin of the electron density fluctuation for the low-angle scatter is consistent with the conclusions for other observations.

However, if the existence of amorphous regions is not recognized so that one is, in general, dealing with a very imperfect crystal, the low-angle scatter arises solely from long-range imperfections in the lattice. The diffraction maxima then represent a periodicity in these imperfections.[19] It has therefore been suggested that regularly folded crystallites represent the major structural elements in bulk crystallized material and that these give rise to the diffraction maxima. This concept has been encouraged and engendered by electron microscopic observations of fracture surfaces and by the concept that the diffraction maxima are restricted in size to the range of 50 to 200 A.

From the kinetic studies of the crystallization process, the conclusion has been reached that the morphology should depend on the crystallizing conditions, particularly the crystallization temperature. Consequently, a dependence of the diffraction maxima on the crystallization temperature is anticipated and is borne out by experimental observations.[14,21,22] In particular, detailed studies of low-angle diffraction maxima over a wide range of crystallization temperatures have been reported for crystalline but nonoriented linear polyethylene. The results of one set of observations are shown in Fig. 9-1 for an unfractionated linear polyethylene specimen 1.0 mm thick.[14]† The solid circles represent the intensity maxima that are actually observed. For specimens crystallized in the range 115 to 120° two well-defined maxima can be resolved. These are numerically equivalent to being first- and second-order reflections. The open circles represent first-order reflections calculated under the assumption that at the higher crystallization temperatures only the second-order reflections are capable of being resolved. A direct observation of the very long spacings thus implied has been obtained by Pollack, Robinson, Chiang, and Flory[15] for a fraction of linear polyethylene (M_v = 126,000 and 360,000) crystallized at 131.3°C. Their results are illustrated in Fig. 9-2, where a discrete maximum at 1,100 A is clearly discernible.

For the unfractionated polymer the prime spacings range from about 200 to 900 A. As anticipated, they depend very strongly on the crystallization temperature. For crystallization at temperatures below about 100° the diffraction maxima correspond to about 250 A and are not very sensitive to the crystallization temperature. Above this crystallization temperature a sharp increase in the magnitude of the spacings occurs. The concept that diffraction maxima in bulk systems are limited to the range 100 to 200 A is thus unfounded and an unnecessary restriction. The differences observed between the high molecular weight fraction and the unfractionated material point out an influence of molecular weight and molecular weight heterogeneity on the morphological features of the crystalline state. This conclusion was inherent in the previously discussed differences in the fusion process between the whole polymer and its molecular weight fractions. These observations are quite important and clearly warrant more detailed study and analysis. For unfractionated Marlex-50 the unusually high proportion of low molecular weight material allows for the possibility of the selective crystallization of the low molecular weight species.

† As a matter of convenience, it has become customary to express the spacings in angstrom units, as calculated from Bragg's law.

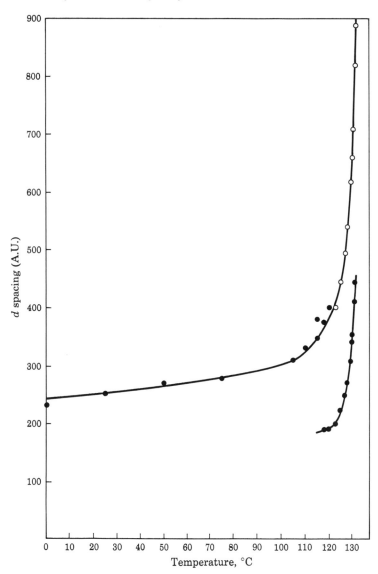

Fig. 9-1   Plot of low-angle diffraction maxima (in angstroms) against crystallization temperature for specimen of unfractionated linear polyethylene (Marlex-50) 1.0 mm thick.   Solid circles, diffraction maxima actually observed; open circles, calculated first-order reflections (14).

The above results emphasize the importance of isothermal crystallization. For a relatively rapid crystallizing polymer, as polyethylene, there are technical problems in achieving isothermal crystallization at the lower temperatures during the cooling process from the melt. The effect of sample thickness in influencing the diffraction maxima is a case in point. The results are illustrated in Table 9-1.

The data in Table 9-1 demonstrate that, for the same crystallization temperature, the thinner specimens yield lower values of the diffraction maxima than their thicker counterparts. The differences

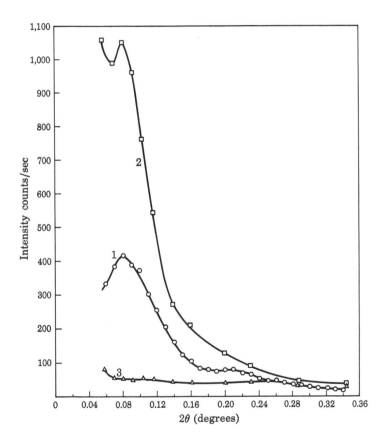

Fig. 9-2 Low-angle scattering intensity against angle for polyethylene specimens. Curve 1, 360,000 molecular weight fraction crystallized at 131.3°. Curve 2, same sample using monochromatic beam instrument. Curve 3, rapidly crystallized unfractionated specimen using latter instrument. [*Pollack, Robinson, Chiang, and Flory* (15).]

are quite large at the lower temperatures but become somewhat smaller as the crystallization temperature is increased. The effect of sample thickness can be related to the difficulties of attaining isothermal crystallization at large values of undercooling for a polymer whose crystallization rate is relatively rapid. The smaller values of the d spacings obtained for the thinner specimens can be attributed to differences in cooling rate from the melt. For thinner samples, the rate of cooling from the melt to the crystallization temperature is greater; hence the heat of crystallization is more easily dissipated. Thus, at the lower

TABLE 9-1
Comparison of first-order reflections for
unfractionated polyethylene specimens of
varying thickness

Crystallization temperature, °C	d Spacings		
	1.0 mm	0.5 mm	0.1 mm
0	230		150
105	308		238
110	330		256
115	345, 380	277	257
118	375		277
120	380, 400		270
123	400		320
125	446		360–400

temperatures, isothermal crystallization conditions are more closely attained with the thinner specimens so that the d spacings observed are more representative.

The most important observation is that the d spacings are very dependent on the crystallization temperature, particularly in the vicinity of T_m. This suggests that they arise from a characteristic dimension related to that of the critical-size nuclei.[14,22] For if, in at least one direction, nuclei do not grow significantly beyond critical size, a well-developed periodicity in crystallite dimensions evolves. According to the nucleation theory previously developed,

$$\rho^* = \frac{4\pi\sigma_u{}^2 T_m}{(\Delta H_u \, \Delta T)^2} \qquad (9\text{-}1)$$

and
$$\zeta^* = \frac{4\sigma_e T_m}{\Delta H_u \, \Delta T} \qquad (9\text{-}2)$$

so that the dimensions of the critical-size nuclei are very dependent on the undercooling at which the crystallization is conducted.

In accordance with this hypothesis, the first-order d spacings for the unfractionated polyethylene specimens are plotted against the temperature variable $T_m/\Delta T$ in Fig. 9-3. The horizontal axis in this plot is nonlinear in temperature; the higher temperatures of crystallization are disproportionally spread out while temperatures corresponding to large undercoolings are restricted to a region in the vicinity of

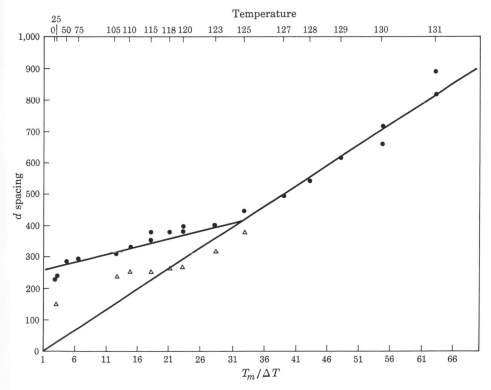

Fig. 9-3 Plot of low-angle diffraction maxima against temperature function $T_m/\Delta T$ for unfractionated linear polyethylene. Solid circles, samples 1.0 mm thick; triangles, samples 0.1 mm thick. Upper scale indicates temperatures in degrees centigrade (14).

the origin. The data for the higher crystallization temperatures obey the expected linear relation which extrapolates to very small d spacings at large undercoolings. For crystallization conducted below about 115°C, deviations from linearity are observed. Only a relatively small change in the spacings occurs over an apparently wide crystallization interval. However, the strong possibility exists that in this temperature interval the ambient temperature and the temperature at which the major portion of the crystallization occurs are not identical.   The latter temperature is, of course, higher.   It thus appears possible that if isothermal crystallization could be achieved at the lower temperatures the straight line in the plot would represent the temperature dependence of the d spacings over the complete range.

At large values of undercooling, the temperature function $T_m/\Delta T$ is essentially independent of the melting temperature and would thus be the same for different polymers.   Spacings of the order of 100 A would therefore be universally expected for crystallizations conducted at the large undercoolings which is in accord with experiment.   For example, Eppe, Fischer, and H. A. Stuart[16] crystallized a polyurethane sample from the glassy state at temperatures well removed from the melting temperature.   The diffraction maxima ranged from 50 to 150 A. The concept that, in bulk crystallized polymers, diffraction maxima are restricted to these values appears to be based on studies conducted at large undercoolings.   Investigations encompassing a wide range of crystallization temperatures indicate clearly that the values of the diffraction maxima are not so restricted.

The linearity demonstrated in Fig. 9-3 supports the suggestion that significant growth of a critical nucleus is restricted in at least one direction.   The dimension involved needs to be identified.   It would appear reasonable to assume that growth is retarded along the chain direction or c axis.   There are no inhibitions on the development of crystal planes in directions normal to the chain axis.   If this identification is made, then from Eq. (9-1) and the slope of the straight line in Fig. 9-3 the ratio of $\sigma_e/\Delta H_u$ is found to be equal to 2.6 when T_m is assigned 137.5°.   For polyethylene, this corresponds to 2500 cal/mole units or, from the known dimensions of the unit cell, 95 ergs/cm². The ratio determined is very sensitive to the value assigned to the equilibrium melting temperature.   For example, if T_m is taken as 143°, which is not an unreasonable value, an interfacial energy of 260 ergs/cm² is deduced.

This range of values for $\sigma_e/\Delta H_u$ appears to be exceptionally high but is consistent with those deduced by other methods.   The analysis of the melting of copolymers[23] gave a value of 170 ergs/cm²,[24] while Cormia, Price, and Turnbull[25] determined 168 ergs/cm² from droplet experiments.   It should be noted that the analysis of the low-angle diffraction data is predicated on homogeneous nucleation theory.   If the chain direction is affected by heterogeneities during nucleation, a still greater value of $\sigma_e/\Delta H_u$ would result.   The droplet experiments demonstrate, on one hand, that much larger supercoolings can be achieved by the isolation of heterogeneities than is usually observed in bulk crystallization. Yet from an analysis of the bulk crystallized specimens a correspondingly high value of $\sigma_e/\Delta H_u$ is obtained. The distinct possibility thus exists that, in the formation of asymmetric nuclei, the catalytic effect of heterogeneities could influence only one of the dimensions. This concept would allow for an explanation of the limited supercooling that can be attained in bulk specimens while similar values of σ_e are obtained from both types of experiments.

The high and very unique value that characterizes σ_e must be related to the molecular nature of the interface of concern. This interface, which involves the passage of a connected sequence of chain units from the crystal to the melt, has no analog in the crystallization of monomeric substances. If it is postulated that a regularly, sharply folded nucleus is formed from a single molecule, then σ_e can be identified with the free energy required to make the sharp bend in the chain.[26,27] On the other hand, if nucleation consists of the participation of many molecules and if the ad hoc requirement of sharp bending is not invoked, σ_e represents the sum of excess free energies for the sequence of units of a given chain which traverses the region of perfect crystallinity to that of complete liquid disorder. As has been pointed out, this change in order cannot occur over the interval of one unit. A high value of σ_e would result if this intermediate region, the interfacial region, possessed a high enthalpy and a low entropy.

The foregoing interpretation of the low-angle diffraction of polymers, with a restrictive growth rate in one direction, leads to the concept of lamellar or platelike crystallites as being a prime morphological entity. This conclusion can be reached without any recourse to direct electron microscopic studies.

Surface replicas of thin polymer films crystallized from the melt or of fracture surfaces of the interior of thicker specimens display lamellar structures as was illustrated in Fig. 1-9. Although these kinds of structures have been observed for a variety of polymers,[16,22,28,29,30] rather scant attention has been given to specifying the crystallization conditions or molecular weights of the specimens. This information is particularly important in attempting to identify and correlate these observations with the low-angle diffraction experiments. The thickness of the lamella most commonly observed is of the order of 100 to 150 A, with the orientation of the chain axis being normal to the wide face.† This indicates that multiple sequences from the same chain participate within a single crystallite. These dimensions corre-

† Recently, lamella thicknesses as great as 700 A have been observed from fracture surfaces of low molecular weight fractions of polyethylene that were isothermally crystallized at high temperatures.[31]

spond generally to the long spacings observed by low-angle X-ray diffraction for specimens crystallized at very large undercoolings. For identical samples studied by both methods, agreement is obtained when the spacings and dimensions are in the 100 to 200 A range. However, Sella[22] has reported that when the diffraction maxima are increased to 300 to 400 A the lamellae that are observed on the surface of a bulk polymer are only in the size range of 80 to 140 A. It is not known whether this situation persists for crystallization conditions that lead to diffraction maxima of the order of 1,000 A. If the lamellae directly observed by electron microscopy are restricted in thickness after crystallization at low undercoolings, then either a different interpretation will have to be given to the diffraction results, or the deformation processes involved in fracture introduce some superficial effects on the morphology and crystalline texture. It should be noted that fracturing is usually accomplished at the temperature of liquid nitrogen, which is below the glass temperature for most polymers of interest.

The relatively recent concept of the formation and existence of lamellar crystallites in bulk crystallized homopolymers appears to be well founded and supported by the evidence cited. However, an additional or corollary assertion has been put forth, namely, that within an individual crystallite the polymer chains are regularly and successively sharply folded. The periodicity observed at low angles is then identified with the fold period. However, it is difficult to reconcile the large spacings of Figs. 9-1 and 9-2 with a regularly folded structure when cognizance is taken of the molecular weight and molecular weight distribution of the samples. This problem could be alleviated by the indiscriminate insertion into the lattice of chain ends and other structural irregularities. This possibility would not be compatible with the experimental observations that higher and sharper melting temperatures are observed for the crystals formed at the lower undercoolings and the experiments that demonstrate the rejection of chain ends by the lattice.

It is not necessary, of course, that lamellar structures be equated and identified with pleated chains. There exists the distinct possibility of backlooping or partial folding of the individual chains. Different crystalline sequences from the same molecule would then occur in nonadjacent positions within a given crystallite. The presence of noncrystalline or amorphous regions existing with the crystallite would thus be allowed for. Moreover, some chains could traverse a crystallite only once and, after passing through the amorphous regions, join other crystallites. Other chains, after leaving the crystallite, could again return to it. In principle, therefore, there is no inconsistency between the presence of a lamellar crystallite whose thickness is appreciably less than the length of an extended molecule and the existence of amorphous or liquidlike regions. Incompatibility develops only when the chains within the crystallite are required to be regularly folded or pleated. Neither fundamental theory nor careful scrutiny

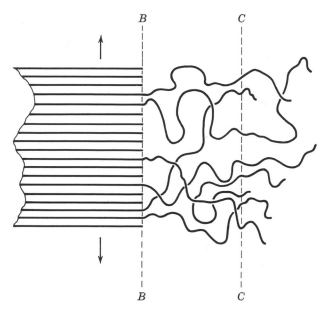

Fig. 9-4 Schematic diagram of the interfacial zone transverse to the *c* axis. [*Flory* (32).]

of the experimental evidence provides any compelling reasons for the adoption of the latter point of view.

The reason for the formation of lamellar-type crystallites can be found by examining the spatial requirements of polymer chains in the interfacial zone and in the region of complete isotropy.[32] Because of the contiguous nature of polymer chain units, the order that exists within a crystallite cannot be dissipated abruptly at the interface normal to the *c* direction. This point has already been made when discussing the high value of the interfacial free energy σ_e. We consider a lamellar crystal of unlimited lateral dimensions, as is illustrated in Fig. 9-4.[32] Chains emerge from the crystal transverse to the plane *BB*, located at the interface, and enter the adjoining regions. Some of the chains then intersect the plane *CC* located in the completely isotropic amorphous regions. The problem that needs to be resolved is whether the flux of chains emanating from the crystal can be accommodated in the amorphous region. If A_c is the cross-sectional area per chain in the crystalline state, the number of chains emanating from the crystal face per unit area is

$$N_c = \frac{1}{A_c} \tag{9-3}$$

To calculate the number of chains per unit area N_A which intersect the plane CC, a freely rotating, segmented chain is taken as a model for the amorphous polymer. The successive bond orientations are uncorrelated, so that the chain configuration is represented by a line of continuously varying direction. The length, cross-sectional area, and volume of a segment are denoted by l, A_a, and V_a, respectively. In order for a bond inclined at an angle θ to the normal of the plane CC to be able to intersect this plane, it must have its terminus within a distance $l \cos \theta$ of the plane. The number of intersections at angles θ to $\theta + d\theta$ per unit area are

$$N_\theta \, d\theta = \frac{V_a^{-1} l \cos \theta \sin \theta \, d\theta}{\int_0^{\pi/2} \sin \theta \, d\theta} = V_a^{-1} l \cos \theta \sin \theta \, d\theta \tag{9-4}$$

where V_a^{-1} is taken to be the concentration of polymer segments in the absence of solvent. Integration over all directions θ yields

$$N_A = \int_0^{\pi/2} N_\theta \, d\theta = \frac{l}{2V_a} = \frac{1}{2A_a} \tag{9-5}$$

Comparison with Eq. (9-3) yields

$$\frac{N_A}{N_c} = \frac{1}{2} \frac{A_c}{A_a} \tag{9-6}$$

as the ratio of the density of chain intersection in the amorphous regions to that in the crystalline region. For example, if A_c/A_a is of the order of unity, then no more than half of the flux of chains emerging from the crystal face can be accommodated in the region of complete isotropy. The remaining chains must then somehow be dissipated.

Before pursuing the implications inherent in Eq. (9-6), the relative displacements of planes BB and CC require examination. As the distance between BB and CC is increased, intrusion of the amorphous chains into the zone between the two planes from sources other than the crystallite in question can be expected. The flux of chains emanating from the crystallite and passing through CC will be reduced below the limit given by Eq. (9-6). This effect will be tempered some-what by the presence of neighboring crystallites which could absorb the flux of chains from the amorphous regions.

Equation (9-6) thus serves as an upper limit to the fraction of chains that emerge from an infinitely (in lateral dimensions) large lamellar crystal and cannot return to it. This conclusion is reached solely as a consequence of the spatial requirements of amorphous poly-mer chains when compared with the ordered array that exists in crys-tallites. The relative number of chains that can be accommodated by the amorphous regions depends on the ratio A_c/A_a. If, for example, the chains are fully extended in the crystalline state, as in polyethylene, and the bond orientations are uncorrelated in the amorphous state, the ratio of cross sections can be identified with the ratio of the corre-sponding specific volumes. This would be of the order of unity for most polymers. Hence, when $A_c/A_a = 1$ and the plane surface is very large, at least half of the chains leaving the crystal must reenter it. It does not necessarily follow, however, that the chains need to be regularly folded or pleated in the crystallite. A significant number are permitted to proceed into the region of isotropy, and some of these will eventually participate in other crystallites. Those chains which reenter the crystallite need not do so immediately but can traverse the interfacial region before returning. It is not required a priori that such a chain must occupy a sequence adjoining that of its previous passage through the crystallite. Perfectly respectable lamellar crys-tallites can thus be formed during the melt crystallization of polymers and be consistent with experimental observation. It is not necessary to endow the chain molecule with an inherent propensity for folding. There is, therefore, no fundamental inconsistency in having lamellar crystallites coexisting with amorphous regions. This requirement of both experiment and theory can be satisfied by the participation of many crystalline sequences from the same chain in a given crystallite without requiring their juxtaposition. Depending on crystallographic detail and the configuration of the amorphous chain, folding can be expected in the crystals. However, there is no fundamental basis for a regularly folded or pleated structure to result.

Cases can be anticipated where the ratio A_c/A_a will exceed unity. It would then be possible for N_c/N_a to be of the order of unity so that the chain flux emanating from the crystallite could be completely absorbed in the amorphous regions. An example of this possibility is the alpha-helical crystalline form of polypeptides. The projected length per repeat unit on the axis of the helix is 1.5 A as compared with 3.8 A for the length of a trans unit of the chain. If A_c/A_a is approximated by the inverse ratio of these lengths, then $N_a/N_c = 1.25$. In this case there would be no difficulty in reconciling the spatial requirements of random chains with the space available.

The above conclusions have been based on the postulate that the transverse dimensions of the crystal are very large compared with its thickness. These conditions do not, however, apply to a nucleus of critical size. Estimates of the lateral interfacial free energy σ_u indicate (see Sec. 8-6) that for polyethylene the nucleus consists of from 20 to 100 sequences in the usual range of undercooling at which crystallization is conducted. For such a small number of chains the spatial restraints operative for large crystallites can be easily circumvented. As the chains emerge into the interfacial zone, they can, as long as they are few in number, be dispersed in directions transverse to the bundle axis. Hence folding of any sort is not required for nucleus formation. A critical nucleus comprised of sequences from different molecules is a perfectly acceptable arrangement from a geometric point of view. It also places the minimum demands on the cooperation required of disordered chains to form a crystallite nucleus. It is consistent with the analysis of crystallization kinetics and is consequently the most plausible candidate for the nucleation of crystallization. It does not follow, from any fundamental principles, that the chain disposition within the crystallite that is evolved needs to be identical with that within the nucleus. The problem of the chain disposition within a nucleus and within a mature crystallite is a separate and distinguishable matter. For crystallization from polymer-diluent mixtures, other factors influence both the spatial requirements of chains emanating from crystallites and the problem of nuclei formation.

In light of the foregoing discussion, the crystallization of random copolymers presents some interesting problems. The infrequency of long sequences of crystallizing units precludes the multiple participation of the same molecule within the same crystallite. Unlimited lateral growth involving the participation of sequences from other chains would be severely restricted because of the spatial requirements of the interfacial and amorphous regions just discussed. The introduction of noncrystallizing copolymeric units in random distribution would suppress the development of the lamellar morphology characteristic of the parent homopolymer. It should be noted again that a high value of σ_e, comparable in magnitude to that assigned to the parent homopolymer, has been deduced for random ethylene copolymers. Clearly, it cannot be identified with the free energy that would be involved in forming a folded structure.

Although it has been demonstrated that there is no incompatibility in the coexistence of large lamellar crystallites with amorphous regions in homopolymers, the experimental evidence for the presence of these noncrystalline regions requires close scrutiny. One of the most compelling sets of observations is the phenomenon of glass formation. Glass formation is a characteristic property of polymeric substances as well as of certain monomeric liquids. Although there is some controversy as to the mechanism involved in glass formation, there is complete agreement on its being a property of the liquid state. Completely molten polymers as well as crystalline polymers display well-defined glass temperatures. Moreover, for polymers that can be compared in both states, as well as for those polymers for which the level of crystallinity can be controlled, essentially the same values are obtained for the glass temperature.[33-35] This is indeed strong evidence for the presence of amorphous regions in crystalline polymers.

If, on the other hand, only a crystalline phase existed, albeit one inundated with various imperfections, the glass temperature would have to be attributed in some manner to the properties of these imperfections. Consequently a polymer melt would have to be envisaged as a collection of dislocated or imperfect crystals. This concept would, of course, be incompatible with melting being a first-order phase transition. Moreover, most, if not all, of the physical, mechanical, and flow properties of the melt would remain inexplicable. They require for their description and explanation, in one form or another, the large configurational entropy associated with randomly coiled macromolecules.

Wide-angle X-ray diffraction patterns of crystalline polymers invariably display a broad halo which corresponds to Bragg spacings in the region of 3 to 5 A. The existence of a halo can, in principle, be attributed to the scattering from either the amorphous regions or from imperfections within the crystallite. When considered as an isolated experimental fact of X-ray measurements, devoid of the vast amount of corollary information available, it is a difficult problem to distinguish the molecular origin of this scattering. However, a very careful analysis by Ruland[36] of both the halo and the discrete diffraction from polypropylene has shown that the halo can be attributed to the amorphous regions which are essentially devoid of structural order.

A variety of techniques can be utilized to estimate the level of crystallinity. These include wide-angle X-ray diffraction, infrared and broad-line nuclear magnetic resonance, as well as the analysis of such thermodynamic properties as density, heat content, and expansivity. The tacit assumption is made that two phases exist and their individual contribution to the property being measured is additive and in proportion to the relative amounts of each of the phases. Since one is inevitably concerned with a nonequilibrium situation, wherein kinetic factors are of the utmost importance, it is obvious that the comparison of the different methods for a given polymer is significant only when the specimens have been crystallized under identical conditions and receive the same thermal treatment.

The results for the degree of crystallinity, obtained by different methods, for natural rubber crystallized at 0° are summarized in Table 9-2. Natural rubber can be classified as a polymer which crystallizes only a modest amount. The data compiled in Table 9-2 indicate that

TABLE 9-2
Values obtained for the degree of crystallinity $(1 - \lambda)$ of natural rubber crystallized at 0°C

Method	$1 - \lambda$	Ref.
X ray	0.30–0.35	(37)
Heat content	0.26	(33, 38)
Density	0.31	(38)
Expansivity	0.31	(38)

essentially the same results are obtained by the diverse methods employed. The small differences observed could be significant in that they might reflect differences in the sensitivity of the individual techniques and differing contributions of imperfections. A significant refinement in the experimental techniques would be required to resolve this question. The major conclusion can be drawn, however, that at these levels of crystallinity it is proper to discuss the coexistence of two phases.

At the other extreme, at very high levels of crystallinity, complications can be anticipated. However, for an annealed specimen of linear polyethylene (which represents about the highest level of crystallinity reported) Wunderlich and Dole[39] calculate, from calorimetric data, that $1 - \lambda$ is the order of 0.90. This result is in qualitative agreement with that deduced from density[14,40] and X-ray measurements[41] for samples receiving a similar crystallization treatment. As the level of crystallinity becomes high, the contributions from the amorphous regions decrease, and the role of imperfections within the crystal lattice can become important. The additivity laws could be seriously questioned, and it is not expected that the different methods will respond in the same manner to the imperfections.

In a broad qualitative sense, imperfections within lattices of chain molecules can be assigned either to intramolecular faults or to a variety of problems involved in the packing of the molecules. The thermodynamic methods automatically take into account equilibrium-type defects, but nonequilibrium defects need not contribute in the same way to each method. On the other hand, methods such as X-ray and infrared analysis would be expected to respond in different ways to all defects. As an example, the infrared method measures primarily intramolecular interactions whereas X-ray diffraction is concerned with three-dimensional ordering. Hence, if a disturbance affects the configuration of a single chain but not its packing properties, different results would be expected for the degree of crystallinity obtained by the two methods. In addition, the unique nature of the interfacial regions has been indicated. These regions obviously cannot be assigned to either the crystalline or amorphous phases and would not be expected to have the characteristic scattering or thermodynamic properties of either.

9-2 Crystals from Dilute Solution

Crystals grown from dilute polymer solutions display a most interesting and important morphology. Their discovery has provided a great stimulus to the study of the morphology and texture of crystalline polymers.[12,13,16,42–46] Under the electron microscope these crystals are observed to consist of thin layers, or lamellae, with a uniform thickness of about 100 A, and to extend up to several microns in the transverse dimensions. The thickening of the crystals, by the deposition of additional lamellae, occurs through the formation of spiral terraces and conforms to the requirements of growth by a screw dislocation mechanism.[47] The gross morphological features are thus quite similar to those found in the low molecular weight *n*-alkanes crystallized from dilute solution.[13,48]

The orientation of the chain molecules within the platelets has been determined from studies of selected-area electron diffraction patterns. A typical pattern for a lozenge-shaped crystal of polyethylene is given in Fig. 9-5. The pattern is exceptionally sharp, and its analysis indicates that the chain direction or *c* axis is perpendicular to the wide face of the crystal. Moreover, the directions of the *a* and *b* crystallographic axes are preserved throughout the platelet so that the designation "single crystals" has been given to such structures. Since the platelets are of the order of only 100 to 200 A thick, which is a small fraction of the extended length of a typical polymer molecule, it is obvious that a given molecule must traverse a crystal

Fig. 9-5 Electron diffraction pattern from a lozenge-shaped polyethylene crystal. *Reprinted with permission from A. Keller, in R. H. Doremio, B. W. Roberts, and D. Turnbull (eds.), "Growth and Perfection of Crystals," John Wiley & Sons, Inc., New York, 1958.*

many times in order to satisfy the orientation requirements. Hence the platelets must consist of folded polymer chains. This conclusion, which is consistent with the structural analysis, does not require that the molecules be regularly folded or pleated; i.e., the external fold plane (001) need not be perfectly regular.

Although crystals of linear polyethylene have been most extensively studied, the platelet type of crystal has been observed subsequent to the dilute solution crystallization of a large number of different polymers. These include cellulose derivatives,[49,50] polyamides,[51] polyethers,[52] polyolefins such as polypropylene[13] and poly-4-methylpentene-1,[53] and polyacrylonitrile[54] as examples. Lamellar crystals have also been observed from dilute solutions of branched polyethylene.[16,55] The lamellae are oval in shape, are less than 90 A thick, and are far less perfect than those found with polymers of regular structure. Well-defined lamellar structures are also observed for the dilute solution crystallization of polytrifluorochloroethylene from mesitylene.[56] The electron diffraction patterns indicate that, for these systems also, the chain axes are directed normal to the wide face of the platelets.

For some of these systems the nature of the solvent used plays an important role in determining the morphological form. For example, although cellulose triacetate crystallized from a nitromethane solution yields well-defined platelets, attempts to grow such crystals from other solvents has as yet been unsuccessful.[49] Although platelets are observed following dilute solution crystallization of polyacrylonitrile from propylene carbonate solutions, in other solvents, such as dimethyl formamide and dimethyl acetamide, morphologically uninteresting gels are formed.[57]   Changes in the morphological form of polyamides that depend on the nature of the solvent have been reported.[55,58]   Thus the thermodynamic nature of the solvent and perhaps its effect on the chain configuration influence to some extent the kind of crystals formed.†

Another important property of the platelets is that, within the limits of experimental error (circa 15 A), electron microscope observations indicate a remarkably uniform thickness.   This also manifests itself in four orders of X-ray diffraction appearing at low angles.   The prime spacings correspond to those observed under the electron microscope.   Various crystal habits have been observed which range from the isolated lozenge-shaped platelets of Fig. 1-10 to the typical dendritic form of Fig. 1-11.   The crystal habit that forms depends on the crystallization temperature and the molecular weight of the polymer. Dendritic structures are favored by rapid crystallization conducted at large undercoolings (low temperature)[28,61,62] and by the very slow crystallization that occurs at small undercoolings.[62]   The electron micrographs obtained at both low and very high supercoolings are very similar irrespective of the possibility that different mechanisms may be operative.   The tendency to form dendrites is increased as the concentration of the solution is increased above about 1 per cent.   In the intermediate range of undercoolings the well-known single crystal platelets are observed.

Studies of molecular weight fractions of polyethylene from xylene have shown that the temperature below which the crystallization changes from single crystal platelets to the more diffuse dendritic-like structure is higher, the greater the molecular weight.   The upper temperature limit at which dendrites are again formed at the expense of platelets also depends on molecular weight.   It ranges from 84 to 92° for molecular weights ranging from 10,000 to 120,000.   Since the equilibrium melting temperature is not very dependent on molecular weight in this range, morphological characteristics depend not only on the undercooling at which the crystallization is conducted but also directly on the molecular weight.   However, in the temperature region where well-defined structural entities are precipitated, the thickness of the crystals is independent of the molecular weight.[61,63,64]

---

† Much larger single crystals, observable under the light microscope, have been grown from dilute solutions of gutta-percha.[46]   In addition, the irradiation of large single crystals of monomeric trioxane leads to polymerization and the formation in situ of macroscopic crystals of polymethylene oxide.   Wide-angle X-ray diffraction patterns demonstrate that these are also single crystals.[59,60] Specimens of this kind appear to be ideally suited for fundamental studies of the physical and mechanical properties of crystalline polymers.

A characteristic property of lamellae is the dependence of their thickness on the crystallization temperature. This is illustrated in Fig. 9-6 for the system polyethylene-xylene. With increasing crystallization temperature the spacings increase from about 90 A at the lower temperatures to 150 A. Above a crystallization temperature of 90° no

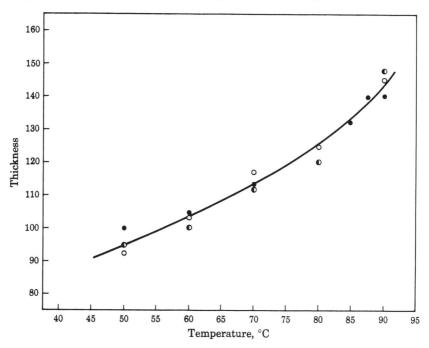

Fig. 9-6   Plot of platelet thickness, in angstroms, against crystallization temperature for polyethylene crystallized from dilute xylene solution. Data obtained from low-angle X-ray diffraction and electron microscopy. [*Holland and Lindenmeyer* (61); *Price* (63); *Keller and O'Connor* (64).]

well-defined structural entities are observed. At very low temperatures isothermal crystallization is difficult to achieve. Despite these limitations on the crystallization range, the change in thickness with crystallization temperature is apparent. However, the spacings are significantly less than those observed in bulk polymers.

In summary, the formation of a platelet or dendritic habit, with the polymer chain traversing a given crystal many times, is a widespread mode of crystallization from dilute solution. Experimental studies indicate that the crystallization temperature and the undercooling, as well as molecular weight, solvent interaction, and chain configuration, influence the mode of crystallization.

Despite the number and sharpness of reflections observed at low angles and the apparent perfection of the platelets as seen under the electron microscope, both electron diffraction and the wide-angle X-ray patterns of such specimens show a halo. The X-ray diffraction patterns from single crystal material of polyethylene are identical with those obtained from highly crystalline bulk crystallized polymer with an amorphous content of 15 to 20 per cent by density.[65] For linear polyethylene, including high molecular weight fractions, the density of dilute-solution-grown material is 2 to 3 per cent less than that of a perfect crystal[62,66] and corresponds to a degree of crystallinity of about 80 per cent. This discrepancy in density between the single crystal and that calculated from the dimensions of the unit cell cannot be accounted for by the small number of units required to make a sharp bend in the folded structure. The concentration of voids and defects that would be required within the interior of the crystal would be of such a magnitude as to raise a question of the existence of a crystal at all. It is also observed that a 7 per cent decrease in the enthalpy of fusion exists between single crystals of polyethylene grown from dilute solution and an annealed specimen crystallized in bulk.[66] These observations find a satisfactory explanation only in the terms of a substantial fraction of amorphous polymer. Because of the regular structure of the platelets, as is revealed by electron microscopy, one can assume that the amorphous regions occur on the platelet surfaces.[32] A smooth amorphous layer, which results from the drying process, is indistinguishable in an electron micrograph from the crystal to which it is attached.

The melting temperatures of crystals formed from dilute solution are significantly less than those grown in the bulk polymer and depend on the temperature of crystallization and the thermodynamic nature of the solvent.[63,67] A comparison of the melting temperatures is conveniently made by observing the solubility point of the polymer in a very dilute solution. For example for polyethylene crystallized from the melt at 131° for two weeks, the solubility point in tetralin is 110°, while that for the material crystallized from dilute solution is 96°.[63]† If this difference in melting temperature is attributed solely to the finite thickness of the solution crystallized specimen, the interfacial free energy associated with the platelet surface is calculated to be 1800 cal/mole emerging chain repeat unit, or 68 ergs/cm².[62] This is significantly less than the corresponding interfacial free energy deduced for bulk crystallized specimens. The difference in melting tempera-

† This temperature varies slightly, depending on the crystallization temperature.

ture between solution grown and melt grown specimens becomes much less pronounced in poorer solvents,[67] indicating again the distinct possibility that the nature of the thermodynamic interaction between polymer and solvent strongly influences the crystallization process.

The theoretical basis for the formation of lamellae in dilute-solution-grown crystals and the attendant folded geometry of the constituent chains needs to be developed. The mechanisms and processes proposed must obviously be consistent with the physical, thermodynamic, and morphological properties of the crystals just summarized. A very significant and relevant question is the relation between the lamellae formed from dilute solution and those formed in the bulk. Earlier theories, which on close scrutiny do not distinguish between solution or bulk crystallization, are predicated on either nucleation kinetics[26,63,68,69] or equilibrium considerations.[70] In the latter case an attempt is made to generalize to three dimensions the disturbances inherently necessary for the existence of a very long one-dimensional lattice. These disturbances in three-dimensional order are then stated to give rise to regular chain folding. Alternatively, it has been assumed that both primary and growth nuclei are comprised of regularly folded chains. Consequently growth can proceed only in directions normal to the chain axis so that a regularly folded structure must evolve. Size control and the dependence of size on the crystallization temperature are developed from the monomeric nucleation theory that was discussed in Sec. 8-5. However, since unimolecular two-dimensional nucleation is involved, the thermodynamic stability of the crystallites is predicted to be significantly less than is experimentally observed. Attempts to remove this difficulty have been made[27,64,70]; however, they involve questionable assumptions in respect to the manner in which a sequence of chain units is deposited on a substrate (see following).

It has been shown how the spatial requirements of polymer chains offer a natural explanation for the formation of lamellar crystallites in bulk polymers. This situation is accentuated in dilute solution. In a solution, the flux of chains in the isotropic regions is severely reduced when compared with a pure system. This results from the need of the polymer to reduce its concentration from $v_2 = 1$, at the crystal, to that of the surrounding solution. Equation (9-6) must therefore be modified to[32]

$$\frac{N_a}{N_c} = v_2 \frac{A_c}{A_a} \tag{9-7}$$

The frequency with which a chain returns to the crystal face of origin thus must increase with dilution. For an infinitely long chain in an infinitely dilute solution only one crystal is formed, since all chains emanating from it must eventually return. For a dilute solution of chains of finite molecular weight the distance between crystallites is sufficiently large as to preclude participation of a given molecule in more than one crystal This rudimentary analysis virtually assures

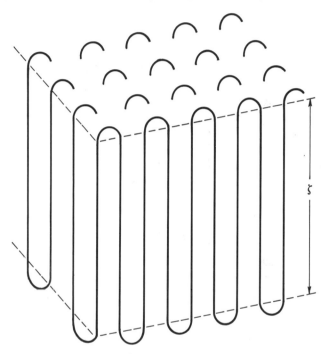

Fig. 9-7 Schematic diagram of a portion of a lamellar crystallite with the polymer chains in a regularly folded array. [*Flory* (32).]

the separation of isolated crystals from dilute solution. The major problem therefore concerns the manner and efficiency by which chain elements of the participating molecules are incorporated into the crystal lattice. The equilibrium requirements must be first established and subsequently viewed in terms of possible crystallization mechanisms.

Two extreme cases, which are consistent with the microscopic and diffraction results, can be envisaged. One of these, which is represented schematically in Fig. 9-7, is the regularly folded array. Each molecule crystallizes to the fullest extent possible. Crystallization is virtually complete except for the small number of chain elements required to make the hairpinlike connections between the crystalline sequences. In the other case, as is illustrated in Fig. 9-8, the crystalline sequences are connected more or less at random, with the connecting loops being of random length. Intermediate situations are also possible. An example is the case where sequences from a given molecule occur within the same layer but the connections between the sequences are of random length.

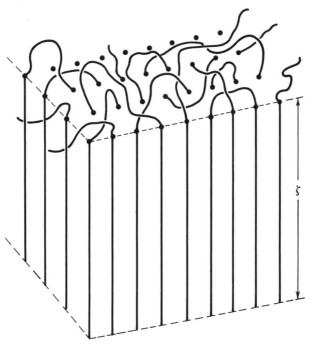

Fig. 9-8 Schematic diagram of a lamellar crystallite with nonregularly folded chains; loop lengths variable. [*Flory* (32).]

Except for the regularly folded array, the other models possess an interfacial region of disordered chain units mixed with diluent. The randomness associated with such a diffuse interface offers the apparent advantage of a greater entropy and consequently greater thermodynamic stability of the crystal. On the other hand, its formation requires that a larger number of molecules participate. An expenditure of free energy is required to bring the necessary number of molecular centers together in one area [see Eq. (8-69)]. In addition, the concentration of polymer chains in the amorphous interfacial zone is greater than that of the solution as a whole. The assemblage of such an array necessitates further osmotic work resulting from the interactions between chain units in this region. Therefore, for a non-regularly folded lattice, the advantage of the disorder entropy must be compared with the free energy expended in osmotic work to form the diffuse interfacial layer.

To estimate the osmotic work involved we take as a model the crystallite schematically depicted in Fig. 9-8.[32] There will be ν crystalline sequences each of length ζ. The crystalline sequences are connected by amorphous loops of average length y. Participating in the crystal therefore are $(\zeta + y)\nu$ chain units and $(\zeta + y)\nu/x$ polymer molecules, the number of units per molecule being x. In a regularly folded array, y has a minimum value which, for purposes of calculation, is taken to be zero. The formation of the diffuse interfacial layer requires the transfer of $y\nu/x$ polymer molecules from the dilute solution of concentration v_2 to the interfacial layer whose concentration is v_2' $(v_2 \ll v_2')$. From conventional polymer solution theory the osmotic work expended is[32]

$$\Delta F_{os} \cong RT\nu y \left\{ \frac{1}{x}\left(\ln \frac{v_2'}{v_2} - 1\right) + \frac{1}{x_1}\left[1 + \left(\frac{1}{v_2'} - 1\right)\ln (1 - v_2') - \chi_1 v_2'\right]\right\}$$
(9-8)

where $x_1 = V_1/V_u$. The significance of ΔF_{os} can be assessed by calculating its influence on the change in solubility or melting temperature. We let T_m be the equilibrium temperature in the solution for a crystal of size ζ in the absence of the osmotic effect. At some temperature $T' = T_m - \Delta T$ the free energy change for the formation of the crystal containing the diffuse interface is

$$\Delta F = \Delta F_{os} - \frac{\nu \zeta \Delta H_u \Delta T}{T_m}$$
(9-9)

The contribution of the finite size of the crystal is assumed to be the same in both instances. By equating the above to zero and substituting from Eq. (9-8), the decrease in the melting temperature caused by the osmotic work in forming the interface is

$$\Delta T = \left(\frac{y}{\zeta}\right)\frac{RT'T_m}{x_1 \Delta H_u}\left[\frac{x_1}{x}\left(\ln \frac{v_2'}{v_2} - 1\right) + 1 \right.$$
$$\left. + \left(\frac{1}{v_2'} - 1\right)\ln (1 - v_2') - \chi_1 v_2'\right]$$
(9-10a)

For large x, the term x_1/x, which represents the first virial coefficient pertaining to the allocation of molecular centers, is negligible.

Therefore

$$\Delta T \cong \frac{y}{\zeta} \frac{RT_m{}^2}{x_1 \Delta H_u} \left[1 + \left(\frac{1}{v_2'} - 1 \right) \ln (1 - v_2') - \chi_1 v_2' \right] \quad (9\text{-}10b)$$

The extent and mean concentration of the interfacial layer cannot be precisely defined. However if a layer thickness is arbitrarily assigned so that $v_2' = 0.5$, then for a good solvent with $\chi_1 = 0$

$$\Delta T = 0.3 \frac{y}{\zeta} \frac{RT_m{}^2}{x_1 \Delta H_u} \quad (9\text{-}11)$$

Utilizing parameters appropriate to polyethylene in a solvent having a molar volume of about 100 cc $(x_1 \cong 7)$, Eq. (9-11) becomes

$$\Delta T = \frac{14y}{\zeta} \quad (9\text{-}12)$$

If the effective concentration of the interfacial layer is greater than that assumed, the constant factor in Eq. (9-12) is increased, while in poorer solvents it is appropriately reduced. The depressed melting temperature amounts at most to a few degrees, depending in detail on the aforementioned factors and the ratio of y/ζ. Although the thermodynamic stability is not seriously jeopardized, it does not necessarily follow that the osmotic effect is a negligible deterrent to the formation of a diffuse interface. The course of crystal growth could easily be influenced by the magnitude of the free energy involved. If amorphous loops result as a consequence of other factors, a slightly reduced stability would be expected. Furthermore, if the nucleation processes involved the presence of the loops, crystallization rates (at the same undercooling) would depend on the nature of the solvent. In particular, they would be influenced by the molar volume and the thermodynamic interaction with polymer.

An important statistical problem exists in the partitioning of the chain elements between the crystalline sequences and the interfacial layer.[32] A single chain is given the opportunity to participate in a lamellar crystallite of fixed thickness ζ and to occupy any number of sequences $\nu < x/\zeta$. Because of the lengths of the intervening amorphous sequences, the number of possible arrangements permitted is

$$C(\zeta,\nu) = \frac{(x - \nu\zeta + \nu)!}{(x - \nu\zeta)!\nu!} \quad (9\text{-}13)$$

To construct the chain partition function, the $\nu - 1$ noncrystalline sequences must be in an acceptable configuration. For a coherent crystallite, the terminal units are all in the (001) plane. Hence all the amorphous loops are required to originate and terminate in this plane. A severe restriction is thus placed on the randomness intuitively associated with Eq. (9-13) and inherently endowed to amorphous chains. Since the ends of the loops are restricted to a plane, the component of the end-to-end vector of the loop along the normal to the plane must be zero. If the growing face tends to develop one layer at a time, the sequences belonging to a given molecule will in general be incorporated in the same (110) layer. Another component of the end-to-end vector is thus constrained to a value close to zero. If each loop joins the terminus of one sequence with its immediate neighbor in the same (110) face, then the end-to-end vector for the loop is fixed at a value which approximates zero. This condition resembles regular folding, with the exception that the lengths of the loop may exceed the minimum size possible and need not be of uniform size.

From the theory of random chains, the probability that one of the cartesian components of the vector connecting the ends of a loop is zero is $(3/2\pi y)^{1/2}$. If d is the number of dimensions of constraint on each loop, the number of arrangements of the chain compatible with ν crystalline sequence is $C(\zeta,\nu)(3/2\pi y)(\nu - 1)d/2$. The average number of units per loop, y, is equal to $(x - \nu\zeta)/(\nu + 1) \cong (x - \nu\zeta)/\nu$. The partition function for the chain can be expressed as

$$Q = C(\zeta,\nu) \frac{3}{2\pi y} \frac{d(\nu - 1)}{2} \exp{(\nu\zeta\phi - 2\nu s_e)} \qquad (9\text{-}14)$$

where $\phi = \Delta F_u/RT$ and $s_e = \sigma_e/RT$. From Eq. (9-14) one seeks the optimum number of sequences participating in the crystal of fixed thickness ζ. For the case $d = 1$, which represents loop connections between pairs of points randomly located in the (001) plane, Q exhibits a maximum with ν at fixed ζ. The range over which the maximum occurs is limited to a small range in ϕ (that is, T). On one side ($T < T_m$) virtually the entire molecule is required to crystallize at equilibrium, with loop lengths being very short. At the other extreme ($T > T_m$) crystalline sequences can occur only rarely.

For $d \geq 2$, a condition representing loop connections along a layer in the (110) plane, the preferred situation is either crystallization to the fullest extent possible or not at all, depending on the value of ϕ. A sharp discontinuity in the state of equilibrium is expected, with the regularly folded array being favored in the crystalline state since it permits the maximum crystallization of the molecule. This deduction is given additional support by the osmotic effect which further diminishes the amount of amorphous material associated with a crystallite.

The conclusion that the folded array, which permits maximum crystallization, is the most stable state for a crystallite of fixed length in contact with a dilute solution is based solely on equilibrium statistical considerations.   Therefore, to achieve this structure, it is not necessary to invoke classical monomeric nucleation theory or to endow the polymer molecules with an inherent propensity for folding.[26,63,68,69] The randomness and concomitant entropy increase that are associated with the partitioning of chains between crystalline and amorphous sequences are not achieved.   This is because the amorphous loops terminate at crystal faces whose locations are fixed by the contiguity of the crystalline sequences.   Consequently, crystallization to the maximum extent is favored.   A similar conclusion is reached[71] even if reentry into the crystallite by a chain is ignored.   For a chain restricted to a single crystallite, whose size is less than the extended length of the molecule, a regularly folded array satisfies the equilibrium condition.

It remains to be ascertained, however, whether the most stable state is achieved under actual conditions of crystallization.   This implies that crystal growth proceeds at a finite rate.   It is well known that for all liquid-crystal transitions kinetic factors intervene, so that the final state realized represents a compromise between equilibrium and the necessity for the process to proceed at a finite rate.   This holds true for both monomeric and polymeric substances.   Even in a dilute polymer solution the relaxation time for long segments is too great to keep up with the fairly rapid rate at which chains are deposited on a growing face.   The effect of the molecular weight on the rate of growth is a case in point.[61]   The abnormally low enthalpies and densities of the platelets precipitated from dilute solution indicate clearly that the most stable state is not formed under actual crystallization conditions.

The morphology and texture of the platelets are determined by the initial nucleation act and the growth processes.   The primary nucleation process merely provides the substrate upon which subsequent growth occurs.   In a dilute system, economy in the osmotic work of transferring molecules from the solution to the crystalline phase tends to minimize the number of molecules utilized in constructing a nucleus.   Hence at most only a few molecules are involved in nucleus formation.   The dimensions of the critical nucleus have been discussed in Sec. 8-5.

The growth of the crystal in directions transverse to the chain direction involves the deposition of polymer segments on an already existing substrate.   In attempts[27,63,69] to treat the growth of lamellar crystallites from polymer chains the assumption has been made that a complete sequence of units is deposited in a single step. The sequence length ζ is determined at the time of the deposition and is closely related to the critical dimensions of a Gibbs-type monolayer surface nucleus. Allowance is made for the competitive removal of the complete sequence prior to the acquisition of the next adjoining one. Alterations in the length of the last sequence in the incomplete outer layer can occur. Preceding sequences, however, cannot adjust their length by this process. Obviously a well-ordered array of fixed dimensions must result from these assumptions. However, the possibility of fluctuations in the lengths of other sequences of the outermost layer through removal of units at the ends of each is ignored, as is the possibility of longitudinal displacement of sequences. The basic assumption in these treatments is that the size of a sequence is uniquely determined at the time of its deposition.

However, fluctuations in the lengths of all the sequences in the outermost layer cannot be ignored.[32] It is highly unlikely that the length of a sequence is solely determined when it is deposited. To investigate this matter, we assume that at some instant the outer layer replicates precisely the layer beneath it, which, for purposes of discussion, is taken to be of uniform thickness ζ. Regular folding may or may not occur, and loop lengths may or may not exceed the minimum requirements. The possibility of fluctuations in sequence lengths depends on the free energy required for the removal of a terminal unit from a sequence in this outer layer. This consists of the free energy of fusion ΔF_u per unit and of the increase in interfacial free energy $2\sigma_u$ resulting from the exposure of one lateral face in each of the two adjacent units from neighboring sequences. If we take polyethylene as an example, $\Delta F_u \cong 2\Delta T$. From the work of Turnbull and Cormia,[72] σ_u can be taken to be 50 to 100 cal/mole. Except for extraordinarily large supersaturations, the free energy change associated with the removal of a terminal unit is extremely small when compared with RT. Hence thermal fluctuations are energetically facile so that the removal of terminal units from the crystalline layer is expected. The partial unpeeling of one chain should facilitate similar action by neighboring sequences since the interfacial area is not further increased by the removal of units adjacent to previously exposed positions. The outer layer is therefore expected to be ragged at its edges and the chains at any instant are not in a sharply folded configuration. Complete removal of a sequence from this outermost layer should be rare, owing to the substantial interfacial free energy $2\zeta\sigma_u$ that is required. For the same reason, large changes in length from one sequence to another should occur rather infrequently.   Longitudinal displacements of a chain sequence could also occur, particularly if the sequence is interrupted by a loop emerging from the crystal face.

The outermost layer of a growing crystallite is therefore in a transient and fluctuating state and subject to change by one or more mechanisms.   Those rearrangements occur that will result in the development of a more stable situation.   This tendency is halted as succeeding layers are deposited.   It is highly unlikely that the deposition of an entire sequence takes place in a single step; acquisition of a sequence must occur through a succession of steps.   The nature of a crystallite in the vicinity of a growing face depends on the rate at which a sequence develops relative to the rate at which a new layer is initiated.   Once initiated the rate of development of a sequence depends on the ratio of the rate of deposition to the rate of removal of a unit.   This ratio is $\exp\left(-\Delta F_u/RT\right)$ and it follows that the net rate of development of a sequence will increase with ΔT.   The temperature coefficient of sequence growth is negative at modest supersaturations.   Conversely in the acquisition of a sequence in a single activated step the temperature coefficient of this rate would be positive.   In either case, the size must exceed $\zeta^* = 2\sigma_e/\Delta F_u$ or sequences will be removed more rapidly than stable ones are acquired.   The temperature coefficient of the net rate of growth of a crystal face also depends on the temperature coefficient of the deposition process.   If deposition is nucleation controlled then its temperature coefficient is also negative.   However, the observation of a negative temperature coefficient of growth does not necessarily imply a nucleation controlled process.

Holland and Lindenmeyer[61] have measured the net growth rate of faces normal to the c axis during the dilute solution crystallization of polyethylene.   Strong negative temperature coefficients were observed for this process with the time scale ranging from seconds to 80° to days at 92°.   These experiments are suggestive that nucleation processes are involved during the development of the lateral crystal faces.

The complexities attendant on the growth of polymer crystals do not allow for a simple quantitative formulation of the problem.   In addition to the problems discussed, it is an oversimplification to postulate that growth occurs one layer at a time.   The simultaneous development of several layers along an advancing front seems highly probable.   Although initiation of a new sequence would be favored at a kink, it would be also expected to occur at a finite rate on a plane surface.   Despite these difficulties, it is still possible to comprehend the control of lamellar thickness without invoking the untenable requirement of the deposition of complete sequences. A layer may be deposited before sufficient time has elapsed for the preceding layer to achieve the size and orderliness of its predecessors. Consequently ζ decreases as the crystal grows, and the net rate of the development of a sequence is retarded. This net decrease in growth rate allows time for the improvement of the organization of the outermost layers and an increase in ζ. As ζ increases, the rate once more increases, and a self-regulating mechanism of lamellar thickness, based on over- all growth kinetics, exists. The value of ζ characterizing the crystallite would be expected to increase with the temperature of crystallization and thus comply with experimental observation. Its value should be somewhere between that of the primary nucleus and the minimum size required for stability. Rates of growth would be expected to depend on molecular weight, as is observed. Therefore it would not be expected that the most stable crystalline state would be achieved at finite rates of crystallization. The latter condition requires values of ζ comparable to that of the molecular chain length. Similarly, neither would a regularly folded array be expected. The presence of a dis- organized overlayer, consistent with the density and enthalpy measure- ments, should result.

9-3 The Dependence of the Melting Temperature on Crystallization Conditions

Since crystallization must be conducted at finite rates, the deviations from equilibrium that result manifest themselves in a reduced thermo- dynamic stability and a lowered melting temperature in the crystallites formed. For polycrystalline substances, factors contributing to the reduced melting temperature arise from the finite size of the crystal- lites, their state of internal perfection, and the interfacial and con- necting regions. For polymers, evidence has been presented for the lamellar nature of the crystallites formed in bulk and in solution. It therefore appears pertinent to investigate the effect of finite crystallite size on the melting temperature. In the analysis, distinction must be made between those aspects of the problem that are unique to poly- meric systems and those applicable to small crystallites of all sub- stances. Inherent in this approach is the assumption that the melting temperature characterizing a given morphology can be experimentally realized. Hence it is assumed that the heating process used in the melting point determination does not disturb the nature of the crystals.

The free energy of forming a cylindrically shaped crystallite of finite size at temperature T is expressed as

$$\Delta F = \zeta \rho \,\Delta f_u - 2\rho\sigma_{ec} - 2\sqrt{\pi\rho}\,\sigma_{uc} \qquad (9\text{-}15)$$

where σ_{ec} and σ_{uc} are the appropriate interfacial energies for a mature crystallite. †

The effects of strain energy and contributions from the circumferential edge energy have been neglected in Eq. (9-15). The possible existence of nonequilibrium internal imperfections and defects within the crystal lattice has been neglected; only the finite size is considered. At the apparent melting point $T = T_m^*$ of such a crystallite, $\Delta F(T_m^*) = 0$ so that

$$\Delta f_u(T_m^*) = \frac{2\sigma_{ec}}{\zeta} + \frac{2\sqrt{\pi}}{\rho^{1/2}}\,\sigma_{uc} \qquad (9\text{-}16)$$

It is convenient to express the crystallite dimensions as ratios to those characteristic of a primary nucleus. Hence $\zeta = n\zeta^*$ and $\rho^{1/2} = m\rho^{*1/2}$. It should be recalled that the minimum conditions for stability at the crystallization temperature are that $n = 1$ and $m = 2$. With this substitution, Eq. (9-16) becomes

$$\Delta f_u(T_m^*) = \left(\frac{1}{2n}\frac{\sigma_{ec}}{\sigma_{en}} + \frac{1}{m}\frac{\sigma_{uc}}{\sigma_{un}}\right)\Delta f_u(T_c) \qquad (9\text{-}17)$$

Here T_c is the crystallization temperature and σ_{en} and σ_{un} are the interfacial free energies for the nucleus. By utilizing the approximation $\Delta f_u(T) = \Delta H_u\,\Delta T$, Eq. (9-17) can be rewritten as

$$T_m{}^\circ - T_m^* = \left(\frac{\alpha}{2n} + \frac{\beta}{2m}\right)(T_m{}^\circ - T_c) \qquad (9\text{-}18)$$

or
$$T_m{}^\circ - T_m^* = \phi(T_m{}^\circ - T_c) \qquad (9\text{-}19)$$

where $\alpha = \sigma_{ec}/\sigma_{en}$ and $\rho = \sigma_{uc}/\sigma_{un}$. The parameters n and m represent the ratio of the actual crystallite dimensions to that of a critical-size nucleus. The latter can be formed either homogeneously or heterogeneously. ‡

---

† This distinction between the interfacial energies of a mature crystallite and of a nucleus is made not only for the purpose of complete generality but also to avoid the proposition that the chain configuration within a crystallite must be identical with that of a stable nucleus.

‡ The validity of this statement can be seen in the following: If ζ_0^* represents a dimension of a homogeneously formed nucleus and ζ^* is the actual dimension of one formed heterogeneously, then $\zeta^*/\zeta_0^* = \kappa$ is equal to or less than unity. If $n' = \zeta^*/\zeta_0^*$, $\zeta/\zeta^* = n'/\kappa = n$. A similar argument applies to the other dimensions involved.

Equations (9-18) and (9-19) represent the depression in the melting temperature of a crystal resulting from its finite size.   It is not specific to polymeric systems.   These equations indicate that T_m^* should be a linear function of T_c with ϕ constrained to lie between 0 and 1.   The condition $\phi = 0$ represents the maximum stability, since $T_m^* = T_m{}^\circ$ for all crystallization temperatures.   When $\phi = 1$, T_m^* always equals T_c and the crystallites formed are inherently unstable. Thus for crystals formed at different temperatures, which differ from one another only in their size, the value of $T_m{}^\circ$ can be obtained by a linear extrapolation of the apparent melting temperature   However, the value of ϕ deduced from such an analysis does not uniquely specify the structural parameters involved.   Within the limits prescribed, a given value of ϕ can be satisfied by a variety of combinations of the quantities α, β, n, and m.

For polymers crystallized in bulk, if the dimensions of the lamellae are very large in the directions normal to the c axis, $m \to \infty$ so that

$$T_m{}^\circ - T_m^* = \frac{\alpha}{2n} (T_m{}^\circ - T_c) = \phi'(T_m{}^\circ - T_c) \qquad (9\text{-}20)$$

For the special case where $n = 1$ and $\alpha = 1$,[73,74]

$$T_m{}^\circ - T_m^* = \tfrac{1}{2}(T_m{}^\circ - T_c) \qquad (9\text{-}21)$$

or
$$T_m^* = \frac{T_m{}^\circ + T_c}{2}$$

However, even if the observation was made that $\phi' = \tfrac{1}{2}$, it does not follow that n and α must be equal to unity.   Other combinations of these quantities can also satisfy this condition.   However, the simplicity of the theory for the melting of finite-size crystals makes an attractive method by which to analyze the melting temperature of polymers.   It is particularly useful in view of the difficulties involved in establishing directly the equilibrium melting temperature.

We recall the early experiments of Wood and Bekkedahl[75] (see Sec. 2-2) on the melting behavior of natural rubber.   These results are ideally suited for analysis according to the foregoing.   Crystallization was conducted isothermally, and the melting temperature subsequent to crystallization was determined utilizing very rapid heating rates.   Natural rubber crystallizes slowly so that the possibility of recrystallization occurring during the heating process is minimized. Their results are summarized in Fig. 9-9 as a plot of T_m^* against T_c. The two straight lines are drawn according to Eq. (9-21) for equilibrium melting temperatures of 28 and 30°, respectively.   Except for the extremely low crystallization temperatures, the data are well represented by this equation.

A similar set of experimental results have been obtained by Hoffman and Weeks[74] for polytrifluorochloroethylene. Complications exist in the interpretation because of the unknown role played by the large concentration of stereoirregular chain units known to be present.

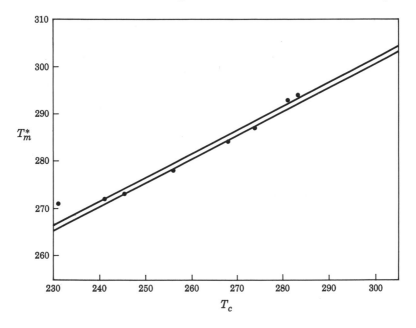

Fig. 9-9   Plot of melting temperature T_m^* against crystallization temperature T_c for natural rubber.   Straight lines are drawn in accordance with Eq. (9-21) for T_m° equal to 301 and 303°K, respectively (73).   Temperature scales in degrees absolute.

Despite this difficulty, a very definite dependence of the melting temperature on the crystallization temperature is found.   In addition, a slight increase in the apparent melting temperature with increasing degree of crystallinity for a fixed crystallization temperature is reported.   These results are summarized in Fig. 9-10 as a plot of $\Delta T_m = T_m^\circ - T_m^*$ against $\Delta T_c = T_m^\circ - T_c$.   In this type of plot, trial values of T_m° are taken, and those giving linear plots which pass through the origin are acceptable according to Eq. (9-20).   As Fig. 9-10 indicates T_m° appears to lie in the range of 224 to 229°C.   This is significantly greater than the value directly determined.[74]   The slightly increased stability with increasing degree of crystallinity

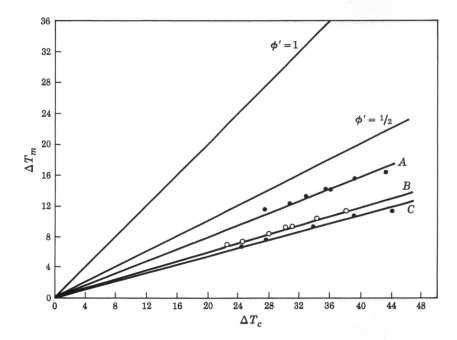

Fig. 9-10 Plot of quantity ΔT_m against ΔT_c for polytrifluorochloroethylene. Dashed lines according to Eq. (9-21) for $\varphi' = 1$ and $\frac{1}{2}$, respectively. Curve A, experimental points for $1 - \lambda = 0.07$ plotted for $T_m{}^\circ = 229^\circ$. Curve B, experimental points for $1 - \lambda = 0.07$ plotted for $T_m{}^\circ = 224$. Curve C, experimental points $1 - \lambda = 0.4$ plotted for $T_m{}^\circ = 224$. [*Data from Hoffman and Weeks* (74).]

may be attributed to compositional and constitutional changes in the melt so that crystallization occurs at an effectively lower undercooling. On the other hand, it could reflect structural improvements and size increases within the crystallite itself. The value ϕ' depends on $T_m{}^\circ$ and ranges from 0.25 to 0.4. It is significantly less than the 0.5 expected if the thickness and interfacial free energy of the crystallite can be identified with those of the primary nucleus. The formation of more stable structures than these simple assumptions predict is indicated.

Despite the fact that ϕ' is not easily interpretable, use of the theory of the melting of finite-size crystals appears to be a useful guide in the estimation of the equilibrium melting temperature of homopolymers and copolymers. The melting temperature determined by the linear extrapolation method outlined is probably a lower limit, since no allowance has been made for the influence of internal imperfections on the apparent melting temperature. It should be emphasized that although Eq. (9-21) is obeyed, irrespective of the value of ϕ', it does not mean that the chains are regularly folded within the crystallite. It can be concluded only that the crystallites are of finite thickness.

In Chap. 2 it was pointed out that, with improved methods of crystallization and annealing, the directly measured melting temperatures of homopolymers have been progressively increased. As an example, the melting temperature of a molecular weight fraction of polyethylene was found to be 138.5° by Chiang and Flory[40] utilizing slow heating procedures subsequent to crystallization at 131°. A linear extrapolation of the apparent melting temperature plotted against crystallization temperature for unfractionated linear polyethylene (Marlex-50) has led to a reported value for $T_m°$ of $143 \pm 2°$.[74]†

The value deduced for $T_m°$ for an infinite molecular weight polyethylene is in qualitative accord with the value predicted by many investigators[76-80] from the analysis of the thermodynamics of melting of the molecular crystals formed by the monomeric n-alkanes. However, for an infinite molecular weight polymer, molecular crystals are not formed since there are no chain ends to be placed in juxtaposition with one another. Consequently, in order properly to carry out the extrapolation, a correction must be made to the entropy of fusion of the low molecular weight homologs to account for this fact.[81] The result is a theoretically extrapolated melting temperature of 145.5°.

In summary, a method is available that allows for an estimation of $T_m°$ and that circumvents the difficulties involved in its direct determination. The values deduced for homopolymers[73,74] and copolymers[82] appear to be reasonable when compared with other theoretical concepts and observations. However, the procedure utilizes a linear extrapolation which has not been established on any firm theoretical grounds. Consequently, except for the fact that finite crystallite size is involved, it is not possible to deduce any detailed information with respect to the internal and interfacial structure of the crystallites.

9-4 Spherulites

The existence of an organized structure on a scale larger than that of individual crystallites is implied by the usual opacity of crystalline polymers and is confirmed by direct observations using the light microscope. An example of such a structure was illustrated in Fig.

† In the determination of the apparent melting temperature of polyethylene there is serious concern as to whether recrystallization occurs subsequent to the initial crystallization despite the utilization of rapid heating rates.

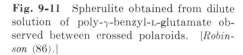

Fig. 9-11 Spherulite obtained from dilute solution of poly-γ-benzyl-L-glutamate observed between crossed polaroids. [*Robinson* (86).]

1-8. When the specimens are observed under crossed polaroids in the polarizing microscope, large birefringent regions are seen. In most cases they consist of circularly birefringent areas possessing a dark Maltese cross with arms parallel and perpendicular to the direction of polarization. The retardation changes continuously along a radius. This is typical of the spherulitic aggregation of crystals or crystallites. A spherulite consists of a large number of crystals radiating in all directions from a point, with a particular direction of each crystal lying consistently along a radius of a sphere. Spherulites can be thought of as a definite organization and orientation of crystallites relative to one another. They possess well-defined boundaries and encompass a domain which, depending on circumstances, can be as large as 0.1 mm in diameter. An obvious primary requirement for spherulite formation is that the substance be polycrystalline. However, not all polycrystalline materials need be or are indeed found to be spherulitic in character. These structures are observed in such a wide variety of homopolymers, crystallized in bulk, that it appears to be a universal mode of crystallization for such substances. The development of spherulites is not limited to polymers. The term was originally used to describe the polycrystalline structures found in igneous rock. Spherulitic structures have been observed in a variety of inorganic and organic crystalline compounds.[83,84] Globular proteins, such as the enzyme carboxypeptidase, have been crystallized from dilute solution in a spherulitic habit.[85] Robinson[86] has shown that subsequent to the dilute solution phase separation of poly-γ-benzyl-L-glutamate in solvents, where the alpha-helical form is maintained, large well-defined spherulites develop. An example of such a spherulite is shown in Fig. 9-11. When viewed between crossed polaroids, the optical character of the spherulite is virtually identical to the banded type that is formed during the crystallizations of chainlike molecules from the melt.   The viscosity of the crystallization medium does not, therefore, appear to be very influential in directing the formation of spherulites.   A characteristic feature of the poly-γ-benzyl-L-glutamate spherulites is the appearance of a single fault, or line of dislocation, which lies along a radius and is easily visible in ordinary light.   In Fig. 9-11 the crossed polaroids are so arranged that one arm of the cross falls slightly to one side of the fault.   The arm has now developed a zigzag appearance similar to that found in many bulk crystallized specimens.

Although the spherulite is a very dominant morphological feature of bulk crystallized homopolymers, it is clearly not unique to them. It can be supposed that certain common features, apparently not directly related to molecular structure, govern the formation of spherulites in a variety of substances.   The question is posed as to why spherulitic aggregates are formed, rather than an unorganized and unrelated collection of individual crystallites or crystallite regions. In attempting to answer this question, it is instructive to examine the optical nature of spherulitic patterns, paying particular attention to how they depend on the crystallization conditions and details of chain structure.

The optical patterns displayed by polymer spherulites depend on certain features of chain structure and on the crystallization conditions.   Of prime importance are the crystallization temperature, the molecular weight, and the structural regularity of the individual chains.   The observations of Takayanagi[87] on polyethylene adipate succinctly point out the influence of the crystallization temperature. Examples are given in Fig. 9-12 for crystallization temperatures of 0, 29, and 45.5°.   In terms of the spherulitic growth rate, these correspond to a temperature below the maximum rate, a temperature in the vicinity of the maximum, and a temperature greater than the maximum.   At 29° the common type of banded spherulite is observed. It consists of a series of concentric light and dark rings with the sign of the birefringence along the radius alternating at each layer.   At low temperatures of crystallization, the spherulites no longer have the banded appearance, and negative birefringence is observed along the radius.   At the higher temperature of crystallization the spherulites are more fibrous and not as well defined, and the birefringence is positive along the radius.   In general, the boundaries of the spherulites that are formed closer to the melting temperature are less well defined than those formed at lower temperatures.   Similar optical patterns have been obtained for gutta-percha crystallized over a wide temperature range.[88]

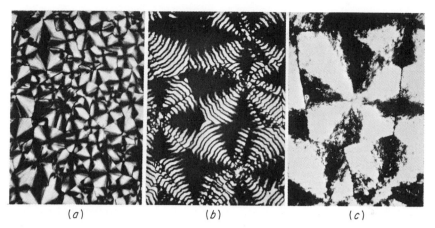

Fig. 9-12 Diffcrent optical patterns obtained from polyethylene adipate spherulites. (*a*) Crystallized at 0°; (*b*) crystallized at 29°; (*c*) crystallized at 45.5°. [*From Takayanagi* (87).]

For high molecular weight polyethylene the banded or ring-type spherulites are observed over the limited temperature range available for isothermal crystallization.   However, for lower molecular weight samples ($M \simeq 20,000$ or less) very fibrous nonbanded spherulites are developed.[89]   Similar observations have been made for a low molecular weight sample of polyethylene oxide crystallized at different temperatures.[90]

Copolymers and structurally irregular polymers also show spherulitic structure but in general they are of the nonbanded type.[91,92] However, branched polyethylene displays banded spherulites.   The spacing of the rings depends on the degree of branching.[93]   As the crystallization temperature is increased, the ring spacings also increase. Over the limited temperature range available, the spacings are inversely related to the undercooling.   As the amount of noncrystallizing component introduced into the chain increases, although crystallization still ensues, the spherulitic structure disappears.   For example, in ethylene copolymers the spherulites are not observed (as far as light microscopic examination is concerned) in specimens containing more than 2 per cent m-C_3H_7 and 5.9 per cent CH_3 side groups.[92]

From the optical properties of the crystal, the magnitude and sign of the refractive index along the major directions of a spherulite allow the chain orientation within it to be described.   For example, in polyethylene, the refractive index of light vibrating along the radius of the spherulite is less than that for vibrations perpendicular to it. Refractive index measurements of highly oriented fibers indicate that the refractive index for light vibrating parallel to the chain axis is greater than that normal to the axis.   It is concluded, therefore, that within the spherulite the *c* axes of the crystallites (the chain axes) are normal to the spherulite radii.[94]   A rationale of this surprising conclusion has been given by Bunn.[94]   He pointed out that the radii of spherulites are directions of crystal growth, with the situation in polyethylene being very similar to the crystal morphology of short chain hydrocarbons.   In the latter the crystals grow as thin plates, with the molecular axes normal to the wide face of the plates.   The crystals grow much faster in directions normal to the molecular axes than they do in parallel directions.   Thus the observations appear quite reasonable in view of the now recognized lamellalike nature of most polymer crystallites.   In spherulites the magnitude of the birefringence is low when compared with the birefringence of drawn fibers so that the perpendicular orientation of the chains is far from perfect.   For polymers with strongly polarizable side groups, as, for example, polyesters and polyamides, a refractive index in one of the directions normal to the chain axis might be comparable with the one along the chain direction.   Thus even with the molecular axis normal to the radius a spherulite would be positively birefringent.   For polyethylene adipate, negative or positive spherulites are observed, depending on the crystallization temperature.[87]   In polyamides examples are known of the existence of positive and negative spherulites in the same material. In both cases the molecules lie tangential to the spherulite radius, but different crystallographic directions are parallel.   These conclusions with respect to chain orientation in a spherulite are confirmed by microbeam X-ray diffraction studies of portions of a spherulite.[95,96] For polyethylene the *b* axis has been identified as the one parallel to the radius.   The spherulites observed from poly-γ-benzyl-L-glutamate solutions possess the same type of orientation.   The long axes of the molecules are normal to the spherulite radius.

The radial symmetry of a fully grown spherulite develops through the initial formation and growth of other geometric forms.   This was recognized in the study of spherulites formed from monomeric substances,[83,84] and, not unexpectedly, polymers follow a similar pattern. Initially, fibrous or needlelike crystals are formed which develop lengthwise by a branching or fanning mechanism analogous to dendritic growth.   The spherical shape is gradually approached through the formation of sheaves which can be observed in the electron microscope.   The assumption of a regular branching mechanism leads to a well-defined spherical aggregate after the completion of a sufficient number of steps.[97]   Furthermore, if the direction of branching of one crystallite relative to another is well defined, then within the aggregate a definite crystallographic orientation will develop. The branching itself will be noncrystallographic in character and must depend on features that involve the crystallite interfaces.

The optical patterns of the concentric ring or banded spherulites have been extensively studied. It is generally believed that the alternating dark and bright bands arise from a periodically varying orientation of the birefringent units along a spherulite radius.[28,98] Extinction arises whenever a birefringent unit is suitably oriented; such

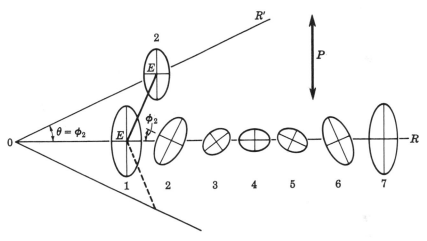

Fig. 9-13 Schematic diagram of the helicoidal arrangement of a set of biaxial refractive index ellipsoids that it utilized to explain birefringence patterns of spherulites. [*From Keller* (95).]

orientation recurs periodically. Replicas of fracture surfaces of melt crystallized polyethylene, containing spherulites with periodic extinction rings, show thin lamellae which change their orientation periodically along the radius of a spherulite. The period is identical with that of the extinction rings observed under the polarizing light microscope.[45]

The radius of a spherulite has been envisioned as consisting of a set of crystallites, as is represented schematically in Fig. 9-13 by the helicoidal arrangement of a set of biaxial refractive index ellipsoids.[99,100,101] In this figure the plane containing the optic axes is set perpendicular to the spherulitic radius, designated by RR, and each ellipsoid is rotated in the same sense by an amount determined by its distance from the center. Consequently, there is a repeat of this position. Detailed analysis of this model, utilizing basic theory of optics, explains the periodic extinction, the appearance of the Maltese cross, the zigzag line, and other fine details of the optical character of banded spherulites.   To explain the circular symmetry of the patterns, i.e., the formation of regular rings, the assumption must be made that adjacent or contiguous radii are in phase.   Thus around any given circle of a two-dimensional spherulite (as it is viewed in the microscope) the orientation between the optical indicatrix and all radii is the same.   This conclusion is merely a statement of experimental observation and does not follow naturally from the model assumed.

A confirmation of the orientation assumptions has been obtained from microbeam X-ray diffraction studies of ringed polyethylene spherulites.   As has been previously indicated, the tangential orientation of the chains is substantiated by these experiments.   In addition, an analysis of the diffraction patterns indicates that the unit cells have a helical orientation about the *b* axis which is directed radially. The distance corresponding to half of the helical pitch, as deduced from the X-ray studies, corresponds to the extinction ring interval directly observed under the light microscope.[96]   It should be noted in this connection that in low molecular weight polyethylene oxide, where the spherulites, instead of being banded, are more fibrous in nature, diffraction patterns taken at various positions along a given radius show no evidence of a periodic orientation of the unit cell.[90]   Hence, if substantiated in other systems, a major difference in crystallite orientation exists between different kinds of spherulites.   We have already noted that the optical character of the spherulite formed depends on factors related to the chain structure and the crystallization conditions.

Although a description of the optical properties of banded spherulites has been developed, it is still necessary to relate this to molecular properties and to generalize it to the other types of spherulites.   Eventually the sequence of events involved in spherulitic formation and growth must be deduced.   The optical description is essentially phenomenological in character so that the specific form of the structural units cannot be unequivocally inferred from it.   Since spherulitic growth is a nucleation controlled process, it is tempting to postulate that the twisted array of optical indicatrices and unit cells directed along a radius results from an incoherent nucleation process on the surface of a crystallographic plane parallel to the chain axis.[69,102]   It is assumed that the corresponding crystallographic planes of the crystal and the nucleus do not match but are rotated relative to one another. Qualitatively, this is consistent with the optical properties of ringed spherulites.   However, the properties of only one arm or radius are explained by this hypothesis.   No explanation is given for the phasing of the adjacent radii. Kinetic studies have also demonstrated that the radius of a spherulite increases linearly with time. For a spherically symmetric body this means that, at constant temperature, the mass transformed per unit spherulite area is constant. The area in this case is the continuous boundary between the spherulite and the melt. With a constant density and orientation of crystallites per unit area and a constant nucleation rate per unit area, the conclusion can be reached that the size of a crystallite (in the growth direction) is constant, independent of the time of its existence.[102] If this hypothesis is correct, then, taken with previous deductions, it implies that growth in the two major directions, parallel and normal to the chain directions, is retarded. Since only one arm of the spherulite is considered, it has been necessary to assume that the spherulite-liquid boundary is continuous in order to account for the linear growth rate. Otherwise, nucleation rates in portions devoid of crystallites would differ from those on or in the vicinity of crystallites so that the mass transformed per unit area would not be independent of time. The three-dimensional character of a spherulite is tacitly ignored as are their volume-filling characteristics. The influence of one growing arm on its neighbor is a problem of serious concern from the point of view of both the nucleation processes and the branching mechanism. Although it is clear that the growth of a spherulite occurs by a nucleation mechanism, classical nucleation theory has not as yet explained the salient features of spherulitic development.

Although many of the fundamentals of spherulitic growth are as yet unexplained, there are certain common characteristic features of spherulitic-forming substances. Most, if not all, polycrystalline aggregates that form spherulites are composed of crystallites that are anisotropic or asymmetric in shape. The lamellar nature of homopolymer crystallites obviously falls into this classification. Liquid-crystals of the cholesterol type are asymmetric and form spherulites, as do the structurally asymmetric alpha-helices of poly-γ-benzyl-L-glutamate. In the latter cases spherulites are observed even though the crystallization occurs from dilute solution. Carbon (in the graphite form) has a sheetlike or layer structure, and in this system spherulites are also observed. Melts of low molecular weight organic substances develop spherulites upon the addition of small amounts of impurities. These impurities concentrate at specific crystal faces and retard their growth; consequently an asymmetric-shaped crystallite should evolve. Spherulites of low molecular weight inorganic salts are formed by metathesis by allowing a dilute solution of one component to diffuse into a dilute solution of the other when suspended in a viscous gel. Convection is eliminated and the growth of a given face retarded by the depletion of the appropriate ions at the surface. Thus, when for various reasons the magnitude of crystal growth rates in two different directions differs appreciably, highly asymmetrically shaped crystallites result. It is under these conditions that spherulites are developed. The absence of spherulites in copolymers containing structurally different units can be attributed to the suppression of the lamella-type crystallite for the reasons previously noted.[92]

The close similarity between these apparently diverse cases is perhaps better understood when it is realized that the first few crystallites formed during the primary nucleation processes in a molten polymer are distributed at random in the untransformed matrix. Hence, one has, in effect, a system of dilute anisotropic crystals with a correspondence to the more molecularly dilute systems. If this generalization is accepted, this question arises: If polycrystallinity is preordained by primary nucleation in remote volume elements, why does the formation of asymmetric crystallites lead to spherulites rather than to a nonorganized arrangement of crystallites? In particular, the problem to be resolved is whether the spherulitic configuration results from an inherent stability relative to other organizations of crystallites or is a consequence of kinetic factors subsequent to primary nucleation. For certain cases, Fullman[103] has shown that the condition of greater stability is fulfilled. For crystallites composed of chain molecules a unique anistropy of interfacial free energies exists. The interfacial free energy characteristic of a surface normal to the chain direction is many factors greater than that assigned to the surfaces transversely directed. Since it has been deduced that the crystallite dimensions in the chain direction are much less than those in the lateral directions, the Wulf theorem[104] stands in gross violation. The characteristic thin lamellar crystallites of chain molecules cannot therefore represent an equilibrium body. Organization into spherulites is a possible mechanism by which this difficulty can be alleviated.

REFERENCES

1. Bear, R. S., and H. S. Rugo: *Ann. N.Y. Acad. Sci.*, **53:** 627 (1951).
2. Bear, R. S.: *J. Am. Chem. Soc.*, **66:** 1297 (1944).
3. Bear, R. S.: *Advan. Protein Chem.*, **7:** 69 (1952).
4. Bear, R. S.: *J. Cellular Comp. Physiol.*, **49** (*Suppl.* 1): 303 (1957).
5. Huxley, H. E.: *Proc. Roy. Soc.* (*London*), *Ser. B*, **141:** 59 (1953).
6. Kiessig, H.: *Kolloid-Z.*, **152:** 62 (1957).
7. Arnett, L. M., E. P. H. Meibohm, and A. F. Smith: *J. Polymer Sci.*, **5:** 737 (1950); **7:** 57 (1951).

8. Wallner, L. G.: *Monatsh. Chem.*, **79**: 279 (1942).
9. Statton, W. O.: *J. Polymer Sci.*, **22**: 385 (1956); W. O. Statton and G. M. Godard: *J. Appl. Phys.*, **28**: 1111 (1957).
10. Belbeoch, B., and A. Guiner: *Makromol. Chem.*, **31**: 1 (1959).
11. Mandelkern, L., C. R. Worthington, and A. F. Diorio: *Science*, **127**: 1052 (1958); *J. Appl. Phys.*, **31**: 536 (1960).
12. Keller, A.: *Phil. Mag.*, **2**: 1171 (1957); *Discussions Faraday Soc.*, **25**: 114 (1958).
13. Ranby, B. G., F. F. Morehead, and N. M. Walter: *J. Polymer Sci.*, **34**: 349 (1960).
14. Mandelkern, L., A. S. Posner, A. F. Diorio, and D. E. Roberts: *J. Appl. Phys.*, **32**: 1509 (1961).
15. Pollock, S. S., W. A. Robinson, R. Chiang, and P. J. Flory: *J. Appl. Phys.*, **33**: 237 (1962).
16. Eppe, R., E. W. Fischer, and H. A. Stuart: *J. Polymer Sci.*, **34**: 721 (1959); H. A. Stuart: *Ann. N.Y. Acad. Sci.*, **83**: 3 (1959); H. A. Stuart: *Kolloid-Z.*, **165**: 3 (1959).
17. Hermanns, P. H., and A. Weidinger: *Makromol. Chem.*, **39**: 67 (1960).
18. Statton, W. O.: *J. Polymer Sci.*, **22**: 385 (1956).
19. Hess, K., and H. Kiessig: *Z. Physik. Chem. (Leipzig)*, **193**: 196 (1944); K. Hess and H. Kiessig: *Naturwissenschaften*, **31**: 171 (1955); K. Hess: *Ric. Sci., Suppl. A*, p. 594, 1954.
20. Hosemann, R.: *Z. Physik*, **128**: 1 (1950); R. Bonart and R. Hosemann: *Makromol. Chem.*, **39**: 105 (1960); R. Hosemann: *Polymer*, **3**: 349 (1962).
21. Arnold, H.: *Kolloid-Z.*, **157**: 111 (1958).
22. Sella, C., and J. J. Trillat: *Compt. Rend.*, **246**: 3246 (1958); **248**: 410, 1819, 2348 (1959).
23. Flory, P. J., and A. D. McIntyre: *J. Polymer Sci.*, **18**: 592 (1955).
24. Richardson, M., P. J. Flory, and J. B. Jackson: *Polymer*, **4**: 221 (1963).
25. Cormia, R. L., F. P. Price, and D. Turnbull: *J. Chem. Phys.*, **37**: 1333 (1962).
26. Lauritzen, J. I., and J. D. Hoffman: *J. Res. Natl. Bur. Std.*, A, **64**: 73 (1960).
27. Frank, F. C., and M. Tosi: *Proc. Roy. Soc. (London)*, Ser. A, **263**: 323 (1961).
28. Keller, A.: *Makromol. Chem.*, **34**: 1 (1959).
29. Geil, P. H.: *J. Polymer Sci.*, **44**: 449 (1960); **47**: 65 (1960); **51**: S10 (1961).
30. Kampf, G.: *Kolloid-Z.*, **172**: 507 (1960).
31. Anderson, F.: *Bull. Am. Phys. Soc.*, Ser. 11, **8** (3): (1963).
32. Flory, P. J.: *J. Am. Chem. Soc.*, **84**: 2857 (1962).
33. Bekkedahl, N., and H. Matheson: *J. Res. Natl. Bur. Std.*, **15**: 503 (1935).
34. McCrum, N. G.: *J. Polymer Sci.*, **34**: 355 (1959).
35. Takayanagi, M., M. Yoshino, and S. Minami: *J. Polymer Sci.*, **61**: 57 (1962).
36. Ruland, W.: *Acta Cryst.*, **14**: 1180 (1961).
37. Goppel, J. M., and J. J. Arlman: *Appl. Sci. Res.*, Sect. A, **1**: 462 (1949).
38. Roberts, D. E., and L. Mandelkern: *J. Am. Chem. Soc.*, **77**: 781 (1955).

39. Wunderlich, B., and M. Dole: *J. Polymer Sci.*, **24**: 201 (1957).
40. Chiang, R. F., and P. J. Flory: *J. Am. Chem. Soc.*, **83**: 2857 (1961).
41. Kilian, H. G.: *Kolloid-Z.*, **183**: 1 (1962).
42. Storks, K. H.: *J. Am. Chem. Soc.*, **60**: 1753 (1958).
43. Jaccodine, R.: *Nature*, **176**: 301 (1955).
44. Till, P. H.: *J. Polymer Sci.*, **24**: 301 (1957).
45. Fischer, E. W.: *Z. Naturforsch., a*, **12**: 753 (1957).
46. Schlesinger, W., and H. M. Leeper: *J. Polymer Sci.*, **11**: 203 (1953).
47. Frank, F. C.: *Discussions Faraday Soc.*, **5**: 48 (1949).
48. Dawson, I. M., V. Vand, and N. G. Anderson: *Proc. Roy. Soc. (London), Ser. A*, **206**: 555 (1951); **214**: 72 (1952); **218**: 255 (1953).
49. Manley, R. St. John: *J. Polymer Sci.*, **47**: 149 (1960); *Nature*, **189**: 390 (1961).
50. Ranby, B. G., and R. W. Noe: *J. Polymer Sci.*, **51**: 337 (1961).
51. Geil, P. H.: *J. Polymer Sci.*, **44**: 449 (1960).
52. Geil, P. H., N. K. J. Symons, and R. G. Scott: *J. Appl. Phys.*, **30**: 1516 (1959).
53. Keller, A.: *Makromol. Chem.*, **34**: 1 (1959).
54. Holland, V. F., S. B. Mitchell, W. L. Hunter, and P. H. Lindenmeyer: *J. Polymer Sci.*, **62**: 145 (1962).
55. Geil, P.: *J. Polymer Sci.*, **51**: S10 (1961).
56. Kargin, V. A., N. F. Barkeev, and L. Li shen: *High Molecular Weight Compounds*, **3**: 1102 (1961).
57. Bisschops, J.: *J. Polymer Sci.*, **17**: 89 (1955).
58. Keller, A.: *J. Polymer Sci.*, **36**: 361 (1959).
59. Okamura, S., K. Hayashi, and Y. Kitanishi: *Makromol. Chem.*, **47**: 230, 237 (1961); *J. Polymer Sci.*, **58**: 925 (1962); **60**: 526 (1962).
60. Lando, J., N. Morosoff, H. Morawetz, and B. Post: *J. Polymer Sci.*, **60**: 169 (1962).
61. Holland, V. F., and P. Lindenmeyer: *J. Polymer Sci.*, **57**: 589 (1962).
62. Jackson, J. B., P. J. Flory, and R. Chiang: *Trans. Faraday Soc.*, **59**: 1906 (1963).
63. Price, F. P.: *J. Chem. Phys.*, **35**: 1884 (1961).
64. Keller, A., and A. O'Connor: *Polymer*, **1**: 163 (1960).
65. Statton, W. O., and P. Geil: *J. Appl. Polymer Sci.*, **3**: 357 (1960).
66. Wunderlich, B., and M. Kashdan: *J. Polymer Sci.*, **50**: 71 (1961).
67. Chiang, R. F., and P. J. Flory: Abstract of paper presented before Division of Polymer Chemistry, American Chemical Society, New York, September, 1960.
68. Price, F. P.: *J. Polymer Sci.*, **38**: 139 (1960).
69. Hoffman, J. D., and J. I. Lauritzen: *J. Res. Natl. Bur. Std., A*, **65**: 297 (1961).
70. Peterlin, A., and E. W. Fischer: *Z. Phys.*, **159**: 272 (1960); A. Peterlin, E. W. Fischer, and C. Reinhold: *J. Chem. Phys.*, **37**: 1403 (1962).
71. Flory, P. J.: *J. Chem. Phys.*, **17**: 223 (1949).
72. Turnbull, D., and R. L. Cormia: *J. Chem. Phys.*, **34**: 820 (1961).

73. Mandelkern, L.: *J. Polymer Sci.*, **47**: 494 (1960).
74. Hoffman, J. D., and J. J. Weeks: *J. Res. Natl. Bur. Std.*, *A*, **66**: 13 (1962).
75. Wood, L. A., and N. Bekkedahl: *J. Appl. Phys.*, **17**: 362 (1946).
76. Garner, W. E., K. van Bibber, and A. M. King: *J. Chem. Soc.*, 1533 (1931).
77. Meyer, K. H., and A. J. A. vander Wyk: *Helv. Chim. Acta*, **20**: 83 (1937).
78. Billmeyer, F. W.: *J. Appl. Phys.*, **28**: 1114 (1957).
79. Van Nes, K., and H. A. Van Westen: "Aspects of the Constitution of Mineral Oils," p. 105, Elsevier Publishing Company, New York, 1951.
80. Broadhurst, M.: *J. Chem. Phys.*, **36**: 2578 (1962).
81. Flory, P. J., and A. Vrij: *J. Am. Chem. Soc.*, **85**: 3548 (1963).
82. Mandelkern, L., and F. A. Quinn, Jr.: Unpublished results, 1963.
83. Bernauer, F.: "Gedrille Kristalle," Gebrüder Borntraeger, Berlin, 1929.
84. Morse, H. W., and J. D. H. Donnay: *Am. Mineralogist*, **21**: 392 (1936); H. W. Morse, C. H. Warren, and J. D. Donnay: *Am. J. Sci.*, **23**: 421 (1932).
85. Coleman, J. E., B. J. Allan, and B. L. Vallee: *Science*, **131**: 350 (1960).
86. Robinson, C.: *Trans. Faraday Soc.*, **52**: 571 (1956); *Discussions Faraday Soc.*, **25**: 29 (1958).
87. Takayanagi, M.: *Mem. Fac. Eng., Kyushu Univ.*, **16**(3): 111 (1957).
88. Schuur, G.: *J. Polymer Sci.*, **11**: 385 (1953).
89. Banks, W., J. N. Hay, A. Scharples, and G. Thomson: *Nature*, **194**: 542 (1962).
90. Price, F. P., and R. W. Kilb: *J. Polymer Sci.*, **57**: 395 (1962).
91. Holland, V. F.: *J. Polymer Sci.*, **43**: 572 (1960).
92. Jackson, J. B., and P. J. Flory: *Polymer*, vol. 4, (1963).
93. Naono, T.: *J. Sci. Hiroshima Univ.*, Ser. *A*, **24**: 653 (1960).
94. Bunn, C. W., and T. C. Alcock: *Trans. Faraday Soc.*, **41**: 317 (1945).
95. Keller, A.: *J. Polymer Sci.*, **17**: 351 (1955).
96. Fujiwara, Y.: *J. Appl. Polymer Sci.*, **4**: 10 (1960).
97. Keller, A., and J. R. S. Waring: *J. Polymer Sci.*, **17**: 447 (1955).
98. Clark, R. J., R. L. Miller, R. S. Stein, and P. R. Wilson: *J. Polymer Sci.*, **42**: 275 (1960).
99. Keller, A.: *J. Polymer Sci.*, **39**: 160 (1959).
100. Keith, H. D., and F. J. Padden, Jr.: *J. Polymer Sci.*, **39**: 101 (1959); **39**: 123 (1959).
101. Price, F. P.: *J. Polymer Sci.*, **39**: 139 (1959).
102. Price, F. P.: *Ann. N.Y. Acad. Sci.*, **83**: 20 (1959).
103. Fullman, R. L.: *Acta Met.*, **5**: 638 (1957).
104. Wulf, G.: *Z. Krist.*, **34**: 449 (1901).

NAME INDEX

Adams, H. E., 114
Aelion, R., 143
Alcock, T. C., 337
Alexander, L. E., 115
Alexander, P., 202, 214
Allan, B. J., 337
Allen, P. W., 289
Aloisio, C. J., 289
Anderson, F., 335
Anderson, N. G., 336
Arlman, J. J., 335
Arnett, L. M., 334
Arnold, H., 335
Astbury, W. T., 145, 197, 213, 214
Avrami, M., 226, 227, 230, 289

Bailey, K., 214
Baker, W. O., 36, 143
Bamford, C. H., 145

Banks, W., 289, 337
Barclay, R. K., 71
Barkeev, N. F., 336
Barnes, W. B., 290
Beaman, R. G., 116
Bear, R. S., 214, 334
Bedon, H. D., 44, 71, 114, 142
Beevers, R. B., 64
Bekkedahl, N., 24, 25, 36, 218, 219, 221, 288, 323, 335, 337
Belbeoch, B., 335
Bennett, B., 143
Benoit, H., 144
Bernauer, F., 337
Billmeyer, F. W., 143, 337
Binder, J. L., 114
Bisschops, J., 115, 336
Bloom, S. M., 145
Blout, E. R., 72, 145
Boedtker, H., 55, 72, 144

SUBJECT INDEX

347